THERMODYNAMIC FUNCTIONS
OF GASES

Volume 2

THERMODYNAMIC
FUNCTIONS OF GASES

Edited by

F. DIN

The British Oxygen Company Limited
Research and Development Centre, London

Volume 2

AIR, ACETYLENE, ETHYLENE,
PROPANE AND ARGON

LONDON
BUTTERWORTHS SCIENTIFIC PUBLICATIONS
1956

BUTTERWORTHS PUBLICATIONS LTD.
88 KINGSWAY, LONDON, W.C.2

AFRICA :   BUTTERWORTH & CO. (AFRICA) LTD.
                DURBAN : 33/35 Beach Grove
AUSTRALIA :   BUTTERWORTH & CO. (AUSTRALIA) LTD.
                SYDNEY : 8 O'Connell Street
                MELBOURNE : 430 Bourke Street
                BRISBANE : 240 Queen Street
CANADA :   BUTTERWORTH & CO. (CANADA) LTD.
                TORONTO: 1367 Danforth Avenue
NEW ZEALAND :   BUTTERWORTH & CO. (AUSTRALIA) LTD.
                WELLINGTON : 49/51 Ballance Street
                AUCKLAND : 35 High Street

TJ270
D5
v.2
CHEMISTRY
LIBRARY

CONTENTS

CONTENTS

AIR

F. Din

The British Oxygen Company Limited,
Research and Development Centre, London

A NUMBER of thermodynamic diagrams for air have been prepared by various authors during the last thirty years, most of which have been intended to meet the requirements of the air liquefaction and separation industry. The diagrams that have come to the present author's notice are those of SELIGMANN[46], HAUSEN[21], WILLIAMS[52], RUSHTON[44], GERHART and others[18], CLAITOR and CRAWFORD[8], HALL and IBELE[20], TANISHITA[49] and finally of MORI[38]. The earliest of these, the Seligmann diagram, covers a very wide range of temperature and pressure, from 65° K to 660° K and from 0·1 kg/cm^2 to 1000 kg/cm^2. It was calculated, even in the two-phase region, from a Clausius modified Van der Waals equation and a single empirical relationship for the specific heat at constant volume in the ideal gaseous state. As Seligmann points out, his diagram could scarcely be expected to agree with the experimental data over its entire range, but nevertheless the general agreement is remarkably good considering that the diagram was calculated entirely from an equation of state.

Hausen's diagram was based very largely on his own determination of the Joule–Thomson coefficient, data which had first to be integrated before they could be conveniently used. For the specific heat at constant pressure Hausen took the value 0·241 cal/g, °C for 1 atm pressure, given in the Reichsanstalt tables, and he assumed this value could be applied for zero pressure and was independent of temperature. In fact, Hausen noted that at 1 atm there is a slight rise in the value of C_p at low temperatures but he considered that this did not seriously affect his diagram. Along the 0° C isotherm Hausen used an equation of state derived by Jakob from the *P-V-T* data of HOLBORN and SCHULTZE[26] to calculate the thermodynamic functions, whilst in the two-phase liquid–vapour region he had to rely on some very early data by BALY[3], OLSZEWSKI[40] and KUENEN and CLARK[33] for the vapour pressure. The range of Hausen's diagram is that generally needed in the air separation industry, namely, temperatures between ambient temperature and the normal boiling point of liquid air, 79° K, and pressures up to 200 atm.

The Williams diagram covers a similar range to that of Hausen and was constructed in much the same manner, although from quite different original data. Williams used the integral Joule–Thomson effect as measured by ROEBUCK[42] for the main part of his diagram, and for his base isotherm at 500° Rankine (absolute degrees on the Fahrenheit scale) the Beattie–Bridgeman equation of state. For the specific heat at constant pressure at zero pressure Williams derived values based on the spectroscopic values for argon, oxygen and nitrogen, and for his vapour pressure data he derived equations based on the work of DODGE and DUNBAR[13] on the liquid–vapour equilibrium of the oxygen–nitrogen system. Williams also had the advantage of a value for the latent heat of vaporization at 1 atm due to DANA[11].

The diagram of Gerhart and others is virtually an extension of the Williams diagram to temperatures above normal ambient temperature. It is based on Roebuck's Joule–Thomson data obtained at these higher temperatures and for the base isotherm at 212° F the compressibility data of AMAGAT[2] and Holborn and Schultze[26] were used. The diagram of Claitor and Crawford covers a similar temperature range to those of Hausen and Williams but the pressure range is from 1 atm to 12 atm only. It is based on a reduced virial equation of state derived by the authors, valid equally for oxygen and nitrogen and, by implication, for air. They claim that the various physical and thermodynamic coefficients deduced from their equation agree with the experimentally observed values, where these are available, within the probable limits of experimental accuracy. The work of Hall and Ibele is likewise based on a theoretical virial equation of state developed for air, nitrogen and oxygen. The pressure range covered is comparable with that of the other compilations but the temperature range extends upwards to 000° R. No saturation data are given and the method of tabulation of the thermodynamic data in the form of correction terms is not convenient for practical use. Tanishita's diagram is for pressures up to 0 atm and temperatures from − 100° C to 500° C so that it also does t include any saturation data. It was calculated from an equation state, but in this case the equation was based on the P-V-T data of agat above 0° C and those of WITKOWSKI[53] at lower temperatures. e computations of Mori cover a similar pressure and temperature r ge to those of Claitor and Crawford with which they have much in c mon. In fact, in the development of his equation of state Mori m es use of the reduced virial coefficients derived by those authors. A ar as the present author is aware, the basis of Rushton's diagram ha not been published.

will be seen, therefore, that only the diagrams of Hausen and W ams, which cover the range needed by the air separation industry,

2

are based directly on experimental data, in both cases measurements of the Joule–Thomson effect. As will be explained later, these two independent investigations are not entirely in agreement. In an attempt to resolve some of the discrepancies between the existing diagrams, the present author undertook the preparation of a thermodynamic diagram for air based directly on the P-V-T measurements of Amagat above 0° C and those of Witkowski at lower temperatures. When finished, however, this diagram proved to be yet another of doubtful accuracy. Indeed, critical consideration of the P-V-T data of Amagat and Witkowski shows that it could not have been otherwise since these data have neither the accuracy nor precision to justify an accurate compilation of the thermodynamic functions.

The problem of deriving a good comprehensive thermodynamic diagram for air has been completely altered following the measurement of P-V-T data by MICHELS and his co-workers[37] at the Van der Waals laboratory. These data have a quite different order of accuracy and precision from the early pioneer work of Amagat and Witkowski, and for the first time it has become possible to construct a thermodynamic diagram for air having a sound experimental basis. These new data are the major source used for the present compilation. There may still be some uncertainty about the values of the functions in the compressed liquid and critical regions and along the saturation boundary, but elsewhere it is believed that this new diagram for air is second to none in its accuracy.

SURVEY OF EXISTING DATA

1. The Compressibility Data

Values of the product pressure times volume, PV, for air were obtained by Amagat[2] for temperatures 100° C and 200° C up to pressures of 1000 atm and at 0° C, 16° C and 45° C up to 3000 atm. Holborn and Schultze[26] also made measurements in the same temperature range but up to 100 atm only. These results were among the first that were obtained at the Reichsanstalt and there is little doubt that their accuracy is superior to that of Amagat's data. Below 0° C the pioneer work was done by Witkowski[53] at Crakow at the end of the nineteenth century. This author considered the errors that arise in compressibility measurements and devised his own apparatus to reduce these to a minimum. He measured the coefficient of expansion of air at constant pressure with the aid of a differential manometer and from his results deduced values of the product PV. His lowest temperatures were realized in an ethylene cryostat operating at reduced pressure whereby a temperature of – 140° C was reached. The maximum pressure in Witkowski's work was 130 atm. PENNING[41] at Leiden in 1923 measured three isochores of air in the same temperature range. He attributed the discrepancies between his results and those of Witkowski to the latter's uncertain temperature measurements, but BEATTIE and BRIDGEMAN[4] on the other hand have pointed out errors in Witkowski's actual calculations. Two isotherms of air at 0° C and −79° C have also been measured by KOCH[32] but these are of doubtful accuracy since even at 0° C they show in places an almost 1 per cent discrepancy from the work of Amagat and Holborn and Schultze. HOLBORN and OTTO[25] deduced the virial coefficients of air and other gases for temperatures from 0° C to 200° C, choosing metres of mercury as the pressure unit, but slight errors in all their analytical expressions have been pointed out by CRAGOE[9].

The measurements of Michels and his co-workers[37] at the Van der Waals laboratory have a different order of accuracy and precision from any of the above determinations except possibly those of Holborn and Schultze. Above 0° C the standard method using the variable volume piezometer with electrical contacts was adopted. It was found that accuracy was impaired at temperatures above 75° C due to oxidation of the mercury surface in the piezometer so that the usual 100° C, 125° C and 150° C isotherms are not reported. For the same reason the maximum pressure at 75° C is only 250 atm, although at 0° C it was found that satisfactory operation could be achieved up to 2000 atm. Below 0° C a new method using a constant volume piezometer with a diaphragm manometer was used; in fact the measurements with air were the first to be undertaken by the new method. The precision and reproducibility of the results show that the new method is at least as good, if not better, than the standard method, and so for the first time there are available P-V-T data for air at temperatures below 0° C in which the utmost confidence can be placed. Since the new method is virtually one at constant volume the maximum pressure reached on the isotherms gets progressively less, ranging from 1000 atm at −25° C to 200 atm at −145° C and 125 atm at −155° C. At the lower temperatures the pressure intervals at constant temperature and at constant volume become rather large, making interpolation less certain.

Some of the measurements were made in the two-phase region, and since air is a mixture of gases, this immediately calls the composition of the phases into question. There is no doubt, however, that no matter what the individual compositions of the phases may have been during the measurement of these two-phase points, the total composition of the two phases together was that of air, which in the case of all the Van der Waals work means dry air free from carbon dioxide but with argon and the other inert gases included. As will be described later, the two-phase points determined at the Van der Waals laboratory were very valuable in enabling the vapour–pressure relationship, the specific volumes of the saturated phases and, indirectly, the latent heats of vaporization to be deduced.

4

2. The Specific Heat of Gaseous Air

Numerous investigators have determined the specific heat of air and the ratio γ at 1 atm pressure, mostly at temperatures of $0°$ C upwards. Ignoring the pioneer investigations of the nineteenth century, there are results by HOLBORN and AUSTIN[23], SWANN[48], SCHEEL and HEUSE[45], HOLBORN and JAKOB[24], SHILLING and PARTINGTON[47] and EUCKEN and VON LÜDE[15]. Between them these authors adopted a variety of well-known methods such as the method of mixtures, adiabatic expansion, constant flow and velocity of sound measurements. They measured either C_p or γ and deduced C_v with the aid of an equation of state, usually that of Berthelot. Direct values of C_v have been reported by GIACOMINI[19] and by HENRY[22]. At low temperatures Scheel and Heuse report values for C_p at $-76°$ C and $-181°$ C measured with their glass flow calorimeter, whilst for C_v Giacomini reports values at $-30°$ C, $-40°$ C and $-190°$ C, the latter being at a pressure of $\frac{1}{3}$ atm. At higher pressures than 1 atm there are experimentally determined values by Holborn and Jakob for a mean temperature of $60°$ C, and values calculated by BRIDGEMAN[6] from the Beattie–Bridgeman equation, by Witkowski[54] and by JAKOB[29] from the P-V-T data and by Roebuck[42] from his measurements of the Joule–Thomson effect.

The specific heat of air as a mixture has also been calculated from the spectroscopic and statistical data of the constituent gases. As already mentioned, Williams relied on the zero pressure spectroscopic values for oxygen and nitrogen reported by JOHNSTON and his co-workers[30]. These workers state that their spectroscopic values for oxygen and nitrogen are more reliable than the experimental values. On the other hand, the spectroscopic values of TRAUTZ and ADER[50] for air are in no better agreement with those based on Johnston's results than with the experimental values, and these German authors conclude that their own calculated values are probably at fault due to incomplete knowledge of the energy levels in the oxygen and nitrogen molecules.

The various values for C_p at 1 atm as well as the zero pressure values of Trautz and Ader are indicated in *Figure 1* as functions of temperature. For the present work it seemed justified to draw an arbitrary curve through the points as shown and to use this as the basis of the C_p values at 1 atm. To convert the values to Joules/mole, °K a factor of $4\cdot184$ J $=1$ cal was used since for most of the results shown in *Figure 1* the precise factor is not indicated by the authors. The C_v values at precisely 1 atm pressure are even less certain. After due consideration it was decided to adopt a constant value of $20\cdot7$ J/mole, °K at all temperatures up to $240°$ K followed by a slight steady rise to $21\cdot0$ J/mole, °K at $450°$ K, the upper limit of the present data.

5

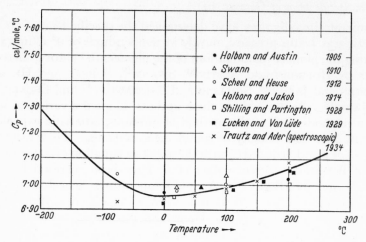

Figure 1.   The specific heat of air at constant pressure at 1 atm

3. The Joule–Thomson Expansion

The differential and integral Joule–Thomson effects for air have been determined by several investigators.   Besides the original work of JOULE and THOMSON[31], measurements have been made by DALTON[10], BRADLEY and HALE[5], VOGEL[51], NOELL[39], Hausen[21], HOXTON[27], EUMORFOPOULOS and RAI[16] and Roebuck[42].   It is clear on examination of the results that the agreement among the various investigations is not good.   For instance, Williams has pointed out that there is a 16 per cent difference between the results of Hausen and Roebuck for the integral effect from 200 atm to 1 atm at 230° K.   Bradley and Hale's results agree with Roebuck's within a maximum difference of 5 per cent in the middle of their common range but the results of Noell are in better agreement with those of Hausen, which is not surprising since the same apparatus was used for both investigations.   Roebuck measured the integral effect for pressures from 200 atm to 1 atm and initial temperatures from 200° C down to – 150° C.   The compressed gas passed radially through cylindrical porous porcelain plugs of varying porosity.   Elaborate precautions were taken to control the pressure and temperature, and errors due to heat leaks were considered and allowed for.   Roebuck himself has reviewed Hausen's differential method and the rather large discrepancy between the two sets of results is attributed to the ignoring of the kinetic effect by Hausen. Since the work on air, Roebuck and his school have determined the Joule–Thomson effect for a number of other gases with numerous modifications and improvements to the apparatus.   It is unfortunate that incorrect calibration of the pressure gauges remained in force for a considerable number of years before the error was discovered[43].   In all of Roebuck's results prior to 1940 the pressure has to be multiplied by a factor of 0·9677 wherever it appears, including the values of the Joule–Thomson coefficient itself, which are actually in degrees per 0·9677 atm instead of degrees per atmosphere as reported. Even if one prefers the Joule–Thomson data of Roebuck to those of the other investigators, the fact remains that the accurate determination of the Joule–Thomson effect is a matter of considerable difficulty and one doubts the reliability of thermodynamic functions calculated on this basis. Where very precise P-V-T data are available, as is now the case for air, the Joule–Thomson data are better used as a check on the computations from the P-V-T data.

4. The Vapour Pressure

Since air is a mixture there are two vapour pressure curves, one for the saturated liquid and the other for the saturated vapour of the same composition, corresponding with the bubble and dew points. The poineer data of Baly[3] and Olszewski[40] as used by Hausen are now known to be in error and there can be little doubt that the more recent work of Dodge and Dunbar[13] on the oxygen–nitrogen liquid–vapour equilibrium is considerably more accurate. Baly, for instance, gives the normal boiling point of oxygen as 91·0° K, almost a degree higher than the now accepted fixed point for boiling oxygen. Williams used the following two formulae based on Dodge and Dunbar's results, applied over the whole range of pressure from 1 atm up to the critical point:

$$\text{Bubble point: } Log_{10} P_{atm} = 3 \cdot 8803 - \frac{305 \cdot 47}{T}$$

$$\text{Dew point: } Log_{10} P_{atm} = 4 \cdot 1139 - \frac{336 \cdot 34}{T}$$

These two formulae, however, are not beyond criticism. First, the work of Dodge and Dunbar is for the binary system oxygen–nitrogen, whereas air contains nearly 1 per cent of argon in addition. Since argon is intermediate in volatility between nitrogen and oxygen it is not considered that the 1 per cent of argon is a serious objection to using Dodge and Dunbar's results as a basis for the vapour pressure of air. A more serious objection arises from the temperature measurements of Dodge and Dunbar. At the higher temperatures of their investigations the thermocouples were calibrated at the then prevailing Leiden value of the methane point which is now known to be nearly 0·5° C in error. Furthermore, latest analysis of Dodge and Dunbar's results[7] shows that they are lacking in thermodynamic self-consistency, again particularly at the higher temperatures and pressures.

There have been very few other investigations of the vapour pressure relationship of air.   Kuenen and Clark[33] carried out investigations on air in the critical region, their results for the dew and bubble pressures being given in Table 1.

TABLE 1

THE VAPOUR PRESSURE OF AIR (Kuenen and Clark[33])

Temperature °C	Dew pressure atm	Bubble pressure atm
− 140·63	37·17	37·17
		point of contact
− 140·64	37·12	37·24
− 140·69	37·02	37·26
− 140·73		37·25
		plait point
− 140·74	36·99	37·42
− 140·75	36·86	
− 140·80	36·65	37·20
− 140·80	36·70	
− 140·83	36·68	
− 140·85	36·75	37·18
− 140·89	36·57	
− 140·99	36·35	
− 141·35	35·24	36·49
− 141·99	34·58	
− 142·35	33·91	35·31
− 143·14	32·06	
− 143·34	31·85	33·79
− 144·12	31·06	33·12
− 144·35		32·52
− 146·32		29·83
− 150·12	23·68	25·04

These authors used the standard Leiden dilatometer for their measurements with arrangements for stirring the condensed liquid magnetically. The phenomenon of retrograde condensation associated with mixtures at the critical point was observed and values were obtained for the two critical points, the so-called plait point where the pressure is a maximum and the point of contact where the temperature is a maximum.   The differences, however, are only about 0·1° K in temperature and 0·1 atm in pressure.   The essential feature of a dew and bubble point determination at constant composition—in this case that of air—is that one phase should predominate, liquid at the bubble point, vapour at the dew point, the other phase being present, theoretically at least, in infinitesimally small quantity.   As those who have observed phenomena in glass vessels in the critical region will appreciate, Kuenen and Clark had great difficulty in satisfying themselves that they had reproduced such conditions. Apart from suggesting that Kuenen and Clark's temperature scale is seriously in error—and the latest work from the Van der Waals laboratory does not suggest this—it is difficult to see how Kuenen and Clark's results in the critical region can be improved upon. Their values for the critical constants of air are those always quoted in published tables.

Apart from the work of Kuenen and Clark there is only one other investigation of the vapour pressure relationship for air so far as is known, which is a determination of some dew points around 1 atm pressure by FURUKAWA and McCOSKEY[17]. These investigators added air at constant pressure in discreet quantities to a vacuum calorimeter until the pressure versus quantity added graph showed a sudden break at the dew point. The data were required for wind tunnel research purposes and only 5 mm accuracy is claimed.

The method of deriving satisfactory vapour pressure data for this survey is described later when the other saturation properties are also considered. It required a fairly involved analysis of the P-V-T data of Michels in this region together with other relevant data. At this stage it may be stated that the values for the dew and bubble points at 1 atm pressure derived by Williams from the work of Dodge and Dunbar have been retained. These are: bubble point 78·8° K; dew point 81·8° K. In this temperature region the work of Dodge and Dunbar is not seriously in error and the above values are believed to be correct to within 0·1° K.

5. The Density of the Saturated Liquid and Vapour

The densities of the saturated liquid and vapour phases—not in equilibrium with each other but each having the composition of air— were determined by Kuenen and Clark[33] in the same investigation as that mentioned in the preceding section. Their results are given in Table 2.

At the normal boiling point for the liquid DEWAR[12] reports the density as 0·91 g/cm³ and LADENBURG and KRÜGEL[34] as 0·92 g/cm³. There is little doubt, however, that these early values are much too high, representing a liquid considerably richer in oxygen than air. For this work a value of 0·847 g/cm³ has been chosen, based on the values for pure nitrogen, argon and oxygen with the assumption that there is no volume change on isothermal mixing at 78·8° K. As mentioned in the previous section, the finally adopted values for the densities of the saturated phases will be discussed more fully later.

6. The Latent Heat of Vaporization

Since air is a mixture it is necessary to state precisely what is meant by the latent heat of vaporization. According to the manner of

9

TABLE 2

THE DENSITY OF THE SATURATED LIQUID AND VAPOUR
(Kuenen and Clark[33])

Note: The phases are not in equilibrium at the same temperature.

Temperature °C	Vapour g/cm³	Liquid g/cm³
− 140·63	0·31	0·31
		point of contact
− 140·69		0·323
− 140·70		0·328
− 140·73		0·35
		plait point
− 140·75	0·277	
− 140·80	0·265	0·365
− 140·84	0·269	
− 140·85		0·359
− 140·89	0·262	
− 140·99	0·253	
− 141·34		0·439
− 141·99	0·217	
− 142·35		0·461
− 143·34	0·188	
− 143·35		0·488
− 144·35		0·503
− 146·32		0·523

definition it is possible to arrive at four or five different values. From the point of view of constructing a thermodynamic diagram, the most convenient definition, and the one which most authors have assumed, is that it is the amount of heat necessary to evaporate completely unit quantity of air as liquid at the bubble point to vapour at the dew point at constant pressure, and therefore with a rise in temperature throughout the process. Dana[11] has reviewed all the previous determinations of the latent heats of oxygen, nitrogen and air and points out that all the earlier values for air are uncertain, if for no other reason than that the nature of the latent heat being measured was not definite. Dana devised a very ingenious glass calorimeter to measure the latent heats of pure oxygen and nitrogen and mixtures of these gases in which a very small quantity of liquid in a thermally insulated chamber was evaporated completely by an electrically heated wire, the liquid being replenished through a very fine capillary from a large bulk outside the chamber. A steady state was soon reached in which the vapour issuing from the calorimeter had the same composition as the main bulk of the liquid which was therefore at a lower temperature than the liquid in the small chamber where evaporation was taking place. The establishment of this steady state was the chief difficulty to be overcome since it was very sensitive to changes in the liquid levels. Care was taken to reduce heat leaks and other sources of error to a minimum. The latent heat values for oxygen–nitrogen mixtures given in Table 3 are Dana's smoothed results.

TABLE 3

THE LATENT HEAT OF VAPORIZATION OF OXYGEN–NITROGEN MIXTURES
(Dana[11])

Oxygen moles %	Latent heat cal/g	Oxygen moles %	Latent heat cal/g	Oxygen moles %	Latent heat cal/g
0	47·74	35	49·83	70	51·08
5	48·06	40	50·07	75	51·17
10	48·37	45	50·28	80	51·23
15	48·68	50	50·48	85	51·23
20	48·98	55	50·67	90	51·18
25	49·28	60	50·83	95	51·12
30	49·57	65	50·97	100	51·01

Expressing the latent heat in cal/g there is thus a maximum at 82 per cent oxygen. Dana's results have been used by all recent authors who have computed the thermodynamic functions of air as the basis of the latent heat value at 1 atm. Again it is necessary to ignore the argon, or at least to class it with the nitrogen. For this work the latent heat of a 21 per cent oxygen mixture has therefore been taken as 49·04 cal/g from Dana's results.

There are no experimental data for the latent heat of air at pressures other than 1 atm. All authors of thermodynamic diagrams have adopted indirect methods based on the values for oxygen and nitrogen. The following method used by Williams and by Claitor and Crawford is typical. When the molar entropy of vaporization, i.e. the latent heat divided by the temperature, is plotted against the reduced temperature, it is observed that a single curve can be drawn through all the points whether they are for oxygen or nitrogen, and also that Dana's experimental value for air at 1 atm also gives a point on the curve. The curve is therefore assumed to be equally valid for air at all temperatures up to the critical point, the temperature of evaporation in the case of air being taken as the mean between the bubble and dew points. Hausen derived a similar relationship for the "reduced latent heat", which he defines as the actual latent heat divided by the product critical volume times critical pressure, and he used this function for his

11

air diagram. In these procedures it is often forgotten, however, that the latent heat values for oxygen and nitrogen are not in general experimental values either. At 1 atm there are values by ALT[1], which although obtained half a century ago are nevertheless very good values indeed, but at other pressures the only data for oxygen and nitrogen are those calculated by MATHIAS, CROMMELIN and ONNES[35] by means of the Clausius–Clapeyron equation from the Leiden density and vapour pressure data obtained at the beginning of the century. These authors point out that the calculated values are least certain at low pressures and near the critical point. Moreover the temperature scale has undergone some modification since the time of this early Leiden work.

The Clausius–Clapeyron equation does not apply for air since pressure and temperature do not both remain constant during evaporation, *i.e.* the Gibbs' thermodynamic potential is not constant. Nevertheless, as will be explained later, the equation has been approximated in this work and used to calculate the latent heats. It is believed that the new values are no more suspect than the earlier ones.

7. *The Specific Heat of the Saturated Liquid*

Liquid air was one of the substances whose specific heat under saturation conditions was determined by the calorimetric measurements of EUCKEN and HAUCK[14]. The values for air which range from 80° K to 120° K were obtained in 1928, twelve years later than the pioneer work of this school, and after certain improvements had been made to the apparatus. Most of the work of this school, however, appears to be in error when compared with more modern precise calorimetric measurements, and so the values for air must be accepted with some reservation.

8. *Solid Air*

There have been no investigations with air solidified under extremely high pressures as in the case of nitrogen, argon and a number of other gases. In recent years there has been some interest in the solid–liquid equilibria under conditions of normal freezing, *i.e.* at triple point temperatures, of a number of systems of the so-called permanent gases. The systems nitrogen–oxygen, argon–oxygen and argon–nitrogen have all been investigated and some very interesting phenomena involving solid solution formation observed. These investigations, however, are still in the pioneer stage and have as yet no thermodynamic significance in the sense of this survey.

CALCULATION OF THE THERMODYNAMIC FUNCTIONS AND CONSTRUCTION OF THE THERMODYNAMIC DIAGRAM

9. *Units, Constants and Conversion Factors*

The pressure unit chosen for the present work is the international atmosphere, $g = 980 \cdot 665$, and the unit of volume the cubic centimetre.

The Kelvin scale of temperature has been used, related to the Celsius scale by an ice point of 0° C=273·15° K.   The unit quantity of air is the "gramme-molecule", namely 28·96 g.   This is the same mean value for the "molecular weight" of air that all recent authors of thermo-dynamic compilations have used and it takes into account the 0·93 per cent of argon present in the atmosphere.   The air is assumed to be free from water vapour and carbon dioxide.   The energy unit is the Joule. Where it has been necessary to correlate this unit with the calorie, namely for the specific heat and latent heat data, a conversion factor of 1 cal =4·184 J has been used as being a probable value covering the work of all the various authors within the limits of their experimental accuracy.

In the low pressure range, *i.e.* at pressures up to about 100 atm at 273·15° K but becoming less than this as the temperature is reduced, the *P-V-T* data can be adequately expressed by series equations:

$$PV = A + BP + CP^2$$
$$= RT(1 + B'P + C'P^2)$$

where A, B and C are functions of the temperature only.   Michels and his co-workers have computed the A, B and C constants for regular intervals of temperature from 348·15° K (75° C) to 138·15° K (– 135° C) from their *P-V-T* measurements.   If the values of the A constant are divided by the corresponding absolute temperature, a value of 0·00366317 is found for the gas constant, R, for air in the Amagat system.   It should be noted that this value is not the same as 1/273·15 =0·0036610 which is the value of R for a perfect gas in the Amagat system.   At 0° C and for pressures below 1 atm the C constant can be ignored and it can easily be shown that under these conditions the volume of the real gas at 0° C and 1 atm is related to the ideal gas volume by the expression:

$$V_{real} = \frac{V_{ideal}}{273·15 \times R}$$

where R is again the gas constant for the real gas in the Amagat system. Taking the volume of 1 gramme-mole of ideal gas at 0° C and 1 atm as 22,414·6 cm³ (oxygen = 16, chemical scale) the molecular volume of air under the same conditions is found to be 22,401·2 cm³, the Amagat unit per mole.   As usual, the *P-V-T* data of Michels are given in the Amagat system, and by using this system throughout, the energy terms are derived in Amagat unit-atmospheres per mole.   Taking the cm³-atm as equivalent to 0·101325 J, a conversion factor of 2,269·8 was found for converting the derived data from Amagat unit-atm per mole to joule per mole.   The density of air at N.T.P. on the basis of the above figures is 1·2928 mg/cm³ which agrees to 1 part in 10,000 with the value given in the Landolt–Bornstein tables.

10. Calculation of the Thermodynamic Functions from P-V-T Data in the Homogeneous Region

The recently obtained *P-V-T* data of Michels and his co-workers, covering as they do a comprehensive range of pressure and temperature, are undoubtedly the best basis for a compilation of the thermodynamic functions of air. The Michels data, as they first became available to the present author, were in the form of isothermal values of the product pressure times volume, *PV*, in Amagat units at rounded off temperatures in °C and at a series of approximately constant densities. Since the final values of the thermodyamic functions were required with rounded off Kelvin degrees and rounded off pressures as the independent variables, it was necessary to do a certain amount of graphical interpolation.

The volume residual, *r*, defined by:

$$r = \frac{RT}{P} - V = \frac{RT - PV}{P}$$

was therefore worked out for each recorded *PV* value. These *r* values were then plotted as isotherms in rounded off °C as reported by Michels and values were read off for rounded off pressures. These values were then plotted against the temperature as isobars and *r* values read off from these curves were therefore at rounded off pressures in atmospheres and temperatures in °K. The lowest temperature isotherm of Michels is at 118·15° K (−155° C) and the highest at 348·15° K (75° C). An extension of the data to higher temperatures up to 100 atm pressure was possible by using the results of Holborn and Schultze which are the only others that can compare with those of Michels in accuracy. The *PV* values of Holborn and Schultze are given for pressures in metres of mercury and with a reference value of *PV* = 1 for 0° C and 1 metre of mercury. Their three isotherms at 0° C, 100° C and 200° C were converted to the Amagat system and *r* values were worked out and plotted along with those of Michels. At 0° C the agreement was quite satisfactory and therefore Holborn and Schultze's results at 100° C and 200° C were accepted.

The values of *r* for rounded off pressures in atmospheres and temperatures in °K were found by this method of graphical interpolation with satisfactory precision over most of the range. In the critical region the values change very rapidly and there was inevitably a loss of precision as a result of the interpolation. In the compressed liquid region, *i.e.* at high pressures and low temperatures, there was also a loss of precision due to the fact that the experimental points are rather far apart, again making interpolation difficult. No extrapolations of the *r* values were made. The finally tabulated *r* values were smoothed along isobars and isotherms by taking differences and the table was then used as the basis of the subsequent calculations.

Before proceeding to discuss the calculation of the other thermo-

dynamic functions, however, it may be as well to describe the derivation
of the final volumes since these were mainly calculated from the r
values. Actually, the volume values were worked out after good
P-V-T data had been established for the saturation boundary since
these were needed for the construction of the product PV versus pressure diagram. Values of the product PV were worked out from the
tabulated r values according to the relation:

$$PV = RT - Pr$$

It will be seen that the r values have to be multiplied by the pressure,
and it is apparent, therefore, that at high pressures any errors in r are
considerably magnified in the effect they have on the calculated PV
values. As already stated, the r values in the critical and compressed
liquid regions were less reliable, which in turn made the recalculated
values of PV uncertain. In these regions r itself is not a particularly
small term compared with PV and a direct interpolation of PV values
from the experimental data is just as reliable, if not more so, than proceeding through the residual. Therefore, when drawing the PV versus
pressure diagram in these regions frequent reference was made to the
original data of Michels which were included on the diagram before
transposing it to a PV versus temperature diagram. After smoothing
this diagram as necessary it was transposed back to the final PV versus
pressure diagram from which PV values were taken. After checking
the values for smoothness in the usual way the volumes were found
simply by dividing by the pressure and converting from Amagat units
to cubic centimetres. It should be emphasized again that it was only
for pressures above 300 atm at all temperatures and above 30 atm for
temperatures below 160° K that any difficulty was experienced; elsewhere the necessary interpolations and smoothing were quite straight-
forward and the final tabulated values of volume over most of the range
are believed to be scarcely less accurate than the original P-V-T
measurements.

In order to calculate the other thermodynamic functions from the
table of volume residuals, it was decided to calculate first the Gibbs'
thermodynamic potential and from it the other functions by differentiation. The equations describing these processes are:

$$G = H - TS \qquad \dots (1)$$

$$dG = VdP - SdT \qquad \dots (2)$$

$$\left(\frac{\partial G}{\partial T}\right)_P = -S \qquad \dots (3)$$

$$\left(\frac{\partial G}{\partial P}\right)_T = V = \frac{RT}{P} - r \qquad \dots (4)$$

15

$$\frac{\partial^2 G}{\partial T^2}\bigg)_P = -\frac{\partial S}{\partial T}\bigg)_P = -\frac{1}{T}\frac{\partial H}{\partial T}\bigg)_P = -\frac{C_p}{T} \qquad \ldots \ldots (5)$$

Integrating equation 4:

$$\Delta G\bigg]_{P_1}^{P_2}\bigg]_T = \int_{P_1}^{P_2} V\mathrm{d}P\bigg]_T = \int_{P_1}^{P_2}\frac{RT}{P}\mathrm{d}P - \int_{P_1}^{P_2} r\mathrm{d}P\bigg]_T = RT\log_e\frac{P_2}{P_1} - \int_{P_1}^{P_2} r\mathrm{d}P\bigg]_T (6)$$

The value of ΔG between successive isobars at any constant temperature may thus be computed from the table of smoothed residuals. The Napierian logarithms of the pressures were first taken and the successive differences between these, $\Delta \ln P$, were recorded and converted to RT ($\Delta \ln P$) values. Columns of $r\Delta P$ values were then drawn up for each temperature, r being the average value between successive isobars.

The values of r were thus virtually integrated to give the $\int_{P_1}^{P_2} r\mathrm{d}P\bigg]_T$ term in equation 6. By taking the $r\Delta P$ values from the RT ($\Delta \ln P$) values the corresponding $\Delta G\bigg]_{P_1}^{P_2}\bigg]_T$ values were obtained.

The advantage of this method of working is that it avoids the somewhat uncertain procedure of measuring the slopes of residual curves. The calculation of the ΔG values described above becomes a purely arithmetical process. Furthermore by this arithmetical procedure, assuming that the possible errors in the original r values are known, it is possible to estimate precisely the errors that are arising at each step, a much more difficult problem when graphical methods are used. The errors, of course, are all contained in the $r\Delta P$ term. In the low pressure range the ΔP's are 5 atm, 10 atm or 20 atm so that the error in r is not unduly magnified. At the higher pressures, however, the ΔP's are 100 atm or 200 atm and small errors in r become much larger errors in ΔG. For instance, at 270° K, ΔG between 10 atm and 15 atm was computed as $0\cdot39801 \pm 0\cdot00005$ Amagat unit-atm/mole but between 1000 atm and 1200 atm the value was $0\cdot38232 \pm 0\cdot00200$ Amagat unit-atm/mole. It appears to the present author that this loss of accuracy at high pressures is inevitable whatever method of computing the thermodynamic functions from the P-V-T data is used; the present method of working merely makes this fact abundantly clear.

Taking the entropy and enthalpy as zero for the liquid boiling at the bubble point at 1 atm, 78·8° K, Dana's experimental latent heat value leads to an entropy of 74·00 J/mole, ° K and an enthalpy of 5942 J/mole for the vapour at the dew point at 1 atm, 81·8° K. From this point the entropy and enthalpy values along the 1 atm isobar were readily calculated by graphically integrating the C_p curve in *Figure 1*.

$$\Delta S \Big]_{T_1}^{T_2} \Big]_P = \int_{T_1}^{T_2} \frac{C_p}{T} \, \mathrm{d}T \Big]_P$$

$$\Delta H \Big]_{T_1}^{T_2} \Big]_P = \int_{T_1}^{T_2} C_p \, \mathrm{d}T \Big]_P$$

The values of the Gibbs' thermodynamic potential followed arithmetically from the entropy and enthalpy values.

$$G = H - TS$$

Using these as reference values, the complete table of values of the Gibbs' thermodynamic potential was drawn up from the already computed values of ΔG along the isotherms. Below the critical temperature it was possible to proceed from the 1 atm isobar to the saturated vapour boundary. For a pure substance there is no change in the Gibbs' thermodynamic potential on going from saturated vapour to saturated liquid at the same temperature and pressure; but this is not so for air. Consequently, it was not possible at this stage to continue the calculation of the Gibbs' thermodynamic potential into the compressed liquid region below the critical point. On the superheated vapour side values could be computed down to 120° K, the limit of Michels' P-V-T data. Extrapolation to lower temperatures followed later after the two-phase boundary had been established.

From the table of values of the Gibbs' thermodynamic potential, values of the derivative $-\dfrac{\Delta G}{\Delta T}\Big)_P$ were worked out arithmetically along the isobars thus giving entropy values at the mean temperatures of the temperature intervals. Tables of successive isothermal and isobaric entropy differences were then drawn up and the differences smoothed out. At the lower pressures very little smoothing was required; it was only above 300 atm where, as already explained, the Gibbs' thermodynamic potential values were liable to error that any roughness appeared in the entropy differences. Even these, however, tended to fluctuate regularly, a manifestly too large difference being followed by a too small one. It was thus comparatively easy to decide which values of the Gibbs' function were most in error and to make the necessary adjustments. Using the table of smoothed isothermal entropy differences and the base values at 1 atm, a fresh table of entropy values was drawn up for the normal temperatures as distinct from the intermediate temperatures obtained after differentiating the Gibbs' thermodynamic potential. The values of the Gibbs' function and entropy at 320° K, the highest temperature over the maximum pressure range, were now accepted as the basic isothermal values and the corresponding enthalpy values were calculated arithmetically.

The next procedure was to calculate the specific heat at constant pressure from the entropy values using the relationship

$$C_p = T \frac{\Delta S}{\Delta T} \bigg)_P$$

where T is again the mean temperature over the temperature interval, the resulting C_p value likewise being for the mean temperature. The C_p values were plotted as isotherms on a large scale C_p versus pressure diagram and as isobars on a C_p versus temperature diagram with numerous slight adjustments until both diagrams were smooth and mutually consistent. Only in the critical region was any difficulty experienced. The 300 atm isobar was then extrapolated into the compressed liquid region down to 120° K and the C_p values used as the basis for calculating the entropy, enthalpy and Gibbs' thermodynamic potential by integration in the usual way. The previously determined ΔG values in the compressed liquid region were then used to calculate the remaining values of the Gibbs' function which could not previously be calculated, and with them the entropy and specific heat as before. The smoothed C_p values were tabulated and then used to recalculate the entropy and enthalpy by integration along the isobars using the already established values at 320° K as basis. In this way smooth, internally consistent specific heat, entropy and enthalpy tables were assured. After the saturation boundary had been established as described later, the values were tested by drawing temperature–entropy, volume–entropy, enthalpy–temperature, enthalpy–pressure and enthalpy–entropy diagrams of the compressed liquid and critical regions with interchanged parameters. A little roughness was still found in the compressed liquid region but this was smoothed out without impairing the internal consistency until all the discrepancies had been transferred to the critical region where they can be tolerated and where they undoubtedly arise in the first place.

Below 120° K in the superheated vapour region the isobars were extrapolated downwards on a log temperature–entropy diagram. On this diagram the isobars are almost straight sloping lines and extrapolation is easy. The isobars were extrapolated to the appropriate dew point temperatures, obtained as described later, and the terminal points were then joined to give the saturated vapour boundary.

11. The Two-phase Boundary and the Latent Heats

The derivation of good values for the thermodynamic functions on the two-phase boundary has been the most interesting feature of the present work. The *P-V-T* measurements of Michels and his co-workers include 32 observations made within the two-phase region, covering 10 isotherms at close intervals of temperature from 118·15° K (– 155° C) to 132·15° K (– 141° C), the latter being a fraction of a degree below the critical point. These 32 observations are spread over six runs, a run being a series of measurements for a given filling of the piezometer and therefore very nearly at constant density. The measured points are spread quite uniformly over the area, some being close to the vapour boundary, others to the liquid boundary, whilst others are well inside the two-phase region. The Van der Waals low-temperature apparatus is not designed to make measurements precisely on the boundary and it is possible to determine such points only by ascertaining where the breaks and discontinuities occur in the measured data when these are analysed by various means. The Van der Waals workers agree with the present author that the results one gets depend very largely on the methods adopted and the ingenuity displayed, particularly since for the most part one is working in the critical region where very sudden changes in magnitudes and trends occur. Therein lies the interest of the problem.

The volume residual terms, r as already defined, of all the Van der Waals observations in the critical and the two-phase regions were first plotted against the pressure and the points joined appropriately to indicate isotherms and lines for a constant run, the latter being almost the same as a line of constant volume. On the isotherms the breaks at the saturated vapour boundary were quite well defined, on the "iso-runs" less so and those at the saturated liquid boundary were impossible to determine. This graph was repeated for the two-phase points only using a very large pressure scale, 1 mm = 0·01 atm, when it appeared, somewhat surprisingly, that with the exception of the points for one particular run, they all lay on straight lines within 0·01 atm. By taking the values of r at the breaks from the first graph, the corresponding pressures were found from the second graph to within 0·01 atm. These were dew point pressures at the corresponding temperatures of the isotherms. Next, pressure was plotted against temperature at constant run on a very large scale. The points when joined gave curves showing a break at the saturation boundary where condensation set in. The values of pressure and temperature at the boundary obtained by these two methods were next plotted on a log P, $\dfrac{1}{T}$ graph, including also Kuenen and Clark's results as given in Table 1. Also it had to be borne in mind that at 1 atm the two vapour pressure curves had to pass through the points 78·8° K for the bubble curve and 81·8° K for the dew curve. The following vapour pressure formulae were accordingly provisionally established:

$$\text{Bubble Curve: } \mathrm{Log}_{10} P_{\text{atm}} = 3 \cdot 8791 - \frac{305 \cdot 68}{T}$$

$$\text{Dew Curve: } \mathrm{Log}_{10} P_{\text{atm}} = 4 \cdot 0816 - \frac{333 \cdot 88}{T}$$

19

These formulae were not considered valid above 30 atm. There is no sharp point of intersection of the dew and bubble curves at the critical point but the vapour pressure values depart from linearity on the $\log P, \dfrac{1}{T}$ graph above 30 atm to meet in a smooth hairpin loop at the critical point.

The values of the residual r at the breaks on the two-phase boundary were next plotted against temperature and a smooth curve was drawn through them. There were only three points on the liquid branch of the curve, none of which was considered reliable. The values of r were converted into densities in g/cm³ and in order to obtain additional values the $P\text{-}V\text{-}T$ data in the superheated vapour region were extrapolated judiciously along isobars and isotherms to the now established dew points to give the saturated vapour volumes. The values were tested by plotting the reciprocal of the volume, *i.e.* the saturated vapour density, against the pressure; this curve being almost a straight line passing through the origin at lower pressures and densities. When the temperature–density diagram for the two-phase boundary was drawn, including also the data of Kuenen and Clark, good values appeared for the saturated vapour but the liquid values were untenable, and the following artifice for determining the liquid densities was therefore adopted. The early reported values for the density of liquid air at 1 atm are certainly false and a much better value can be calculated from the Leiden values for pure oxygen, nitrogen and argon[36] on the assumption that there is no volume change on isothermal mixing. INGLIS and COATES[28] report that at around 50 per cent concentration there is about 1 per cent contraction when liquid oxygen and nitrogen are mixed, which agrees, qualitatively at least, with the known departure of the oxygen–nitrogen system from the ideal solution laws. On the basis of no contraction, however, a value of 0·874 g/cm³ was worked out for the density of liquid air at the bubble point at 1 atm, 78·8° K, and other values were worked out for 90° K and 100° K. These values were inserted on the density–temperature diagram and the law of the rectilinear diameter was then assumed which enabled other liquid densities to be calculated from the established vapour densities. Actually there are two rectilinear diameters for air, one bisecting the isotherms and ending at the point of contact, the other bisecting the isobars and ending at the plait point. It is interesting to observe that at higher pressures the liquid densities thus arrived at become progressively greater than those calculated from the values for oxygen, argon and nitrogen on the assumption of no contraction on mixing. This means, if the present values are regarded as correct, that there is in fact an increasing percentage contraction in volume on mixing the liquids, which is again in accord with the known behaviour of the oxygen–nitrogen system.

Having established the relationship between pressure, temperature and the density or volume around the saturation boundary, it was a simple matter to construct the product PV versus pressure diagram. On plotting the Van der Waals experimental points on this diagram, it was observed that the two-phase values on the liquid side of the area did not quite agree with the proposed data for the liquid branch of the boundary. This was attributed to the fact that the two-constant vapour pressure formula for the bubble curve is not adequate. This can be confirmed from consideration of the experimental results for the run in the two-phase region where the points are nearest to the liquid boundary. For this run the piezometer was nearly full of liquid and therefore these points should be only very slightly lower in pressure than 100 per cent liquid air. The two-constant formula shows them to be lower to a relatively large extent. Accordingly a new formula is proposed for the bubble point of air:

$$\text{Bubble curve:} \quad \text{Log}_{10} P_{\text{atm}} = 3 \cdot 5713 - \frac{290 \cdot 70}{T} + 0 \cdot 001494 T$$

When the PV versus pressure diagram is reconstructed on the basis of this formula the discrepancy previously observed disappears.

Figure 2 shows the two vapour pressure curves proposed for the present work at pressures above 20 atm. The actual points originally determined from the breaks in the P-V-T data are shown, together with the experimental observations for the Van der Waals run nearest the liquid

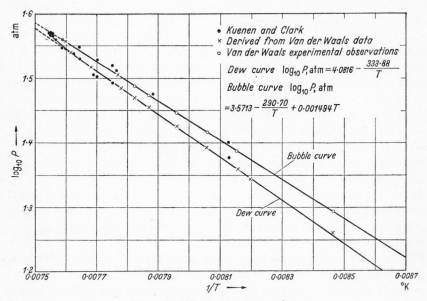

Figure 2. *The vapour pressure of air*

21

boundary. Kuenen and Clark's reported values are also included. As already mentioned the two formulae have only been used for pressures up to 30 atm. At higher pressures values are taken directly from the graph. *Figure 3* shows the density–temperature diagram above 118° K. The points obtained from the breaks in the P-V-T data are shown although it must be remembered that these were smoothed when

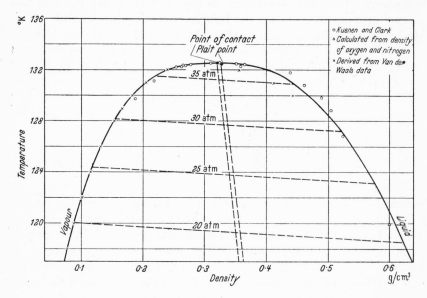

Figure 3. The density of air round the saturation boundary

in the form of volume residuals. On the vapour side these are the accepted values, but not on the liquid side. The two rectilinear diameters are shown which enable the liquid branch of the curve to be drawn, and at 120° K a point is indicated calculated from the densities of pure oxygen, argon and nitrogen on the assumption of no volume change on mixing. The proposed data are seen to be in agreement with the observations of Kuenen and Clark within the probable limits of their experimental accuracy. Finally, *Figure 4* is the product PV versus pressure diagram on the basis of the values proposed for this work, and this is in fact their real justification. This diagram may be drawn on quite a large scale—2 cm = 1 atm and 2 cm = 0·01 Amagat unit—and when the relevant Van der Waals observations are plotted there are no obvious discrepancies. It is believed that on the saturation boundary the pressures are correct to 1 part in 1000 and the product PV to 1 part in 500 along the vapour branch and 1 part in 200 along the liquid branch. This, of course, is considerably less than the precision of the individual P-V-T measurements, but it is doubtful whether anything better can be achieved short of actual experimental data on the boundary itself. The values have also been tested on a pressure versus volume diagram on which the Van der Waals results in the two-phase region show that the isotherms are humped up slightly towards the critical point. On the temperature–entropy diagram, therefore, the isobars should have a slight sag and this feature has been incorporated, although in a purely arbitrary manner.

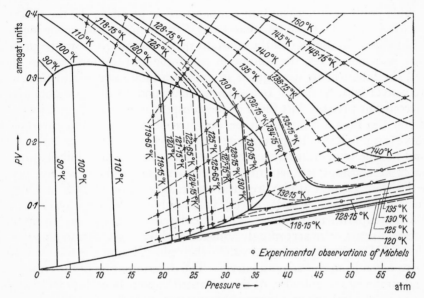

Figure 4. PV versus pressure diagram for air

After the P-V-T data for the saturation boundary had been established, there remained the latent heats to be considered and thence the entropy and enthalpy values. It was decided to use the P-V-T data and an approximation of the Clausius–Clapeyron equation to calculate the latent heats, rather than rely on the indirect methods that have been used by past authors as described in section 6. The derivatives $\dfrac{dP}{dT}$ were first calculated by differentiating the two vapour pressure formulae:

Bubble curve: $\dfrac{dP}{dT} = 2\cdot30258P\left[\dfrac{290\cdot7}{T^2} + 0\cdot001494\right]$ atm/°K

Dew curve: $\dfrac{dP}{dT} = 2\cdot30258P\left[\dfrac{333\cdot88}{T^2}\right]$ atm/°K

Values of these derivatives were worked out and the mean values between dew and bubble points, both for constant rounded off

23

temperatures and constant rounded off pressures were found. The latent heats were then worked out from the Clausius–Clapeyron equation:

$$L = T\varDelta V \frac{\mathrm{d}P}{\mathrm{d}T}$$

where L is the latent heat, $\frac{\mathrm{d}P}{\mathrm{d}T}$ the mean value between the dew and bubble point at either constant temperature or pressure, $\varDelta V$ the difference in volume between the phases and T the temperature, or the mean temperature in the case of the constant pressure series. With the pressure in atmospheres, the volume in cm³/mole and the temperature in °K, the latent heats were given in cm³-atm/mole, which had then to be converted to J/mole. It was found that good results were obtained at constant pressure but those of the constant temperature series were much too high. This might be expected since at constant pressure there is a much smaller percentage difference between the absolute dew and bubble temperatures than that between the dew and bubble pressures at constant temperature. The discrepancies between the two series were greatest at low pressures and temperatures and yet at 1 atm the constant pressure series gave a value only 0·5 per cent lower than Dana's experimental value. The calculated values for the constant pressure series were accordingly adjusted slightly to give a smooth curve through Dana's experimental value when plotted, and the final values were taken from this smooth curve. The determination of the entropy and similarly the enthalpy at the saturated vapour boundary by extrapolating the isobars on a log temperature–entropy diagram has already been mentioned. The latent heat values enabled the entropy and enthalpy of the saturated liquid boundary to be located from the relationship:

$$\varDelta S = \frac{\varDelta H}{T} = \frac{L}{T}$$

the temperature in this case being the mean between the dew and bubble points at the ends of the isobars according to the usual practice for air diagrams. The entropy values for the saturation boundary were tested for smoothness by computing the specific heat under saturation conditions:

$$C_\sigma = T \frac{\partial S}{\partial T}\bigg)_\sigma$$

the derivative $\dfrac{\partial S}{\partial T}\bigg)_\sigma$ being the reciprocal of the slope of the boundary line on the temperature–entropy diagram. The values are quite smooth and range from 51 J/mole, °K for the liquid at 80° K to 91 J/mole, °K at 121° K. The corresponding values of Eucken and Hauck[14]

24

are 57 J/mole, °K at 80° K and 75 J/mole, °K at 120° K, showing rather serious discrepancies.

12. Drawing the Diagram: the Specific Heat at Constant Volume

The constant volume lines cross the two-phase region on the temperature–entropy diagram were computed on the assumption that volume and entropy increase linearly along the isobars. This is certainly true for a single pure substance and probably sufficiently so for air within the accuracy with which the data can be plotted on a reasonable size temperature–entropy diagram. The enthalpy increments along the isobars in the two-phase region were calculated from the relationship:

$$\Delta H = T \Delta S$$

where T is not the mean value between the bubble and dew points but a value increasing steadily from the bubble point to the dew point with each successive interval.

In the homogeneous region the lines for rounded off values of enthalpy were computed by interpolation from the tables in the usual manner and also by taking the values from an enthalpy–temperature diagram. For the constant volume lines, isotherms on a large log volume versus entropy diagram were first drawn from which the entropy values at the chosen integral volumes could be taken.

When the constant volume lines had been drawn on the diagram, values of the specific heat at constant volume were worked out by measuring the slopes of these isochores and applying the relationship:

$$C_v = T \frac{\Delta S}{\Delta T}\bigg)_v$$

where T is the mean temperature over the temperature interval ΔT. The values of C_v were found to have a considerable scatter when plotted and a certain amount of ingenuity and guesswork was necessary in smoothing them out. Isochores on a C_v versus temperature diagram were first plotted and after this diagram had been smoothed by cross-plotting, i.e. isotherms on a C_v versus density diagram, the points of intersection of the isochores and isobars on the temperature–entropy diagram were inserted appropriately. When joined on the C_v versus temperature diagram these points gave the isobars which then enabled isotherms to be plotted on a C_v versus pressure diagram. The finally tabulated values are reasonably smooth against temperature, pressure, density and volume.

Michels and his co-workers have also calculated C_v from their P-V-T data. The Van der Waals data are usually computed in the first instance with density and temperature as the independent variables, and this makes the computation of C_v directly from the P-V-T data much easier and more accurate than measuring slopes on the temperature–entropy diagram. They find, as they have done for other gases, notably carbon dioxide and nitrogen, that C_v passes through a maximum on isothermal compression. The maxima are limited strictly to the critical region, the peaks in the isotherms diminishing very rapidly with increasing temperature until at 40° above the critical temperature there is a continuous rise in C_v on isothermal compression. On the present temperature–entropy diagram the effect is quite undetectable. The present C_v values must therefore be accepted with considerable reservation; they are probably little more than an indication of the trends in C_v as pressure and temperature are varied. Even Michels himself does not claim better than 5 per cent accuracy for his specific heat values in general, and in the critical region the accuracy may well be less than this.

Discussion

Since the final entropy and enthalpy values have both been computed by integrating the specific heat at constant pressure, these two functions will be thermodynamically consistent. The diagram also includes lines of constant volume and it is therefore possible to apply a still more stringent test for internal consistency using the thermodynamic equation:

$$dH = TdS + VdP$$

in its isothermal integrated form, *i.e.*

$$\Delta H]_T = T\Delta S]_T + \int VdP]_T$$

The equation was used to apply the test along a few isotherms over various pressure ranges by calculating ΔS. Values of the volume in the tables were plotted against the pressure along the isotherms and integrated graphically to give values of $\int VdP$. After converting to J/mole these were then subtracted from the corresponding tabulated enthalpy changes and divided by the temperature to give the entropy changes which could then be compared with the tabulated values. The results of the test are shown in Table 4.

It will be seen that the calculated and tabulated ΔS values agree within 1 per cent except over the pressure range 50 atm to 300 atm at 150° K, where the discrepancy is 2 per cent, probably due to the proximity of this area to the critical region. The calculated ΔS values depend almost entirely on the accuracy of the graphical integration of the $\int VdP$ terms and the agreement within 1 per cent is considered adequate proof that the diagram is internally consistent. It may be noted that all calculated values in Table 4 are slightly lower than the tabulated ones, indicating a probable systematic error in the graphical integrations.

26

TABLE 4

TESTING FOR INTERNAL CONSISTENCY

(1) Temperature °K	(2) Pressure range atm	(3) ΔH Tables J/mole	(4) ∫VdP J/mole	(5) ΔH − ∫VdP (3) − (4) J/mole	(6) ΔS calc (5) ÷ (1) J/mole, °K	(7) ΔS Tables J/mole, °K
120	1 – 10	− 355	2169	− 2524	− 21·03	− 21·18
150	1 – 10	− 222	2775	− 2997	− 19·98	− 20·17
	10 – 50	− 1582	1640	− 3222	− 21·48	− 21·60
	50 – 300	− 2011	1321	− 3332	− 22·21	− 22·61
200	1 – 10	− 123	3793	− 3916	− 19·58	− 19·60
	10 – 100	− 1361	3449	− 4810	− 24·05	− 24·31
	100 – 500	− 982	2566	− 3548	− 17·74	− 17·96
300	1 – 10	− 53	5721	− 5774	− 19·25	− 19·30
	10 – 100	− 517	5705	− 6222	− 20·74	− 20·75
	100 – 1000	+ 136	7085	− 6949	− 23·16	− 23·22

Figure 5 shows the temperature–entropy diagram in skeleton form indicating the sources of data that have been used in its preparation. Over the major portion of the diagram the *P-V-T* data of Michels have been used. At higher temperatures the *P-V-T* data from the Reichsanstalt were used and at the lowest temperatures there are two small regions where the data are based on extrapolations. Even in the two-phase region the diagram is based largely on data derived from the Van der Waals measurements. The critical data of Kuenen and Clark, Dana's latent heat value at 1 atm, the bubble and dew points at 1 atm which can be attributed to Dodge and Dunbar and the specific heat values at 1 atm are the only other data that have been considered in the present compilation. This extensive use of the data from one source is always to be recommended where these are of satisfactory accuracy and precision, since it means that anomalous trends in regions of overlapping data by different authors can be avoided and the whole process of calculating the thermodynamic functions can be made much more methodical and uniform, with a corresponding chance of greater accuracy.

Since so many compilations of the various thermodynamic properties of air have been made in the past, it is possible to compare the present work with that of other authors in many ways. Table 5 gives some

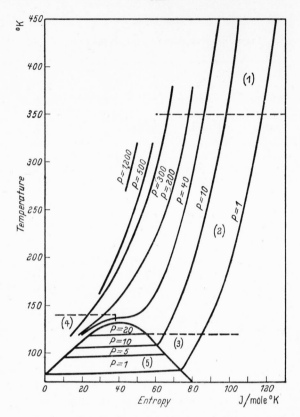

Figure 5. Skeleton temperature–entropy diagram for air

(1) *P-V-T* data—Holborn and Schultze.
(2) *P-V-T* data—Michels and co-workers, C_p at 1 atm, various authors.
(3) Extrapolated to saturation boundary.
(4) Extrapolated C_p values.
(5) Dew and bubble points at 1 atm—Dodge and Dunbar. Vapour pressure and saturation volumes derived from *P-V-T* data of Michels. Latent heat of vaporization at 1 atm—Dana. Latent heats of vaporization—approximate Clausius–Clapeyron equation. Critical constants—Kuenen and Clark.

comparisons of entropy values between the present work and the earlier diagrams and also the recent compilation of Michels and his co-workers based on their own data.

In the case of the Gerhart, Seligmann and Hausen diagrams only small reproductions were available to the present author, which necessarily limited the accuracy with which values could be taken from them. The various data have all been converted to J/mole, ° K and in the case of those of Michels, Gerhart, Seligmann and Claitor and Crawford the values have been adjusted to agree exactly with the present ones at 1 atm and 270° K.   Williams and Hausen used the same reference as in the present case, namely, entropy and enthalpy zero for the liquid at the bubble point at 1 atm, and the comparisons can be made on this

TABLE 5

COMPARISONS OF ENTROPY VALUES IN THE SUPERHEATED REGION, J/mole, °K

D= this work.   G=Gerhart and others[18].   S=Seligmann[46].   M=Michels and co-workers[37].   W=Williams[52]. H=Hausen[21].   C=Claitor and Crawford[8].

Temperature °K	Author	Pressure atm						$\Delta S \dfrac{P=100}{P=1}$
		1	10	30	100	200	1000	(Ideal − 44·05)
380	D	119·52	100·30	90·97	80·30	73·78		− 45·74
	G	119·2	100·2	90·9	80·0	73·4		− 45·8
	S	120·5	101·3	91·6	81·2	74·5		− 46·0
270	D	109·55	90·20	80·59	68·92	61·29	45·30	− 48·26
	M	109·55*	90·19	80·56	68·91	61·31	44·93	− 48·24
	G	109·5*	90·2	81·7	68·7	61·5		− 48·0
	S	109·5*	90·4	81·2	69·9	62·3	46·0	− 47·2
	W	109·20	89·96	80·25	68·32	60·58		− 48·62
	H	106·3	87·4	77·8	66·5	59·0		− 47·3
	C	109·55*	90·09					
200	D	100·79	81·19	70·97	56·88	47·77		− 53·02
	M		81·20	70·94	56·84	47·69		
	S	101·3	82·0	71·5	57·7	49·8		− 51·5
	W	100·50	80·92	70·67	56·65	47·61		− 52·89
	H	97·5	78·7	68·6	54·0	44·8		− 57·7
	C	100·63	81·21					
150	D	92·28	72·11	59·97	37·08	30·51		− 61·77
	M		72·30	60·24	37·47	31·74		
	S	93·3	73·2	61·1	39·3	33·9		− 59·4
	W	92·05	71·96	59·87	37·70	31·46		− 60·59
	H	88·7	69·5	57·3	35·1	30·1		− 58·6
	C	92·21	72·22					
$T=270$ ΔS $T=150$	D	17·27	18·09	20·62	31·84	30·78		
	M		17·89	20·32	31·44	29·57		
	S	16·2	17·2	20·1	30·6	28·4		
	W	17·15	18·00	20·38	30·62	29·12		
	H	17·6	17·9	20·5	31·4	28·9		
	C	17·34	17·87					

* Adjusted for reference.

basis. The agreement with the calculations of Michels is very good when allowance is made for the fact that it was necessary to interpolate from Michels' P-V-T data. Since the same original data have been used in both cases, these two sets of values should agree absolutely. The discrepancies must be attributed to the errors that arise in the evaluation of the thermodynamic functions from the original data. It

29

is only at the higher pressures and at 150° K that the differences are at all appreciable. The errors in computing the thermodynamic functions from the P-V-T data increase rapidly at high pressures where the gas becomes comparatively incompressible like a liquid. At 150° K the discrepancies arise from the proximity to the critical region where calculation of the thermodynamic functions again becomes much less certain. The discrepancy with the Williams diagram for the isothermal entropy change from 1 atm to 200 atm at 270° K arises from the fact that in this region the Williams diagram is based on the Beattie–Bridgeman equation of state. The Claitor and Crawford diagram over its short range is in very good agreement with the present work. The earlier diagrams of Seligmann and of Hausen are much less satisfactory as far as can be judged.

At 1 atm and 270° K the differences between the Williams and Hausen diagrams and the present one arise from the different specific heat data at 1 atm that have been used, and in the case of Hausen's diagram the latent heat of vaporization at 1 atm also. Otherwise the entropy changes along isobars reflect the agreements and discrepancies which have been noted along the isotherms.

Around the two-phase boundary some comparisons are given in Table 6.

TABLE 6

COMPARISONS OF ENTROPY VALUES AT THE SATURATION BOUNDARY

D = this work. W = Williams[52]. H = Hausen[21]. C = Claitor and Crawford[8].

	Author	Pressure Atm				
		1	5	10	20	30
Entropy of	D	0	10·39	16·34	24·67	31·40
Liquid	W	0	11·21	17·28	24·89	31·05
J/mole, °K	H	0	11·71	17·15	23·85	28·03
	C	0*	10·25	15·40		
Entropy of	D	74·00	64·98	60·42	54·76	49·64
Vapour	W	74·00	65·14	60·79	55·77	51·38
J/mole, °K	H	71·13	62·76	58·16	52·72	48·53
	C	73·39	64·10	59·62		
Latent heat of	D	5942	5325	4735	3593	2328
Vaporization	W	5942	5247	4661	3678	2586
J/mole	H	5682	5042	4513	3636	2548
	C	5899	5234	4736		

* Adjusted for reference.

30

The boundary of the present diagram appears to lie between those of Williams and of Claitor and Crawford, the latter diagram showing the smallest values and that of Williams the greatest. Williams and Claitor and Crawford used the same method to deduce the latent heats and it is rather surprising to see that whereas these two diagrams agree quite well at 5 atm, there is an almost 2 per cent difference at 10 atm. The present diagram shows a 2 per cent greater latent heat than the Williams and Claitor and Crawford values at 5 atm but agrees almost perfectly with that of Claitor and Crawford at 10 atm. At higher pressures the latent heats of the present diagram are distinctly lower than those of Williams and of Hausen. Hausen's values on the other hand are considerably the lowest at 1 atm, 5 atm and 10 atm. In view of this lack of system in the values deduced by other authors on a corresponding states basis, it is believed that the present values based on an approximation of the Clausius–Clapeyron equation are in no way inferior.

A very severe comparison of the various computations of thermodynamic functions is afforded by the specific heats. In Table 7 some values of the specific heat at constant pressure at various temperatures and pressures are compared with the present work, in particular the values of Michels, of Williams and those calculated by Bridgeman[6] from the Beattie–Bridgeman equation.

TABLE 7

COMPARISONS OF THE SPECIFIC HEAT AT CONSTANT PRESSURE, J/mole, °K

D=this work. B=Bridgeman[6]. M=Michels and co-workers[37]. W=Williams[52].

Temperature °K	Author	Pressure atm			
		20	100	500	1000
380	D	29·77	31·84		
	B	29·96	31·88		
280	D	30·19	34·98	40·57	38·45
	M	30·17	34·69	39·96	38·74
	B	30·33	35·90		
	W	29·83	35·86		
180	D	33·51	60·6	44·72	
	M	33·10	61·09	45·94	
	W	32·13	51·50		
140	D	41·73	88·8		
	M	40·29	69·87		

Considering the difficulty in establishing the specific heat from the $P\text{-}V\text{-}T$ data with even nominal accuracy, the agreement between the present values and those of Michels is considered excellent. The only serious discrepancy is at 100 atm and 140° K and here the influence of the critical region—C_p is infinite at the critical point—is considerable. The agreement with Bridgeman's values and those of Williams is good at higher temperatures but less satisfactory at the lower temperatures.

Table 8 shows some comparisons of the specific heat at constant volume with those calculated by Michels and his co-workers. C_v varies considerably less than C_p and the precise computation of such small changes is even more difficult than in the case of the latter.

TABLE 8

COMPARISONS OF THE SPECIFIC HEAT AT CONSTANT VOLUME, J/mole, °K

D=this work.   M=Michels and co-workers[37].

Temperature °K	Author	Pressure Atm				
		20	50	100	500	1000
340	D	20·9	21·2	21·4		
	M	20·9	21·1	21·3		
270	D	20·8	21·6	22·0	23·4	23·7
	M	20·9	21·1	21·6	23·1	24·3
200	D	21·7	22·6	23·6	25·2	
	M	21·2	22·0	23·0	24·6	
160	D	23·1	24·8	26·2		
	M	21·9	24·1	25·4		
140	D	24·6	27·0	28·5		
	M	22·8	27·4	23·6		

The present results show similar trends to those of Michels although, somewhat surprisingly, the discrepancies appear to be relatively greater at the lower pressures. The differences in the values in the critical region have already been discussed in section 12. Since the present values have been computed by measuring slopes on the temperature–entropy diagram they are almost certainly less accurate than those computed by Michels.

Finally, it is possible to compare the integral Joule–Thomson effect according to the present diagram with the experimental measurements of Roebuck[42]. In *Figure 6*, pairs of comparable isenthalps are shown in different temperature ranges. At 370° K Roebuck's experimental isenthalp is almost identical with the 14,000 J/mole isenthalp of the present compilation. At lower pressures there is a very slight discrepancy, scarcely outside the accuracy of plotting on the chosen scale. From 300° K to 260° K the two isenthalps are again very closely parallel and therefore in practically perfect agreement. Even at the

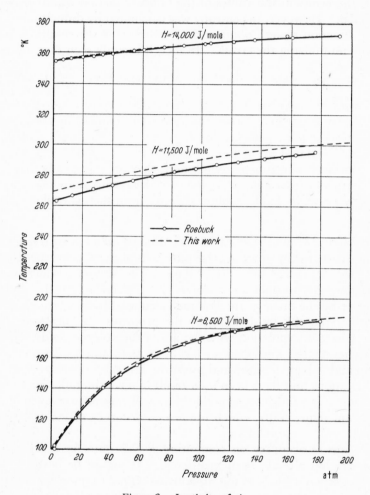

Figure 6. Isenthalps of air

lowest temperature the agreement is still remarkably good, the present isenthalp at 6500 J/mole showing a slightly greater Joule–Thomson effect than that measured by Roebuck over the lower pressure ranges.

The errors in the present diagram, in the homogeneous region at any rate, arise exclusively from the possible error in Dana's latent heat value, the errors in the specific heat values at 1 atm and as a result of the interpolation and smoothing techniques that have been employed in the present work. If a possible 0·5 per cent error is assumed both for Dana's latent heat value and for the C_p values, then it becomes easy to compute the possible entropy errors along the 1 atm isobar. The Gibbs' function was calculated by integrating the values of the volume residual, r, along isotherms, and hence, knowing the possible errors in the latter, the errors in the values of the Gibbs' function could be readily estimated. However, the entropy was calculated by differentiating the Gibbs' function along isobars and smoothing out the resulting values, thereby minimizing the errors. In fact, it is easily seen that the errors in the entropy values are the values of the derivative $\dfrac{\partial(\delta G)}{\partial T}\bigg)_P$ where δG is the error in the Gibbs' function. From these considerations, Table 9 was drawn up which shows the estimated maximum errors in the entropy in the homogeneous range.

It is believed that the method of computation used in the present work has reduced these errors to a minimum; they are only really significant in the critical region and the region of high pressure and density. The enthalpy errors in Table 9 follow directly from the expression:

$$\delta H = T\delta S$$

where δH and δS are the errors in the enthalpy and entropy respectively.

The errors in the volume arise purely as a result of the necessity to interpolate from Michels' P-V-T data. The Van der Waals workers claim that the product PV is correct to 1 part in 10,000 which will therefore be the error in the volume calculated from a reported value of the product PV by dividing by the pressure. In the low pressure range where interpolation with the aid of the volume residual is easy, it is believed that this accuracy has been maintained. In the critical region and at high densities and pressures, however, the direct graphical interpolations that have been used result in a considerable reduction in accuracy. It is for this reason that the small volumes are given to three significant figures only, which implies an accuracy of less than 1 part in 1000.

The loss of accuracy on computing P-V-T data for the two-phase boundary has already been mentioned. It should be borne in mind also that below 120° K in the superheated vapour region the isobars on the log temperature–entropy diagram were extrapolated to the saturated vapour boundary, and it is probably safest to assume that the latent heats calculated from the approximation of the Clausius–Clapeyron equation may be as much as 1 per cent in error. These considerations led to the drawing up of Table 10 giving the possible errors round the two-phase boundary.

The measurements of the P-V-T data at the Van der Waals laboratory have made good a very serious deficiency in the fundamental data for air. Although the range is not quite as great as the Van der Waals

TABLE 9

VALUES OF ENTROPY, ENTHALPY AND VOLUME AND THEIR POSSIBLE ERRORS

(Entropy: J/mole, °K.   Enthalpy: J/mole.   Volume: cm³/mole)

Pressure atm		Temperature °K					
		120	130	140	160	200	450
1	S	85·60 (±0·45)	88·01 (±0·47)	90·23 (±0·48)	94·20 (±0·54)	100·79 (±0·54)	124·47 (±0·65)
	H	7,095 (±54)	7,395 (±61)	7,695 (±67)	8,290 (±80)	9,471 (±108)	16,775 (±292)
	V	9,726 (±2)	10,565 (±1)	11,400 (±0)	13,064 (±0)	16,373 (±0)	36,937 (±0)
20	S		58·93 (±0·51)	62·22 (±0·51)	67·36 (±0·52)	74·89 (±0·55)	99·46 (±0·66)
	H		6,641 (±66)	7,086 (±71)	7,856 (±83)	9,204 (±110)	16,749 (±297)
	V		411·3 (±0·3)	475·9 (±0·2)	587·0 (±0)	782·1 (±0)	1,857·3 (±0)
30	S	22·73 (±0·70)	51·24 (±0·55)	56·45 (±0·53)	62·78 (±0·53)	70·97 (±0·55)	96·04 (±0·66)
	H	2,330 (±84)	5,946 (±72)	6,649 (±74)	7,593 (±85)	9,057 (±110)	16,736 (±297)
	V	45·2 (±0·4)	205·9 (±0·5)	275·5 (±0·3)	366·4 (±0)	509·0 (±0)	1,242·1 (±0·1)
50	S	20·40 (±0·65)	28·67 (±0·77)	40·19 (±0·88)	55·43 (±0·60)	65·57 (±0·56)	91·67 (±0·67)
	H	2,108 (±78)	3,143 (±100)	4,698 (±123)	6,952 (±96)	8,756 (±112)	16,708 (±301)
	V	42·8 (±0·4)	51·8 (±0·5)	77·4 (±0·5)	188·0 (±0)	291·4 (±0)	750·4 (±0·1)
100	S	17·99 (±0·60)	24·45 (±0·72)	30·84 (±0·68)	42·79 (±0·58)	56·88 (±0·57)	85·63 (±0·68)
	H	2,025 (±72)	2,832 (±94)	3,694 (±95)	5,484 (±93)	7,987 (±114)	10,639 (±306)
	V	40·7 (±0·4)	44·7 (±0·4)	50·4 (±0·3)	72·1 (±0·1)	133·3 (±0)	382·7 (±0·1)
200	S	15·30 (±0·55)	20·80 (±0·67)	25·86 (±0·63)	34·75 (±0·57)	47·77 (±0·58)	
	H	2,086 (±66)	2,770 (±87)	3,451 (±88)	4,779 (±91)	7,105 (±116)	
	V	38·5 (±0·4)	40·5 (±0·3)	43·2 (±0·2)	50·2 (±0·2)	70·4 (±0·1)	
500	S				28·93 (±0·55)	38·92 (±0·59)	
	H				5,217 (±88)	7,005 (±118)	
	V					46·1 (±0·2)	
800	S					35·33 (±0·60)	
	H					7,613 (±120)	
	V						

workers usually cover, the data are nevertheless more than adequate for most purposes for which they are required. Scope still remains, however, for further experimental work in other fields. In particular there is a need, as with most other industrial gases, for density–temperature data round the saturation boundary having a comparable degree oı accuracy with the *P-V-T* data in the homogeneous region. In the case of air also the precise vapour pressure relationships for the dew curve and bubble curve cannot be considered by any means finally established.

TABLE 10

VALUES OF ENTROPY, ENTHALPY AND VOLUME AT THE SATURATION
BOUNDARY AND THEIR POSSIBLE ERRORS

(Entropy: J/mole, °K.   Enthalpy: J/mole.   Volume: cm^3/mole)

Pressure atm		1	5	10	20	30
Liquid	S	0	10·39	16·34	24·67	31·40
		(±0)	(±0·4)	(±0·5)	(±0·5)	(±0·55)
	H	0	926	1549	2527	3412
		(±0)	(±35)	(±50)	(±60)	(±70)
	V	33·14	36·94	40·00	46·63	55·69
		(±0·2)	(±0·2)	(±0·2)	(±0·3)	(±0·4)
Vapour	S	74·00	64·98	60·42	54·76	49·64
		(±0·4)	(±0·4)	(±0·5)	(±0·6)	(±0·7)
	H	5942	6251	6284	6120	5740
		(±30)	(±40)	(±55)	(±70)	(±90)
	V	6457	1428	718	330	186·6
		(±12)	(±3)	(±2)	(±1)	(±1·0)

As just stated, a possible error of 0·5 per cent is also considered possible in the specific heat and latent heat data and, again as for most other gases, specific heat values at pressures other than atmospheric would be a welcome addition to the thermodynamic data. It is to be hoped that the growing interest in mixtures of gases as distinct from pure gases will help to stimulate this work for air.

In keeping with its great technical importance several thermodynamic diagrams for air have appeared in the past. None of these, however, except the early diagram of Seligmann can compare with the present one in range, and the present one has by far the soundest experimental basis. It is considered also that the methods that have been adopted for obtaining the thermodynamic functions from the excellent data now available are thoroughly sound and that the final diagram is of high accuracy. Even if more accurate data than those from the Van der Waals laboratory should come to hand, it is doubtful whether the functions could be evaluated with any greater precision by the standard methods. It seems to the present author that improvement can now come only through the use of a modern electronic computing machine. Meanwhile, the present diagram is presented with confidence.

REFERENCES

[1] ALT, *Ann. Phys. Lpz.*, 13 (1904) 1010; 19 (1906) 739; *Phys. Z.*, 6 (1905) 346.
[2] AMAGAT, *Ann. Chim. Phys.* (6) 29 (1893) 68.
[3] BALY, *Phil. Mag.*, 49 (1900) 517.
[4] BEATTIE and BRIDGEMAN, *J. Amer. chem. Soc.*, 50 (1928) 3133.
[5] BRADLEY and HALE, *Phys. Rev.*, 29 (1909) 258.
[6] BRIDGEMAN, *Phys. Rev.* (2), 34 (1929) 533.
[7] BRITISH OXYGEN CO. LTD., Unpublished research work.
[8] CLAITOR and CRAWFORD, *Trans. Amer. Soc. mech. Engrs.*, 71, (1949) 885.
[9] CRAGOE, "Temperature—Its Measurement and control in Science and Industry", Reinhold, New York, 1941, p. 97.
[10] DALTON, *Commun. phys. Lab. Univ. Leiden*, 109c (1909).
[11] DANA, *Proc. Amer. Acad.*, 60 (1925) 241.
[12] DEWAR, *Chem. News*, 73 (1897) 43.
[13] DODGE and DUNBAR, *J. Amer. chem. Soc.*, 49, (1927) 591.
[14] EUCKEN and HAUCK, *Z. phys. Chem.*, 134 (1928) 161.
[15] EUCKEN and VON LÜDE, *Z. phys. Chem.*, B, 5 (1929) 413.
[16] EUMORFOPOULOS and RAI, *Phil. Mag.* (7) 2 (1926) 961.
[17] FURUKAWA and McCOSKEY, *Tech. Note, U.S. Comm. Aero.*, No. 2969 (1953).
[18] GERHART and others, *Mech. Engng.*, 64 (1942) 270.
[19] GIACOMINI, *Phil. Mag.*, 50 (1925) 146.
[20] HALL and IBELE, *Pap., Univ. Minnesota Inst. Tech.*, No. 85 (1951).
[21] HAUSEN, *ForschArb. IngWes.*, 274 (1926).
[22] HENRY, *Proc. roy. Soc.* A, 133 (1931) 492.
[23] HOLBORN and AUSTIN, *S.B. preuss. Akad. Wiss.* (1905), p. 175; *Ann. Phys. Lpz.*, 23 (1907) 809.
[24] HOLBORN and JAKOB, *S.B. preuss. Akad. Wiss.* (1914), p. 213.
[25] HOLBORN and OTTO, *Z. Phys.*, 33 (1925) 1; 38 (1926) 359.
[26] HOLBORN and SCHULTZE, *Ann. Phys. Lpz.*, 47 (1915) 1089.
[27] HOXTON, *Phys. Rev.*, 13 1919) 438.
[28] INGLIS and COATES, *J. chem. Soc.*, 89 (1906) 886.
[29] JAKOB, *Z. tech. Phys.*, 4 (1923) 460.
[30] JOHNSTON and co-workers, *J. Amer. chem. Soc.*, 55 (1933) 172; 56 (1934) 272; 57 (1935) 682.
[31] JOULE and THOMSON, *Math. Phys. Pap.*, 1 (1882) 1.
[32] KOCH, *Ann. Phys. Lpz.*, 27 (1908) 335.
[33] KUENEN and CLARK, *Commun. phys. Lab. Univ. Leiden*, No. 150b (1917).
[34] LADENBURG and KRÜGEL, *Ber. dtsch. chem. Ges.*, 32 (1899) 1415.
[35] MATHIAS, CROMMELIN and ONNES, *Commun. phys. Lab. Univ. Leiden*, No. 162 (1923).

36 MATHIAS and ONNES, *Commun. phys. Lab. Univ. Leiden*, No. 117 (1911) (oxygen).

MATHIAS, CROMMELIN and ONNES, *Commun. phys. Lab. Univ. Leiden*, No. 131a (1912) (argon); No. 145c (1914) (nitrogen).

37 MICHELS and co-workers, *Appl. Sci. Res.* A, 4 (1953) 52. Also private communications.

38 MORI, *J. sci. Res. Inst. (Tokio)*, 46 (1952) 68.

39 NOELL, *ForschArb. IngWes.*, 184 (1916).

40 OLSZEWSKI, *C.R. Acad. Sci. Paris*, 99 (1884) 184.

41 PENNING, *Commun. phys. Lab. Univ. Leiden*, No. 166 (1923).

42 ROEBUCK, *Proc. Amer. Acad.*, 60 (1925) 537; 64 (1929) 287.

43 ROEBUCK and MURRELL, "Temperature—Its Measurement and Control in Science and Industry", Reinhold, New York, 1941, p. 60.

44 RUSHTON, *Refrig. Engr.*, 53 (1947) 28.

45 SCHEEL and HEUSE, *Ann. Phys. Lpz*, (4), 37 (1912) 79.

46 SELIGMANN, *Z. ges. Kälteind.*, 29 (1922) 77; 31 (1924) 129.

47 SHILLING and PARTINGTON, *Phil. Mag.* (7) 6 (1928) 920.

48 SWANN, *Phil. Trans.* A, 210 (1910) 199.

49 TANISHITA, *Trans. Soc. mech. Engrs. Japan*, 17 (1953) 64.

50 TRAUTZ and ADER, *Z. Phys.*, 89 (1934) 1.

51 VOGEL, *Diss. München* (1910).

52 WILLIAMS, *Trans. Amer. Inst. chem. Engrs.*, 39 (1934) 93.

53 WITKOWSKI, *Phil. Mag.*, 41 (1896) 288 (*P-V-T* data).

54 WITKOWSKI, *Phil. Mag.*, 42 (1896) 1 (C_p calculation).

TABLES OF THERMODYNAMIC FUNCTIONS OF AIR

The properties are given for 1 gramme mole of air (28·96 g) as functions of the pressure in international atmospheres ($g=980·665$) and temperature in degrees Kelvin (0° C$=273·15°$ K). Entropy and enthalpy are zero for the liquid boiling at 1 atm.

"Molecular weight" $=28·96$

Density of the gas at N.T.P.
(International atm $g=980·665$) $=0·0012928$ g/cm³

Molecular volume at N.T.P.
(International atm $g=980·665$) $=22,401·2$ cm³

Boiling point of liquid at 1 atm (bubble point) $=78·8°$ K

Condensation point of vapour at 1 atm (dew point) $=81·8°$ K

Critical constants Plait point: temperature $=132·42°$ K

pressure (max) $=37·25$ atm

volume $=88·28$ cm³/mole

Point of contact: temperature
(max) $=132·52°$ K

pressure $=37·17$ atm

volume $=90·52$ cm³/mole

PROPERTIES OF THE SATURATED LIQUID AND VAPOUR

Pressure atm	Temperature °K		Entropy J/mole, °K		Enthalpy J/mole		Volume cm³/mole	
	Liquid (Bubble)	Vapour (Dew)	Liquid	Vapour	Liquid	Vapour	Liquid	Vapour
1	78·8	81·8	0	74·00	0	5942	33·14	6456·7
2	85·55	88·31	4·19	70·30	349	6096	34·39	3389·1
3	90·94	92·63	6·81	68·03	585	6176	35·40	2319·0
5	96·38	98·71	10·39	64·98	926	6251	36·94	1427·6
7	101·04	103·16	13·05	62·84	1196	6280	38·21	1029·1
10	106·47	108·35	16·34	60·42	1549	6284	40·00	718·4
15	113·35	114·91	20·83	57·37	2063	6233	43·21	464·8
20	118·77	120·07	24·67	54·76	2527	6120	46·63	330·4
25	123·30	124·41	28·08	52·25	2966	5960	50·37	246·6
30	127·26	128·12	31·40	49·64	3412	5740	55·69	186·6
35	130·91	131·42	35·40	46·60	3930	5399	64·90	134·2
37·17	132·52 (max) point of contact		41·36		4755		90·52	
37·25 (max)	132·42 plait point		41·00		4707		88·28	

39

SPECIFIC HEAT AT CONSTANT VOLUME, JOULES/MOLE, °K

Pressure atm	Temperature °K									
	90	100	110	120	130	140	150	160	170	180
1	20·7	20·7	20·7	20·7	20·7	20·7	20·7	20·7	20·7	20·7
5		25·6	24·2	23·1	22·3	21·8	21·5	21·3	21·2	21·1
10			28·1	25·3	23·8	22·9	22·3	21·9	21·7	21·5
20					25·8	24·6	23·7	23·1	22·6	22·6
30					27·3	25·6	24·5	23·8	23·2	22·8
40				31·6	28·3	26·4	25·2	24·4	23·7	23·2
50				32·5	29·0	27·0	25·7	24·8	24·1	23·6
60				32·9	29·4	27·4	26·1	25·2	24·5	23·9
80				32·9	29·9	28·1	26·8	25·8	25·0	24·4
100				32·8	30·2	28·5	27·2	26·2	25·4	24·7
150				32·6	30·5	28·9	27·7	26·8	26·0	25·3
200				32·4	30·6	29·2	28·1	27·2	26·4	25·7
250				32·1	30·6	29·4	28·4	27·5	26·7	26·0
300				31·8	30·6	29·5	28·6	27·7	26·9	26·2
400						29·6	28·7	27·9	27·1	26·4
500						29·6	28·8	28·0	27·2	26·5
600										26·6
800										
1000										
1200										

SPECIFIC HEAT AT CONSTANT VOLUME, JOULES/MOLE, °K—*cont.*

190	200	220	240	260	280	300	350	400	450	Pressure atm
				Temperature °K						
20·7	20·7	20·7	20·7	20·8	20·8	20·8	20·9	20·9	21·0	1
21·0	21·0	20·9	20·9	20·9	20·9	20·9	20·9	20·9	21·0	5
21·3	21·2	21·1	21·0	20·9	20·9	20·9	20·9	20·9	21·0	10
21·9	21·7	21·5	21·3	21·1	21·1	21·0	21·0	21·0	21·1	20
22·2	22·1	21·8	21·5	21·3	21·2	21·1	21·0	21·0	21·1	30
22·8	22·4	22·0	21·7	21·5	21·4	21·2	21·1	21·1	21·2	40
23·1	22·6	22·2	21·9	21·7	21·5	21·3	21·2	21·2	21·2	50
23·4	22·9	22·4	22·1	21·8	21·6	21·4	21·3	21·2	21·2	60
23·8	23·3	22·8	22·4	22·0	21·8	21·5	21·4	21·3	21·2	80
24·1	23·6	23·1	22·6	22·2	21·9	21·6	21·4	21·3	21·2	100
24·7	24·1	23·5	23·0	22·6	22·2	21·8	21·6			150
25·1	24·5	23·9	23·3	22·8	22·4	22·0	21·8			200
25·3	24·7	24·1	23·9	23·0	22·6	22·2	21·9			250
25·5	24·9	24·3	23·7	23·2	22·8	22·4	22·0			300
25·7	25·1	24·5	23·9	23·4	23·0	22·6				400
25·8	25·2	24·6	24·1	23·6	23·2	22·8				500
25·9	25·3	24·7	24·2	23·7	23·3	22·9				600
		24·8	24·3	23·8	23·4	23·0				800
			24·4	23·9	23·5	23·1				1000
				24·0	23·6	23·2				1200

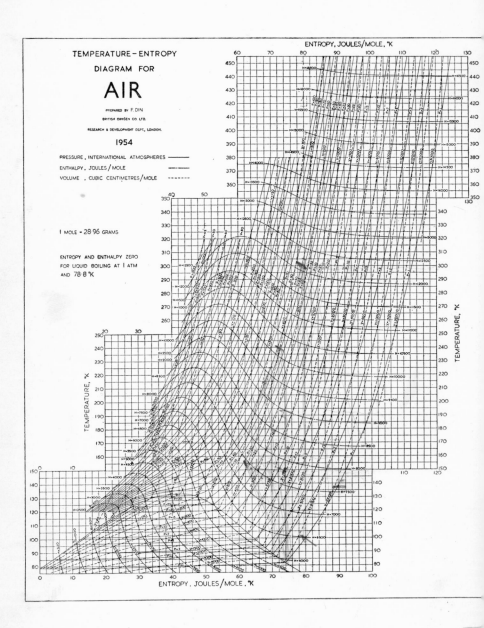

SPECIFIC HEAT AT CONSTANT PRESSURE, JOULES/MOLE, °K

Pressure atm	Temperature °K									
	90	100	110	120	125	130	135	140	145	150
1	30·47	30·25	30·12	30·02	29·97	29·93	29·88	29·84	29·80	29·76
2	30·92	30·66	30·50	30·37	30·30	30·24	30·17	30·10	30·04	29·98
3		31·44	31·13	30·86	30·73	30·61	30·50	30·40	30·31	30·23
5		34·39	33·08	32·20	31·85	31·55	31·31	31·12	30·97	30·84
7			35·80	33·92	33·27	32·75	32·35	32·04	31·79	31·57
10			41·43	37·00	35·69	34·78	34·12	33·61	33·18	32·81
15				44·52	41·81	39·74	38·14	36·92	36·00	35·27
20					52·2	47·7	40·34	41·73	39·71	38·24
25				121	72·4	61·7	53·8	48·3	44·42	41·78
30				111	170	90·7	68·9	57·3	50·3	46·0
35				104	131	—	⊙107	71·2	58·0	51·1
40				98·6	117	170	—	117	71·6	59·6
45				94·8	108	142	240	182	111	79·6
50				91·8	102	125	157	176	151	110
60				87·5	95·0	105	119	136	138	122
70				84·3	89·7	96·5	106	114	118	114
80				81·9	85·6	90·6	96·6	102	106	105
90				80·0	82·8	86·4	90·2	93·9	96·6	96·5
100				78·5	80·7	83·4	86·2	88·8	90·8	90·8
120				75·9	77·3	78·8	80·4	81·7	82·4	82·1
140				73·8	74·5	75·3	76·1	76·6	76·8	76·5
160				71·9	72·2	72·5	72·7	72·8	72·8	72·4
180				70·1	70·1	70·2	70·1	70·0	69·8	69·2
200				68·7	68·5	68·3	68·1	67·8	67·3	66·6
250				66·5	65·8	65·1	64·4	63·7	62·8	61·8
300				65·2	64·2	63·1	62·0	60·8	59·6	58·3
350										
400										
450										
500										
600										
700										
800										
900										
1,000										
1,100										

SPECIFIC HEAT AT CONSTANT PRESSURE, JOULES/MOLE, °K—*cont.*

Pressure atm	Temperature °K									
	160	170	180	190	200	210	220	230	240	250
1	29·68	29·60	29·52	29·45	29·38	29·32	29·26	29·20	29·16	29·13
2	29·88	29·79	29·69	29·59	29·50	29·41	29·34	29·28	29·23	29·20
3	30·10	29·98	29·86	29·74	29·63	29·52	29·43	29·36	29·31	29·27
5	30·61	30·41	30·22	30·04	29·87	29·73	29·62	29·53	29·47	29·42
7	31·20	30·89	30·62	30·37	30·15	29·97	29·82	29·71	29·63	29·57
10	32·17	31·66	31·24	30·89	30·59	30·34	30·14	29·99	29·88	29·79
15	34·02	33·07	32·34	31·77	31·32	30·96	30·68	30·46	30·30	30·17
20	36·11	34·59	33·51	32·72	32·10	31·61	31·23	30·94	30·72	30·55
25	38·48	36·26	34·77	33·71	32·90	31·28	31·80	31·43	31·15	30·94
30	41·22	38·14	36·14	34·75	33·73	32·97	32·38	31·94	31·60	31·34
35	44·38	40·31	37·65	35·87	34·60	33·67	32·98	32·46	32·06	31·74
40	48·2	42·87	39·32	37·04	35·51	34·42	33·61	33·00	32·53	32·15
45	53·1	45·8	41·16	38·28	36·46	35·18	34·25	33·56	33·01	32·56
50	59·5	49·2	43·13	39·57	37·44	35·97	34·93	34·15	33·51	32·98
60	75·0	56·2	47·1	42·30	39·49	37·61	36·32	35·33	34·52	33·85
70	88·4	62·3	51·3	45·2	41·66	39·29	37·71	36·51	35·53	34·72
80	91·9	66·9	55·4	48·3	43·88	40·99	39·09	37·65	36·52	35·60
90	87·8	70·1	59·0	51·2	45·9	42·60	40·41	38·78	37·51	36·48
100	84·2	70·7	60·6	53·1	47·7	44·08	41·63	39·83	38·43	37·30
120	78·1	69·3	61·9	55·5	50·4	46·5	43·68	41·58	40·00	38·73
140	73·2	67·1	61·5	56·4	51·8	47·9	45·00	42·90	41·25	39·90
160	69·7	65·0	60·5	56·2	52·2	48·7	45·9	43·84	42·21	40·84
180	66·8	63·1	59·4	55·7	52·2	49·1	46·5	44·48	42·91	41·57
200	64·3	61·4	58·1	54·9	51·9	49·2	46·8	44·95	43·46	42·17
250	59·8	57·4	55·0	52·7	50·6	48·6	46·8	45·3	44·03	42·92
300	56·1	54·1	52·3	50·6	49·0	47·6	46·2	45·1	43·99	43·04
350	52·9	51·3	49·9	48·7	47·5	46·5	45·5	44·54	43·69	42·90
400	50·1	48·9	47·9	47·0	46·2	45·4	44·63	43·91	43·23	42·59
450	47·7	46·9	46·2	45·5	44·93	44·35	43·79	43·25	42·72	42·21
500	45·5	45·1	44·72	44·30	43·87	43·45	43·02	42·60	42·18	41·77
600			43·01	42·71	42·40	42·09	41·78	41·47	41·17	40·87
700				41·54	41·32	41·09	40·84	40·60	40·36	40·12
800				40·62	40·44	40·27	40·09	39·91	39·73	39·55
900									39·26	39·12
1,000									38·92	38·81
1,100										

SPECIFIC HEAT AT CONSTANT PRESSURE, JOULES/MOLE, °K—cont.

Temperature °K											Pressure atm
260	270	280	290	300	320	340	360	380	400	450	
29·12	29·11	29·11	29·12	29·13	29·16	29·19	29·22	29·25	29·28	29·36	1
29·18	29·17	29·17	29·17	29·18	29·20	29·22	29·25	29·28	29·31	29·38	2
29·25	29·23	29·22	29·22	29·22	29·24	29·26	29·28	29·31	29·34	29·39	3
29·38	29·36	29·34	29·32	29·31	29·32	29·33	29·34	29·36	29·38	29·43	5
29·52	29·48	29·45	29·42	29·40	29·40	29·40	29·41	29·42	29·43	29·47	7
29·72	29·66	29·61	29·57	29·54	29·52	29·51	29·50	29·49	29·50	29·54	10
30·07	29·98	29·90	29·84	29·78	29·72	29·68	29·65	29·63	29·63	29·65	15
30·41	30·29	30·19	30·10	30·02	29·92	29·85	29·80	29·77	29·75	29·76	20
30·76	30·61	30·48	30·37	30·27	30·13	30·03	29·96	29·91	29·88	29·87	25
31·12	30·93	30·76	30·62	30·51	30·33	30·20	30·11	30·04	30·00	29·97	30
31·48	31·25	31·06	30·89	30·75	30·53	30·37	30·26	30·18	30·13	30·08	35
31·83	31·56	31·34	31·15	30·99	30·73	30·55	30·42	30·32	30·25	30·18	40
32·19	31·88	31·63	31·41	31·23	30·94	30·73	30·58	30·46	30·37	30·28	45
32·55	32·20	31·91	31·67	31·47	31·14	30·90	30·73	30·59	30·49	30·38	50
33·30	32·86	32·50	32·20	31·95	31·54	31·24	31·02	30·85	30·72	30·58	60
34·06	33·53	33·10	32·74	32·44	31·94	31·57	31·30	31·10	30·95	30·78	70
34·85	34·23	33·72	33·30	32·94	32·33	31·89	31·58	31·35	31·18	30·97	80
35·63	34·93	34·35	33·86	33·44	32·72	32·21	31·85	31·60	31·41	31·15	90
36·37	35·61	34·98	34·43	33·94	33·10	32·52	32·12	31·84	31·64	31·32	100
37·67	36·79	36·03	35·39	34·81	33·83	33·13	32·64	32·29			120
38·77	37·81	36·99	36·27	35·61	34·53	33·72	33·14	32·71			140
39·68	38·69	37·84	37·06	36·35	35·18	34·29	33·62	33·11			160
40·43	39·44	38·57	37·77	37·02	35·78	34·84	34·09	33·49			180
41·05	40·06	39·18	38·37	37·61	36·34	35·35	34·54	33·85			200
41·93	41·02	40·18	39·40	38·66	37·42	36·39	35·50	34·69			250
42·19	41·41	40·69	40·01	39·37	38·20	37·18	36·26	35·40			300
42·17	41·50	40·88	40·31	39·77	38·79						350
42·00	41·45	40·94	40·45	39·98	39·11						400
41·72	41·25	40·80	40·37	39·95	39·16						450
41·36	40·96	40·57	40·20	39·84	39·14						500
40·57	40·28	40·00	39·71	39·43	38·90						600
39·89	39·67	39·45	39·24	39·03	38·61						700
39·37	39·99	39·01	38·84	38·67	38·32						800
38·98	38·83	38·68	38·53	38·38	38·08						900
38·69	38·57	38·45	38·32	38·19	37·94						1,000
	38·30	38·21	38·12	38·02	37·81						1,100

45

VOLUME, CUBIC CENTIMETRES/MOLE

Pressure atm	Temperature °K							
	90	100	110	120	125	130	135	140
1	7,171	8,031	8,882	9,726	10,146	10,565	10,983	11,400
2	3,472	3,926	4,368	4,801	5,016	5,230	5,443	5,655
3	—	2,555	2,862	3,159	3,306	3,452	3,596	3,740
5		1,456	1,655	1,844	1,937	2,028	2,118	2,008
7			1,135	1,279	1,349	1,417	1,484	1,550
10			738·8	851·9	905·5	957·2	1,007·4	1,056·5
15				511·1	555·4	595·9	634·1	670·7
20					374·0	411·3	444·8	475·9
25				46·3	253·5	294·4	328·0	356·9
30				45·2	50·7	205·9 ⊙	246·0	275·5
35				44·4	49·2	59·9	182·3	215·0
40				43·7	48·0	56·0	112·0	164·8
45				43·2	47·0	53·6	65·1	109·0
50				42·8	46·3	51·5	58·5	77·4
60				42·2	45·3	49·4	54·8	63·6
70				41·7	44·5	47·9	52·0	58·1
80				41·3	43·7	46·6	50·1	54·5
90				41·0	43·0	45·5	48·5	52·2
100				40·7	42·5	44·7	47·3	50·4
120				40·2	41·6	43·4	45·5	47·9
140				39·7	40·9	42·4	44·1	46·1
160				39·3	40·4	41·7	43·2	44·9
180				38·9	39·9	41·1	42·4	44·0
200				38·5	39·4	40·5	41·8	43·2
250				37·5	38·4	39·4	40·4	41·5
300				36·6	37·5	38·4	39·3	40·3
350								
400								
450								
500								
600								
700								
800								
900								
1,000								
1,200								

VOLUME, CUBIC CENTIMETRES/MOLE—*cont.*

145	150	160	170	180	190	200	Pressure atm
11,817	12,233	13,064	13,893	14,720	15,547	16,373	1
5,867	6,078	6,499	6,917	7,334	7,751	8,167	2
3,883	4,026	4,310	4,592	4,873	5,153	5,432	3
2,297	2,385	2,559	2,732	2,904	3,074	3,244	5
1,616	1,681	1,808	1,934	2,059	2,183	2,306	7
1,104·7	1,152·2	1,245·2	1,336·5	1,426·3	1,514·9	1,602·6	10
706·0	740·3	806·7	870·9	933·6	995·1	1,055·6	15
505·3	533·5	587·0	637·9	687·1	735·1	782·1	20
383·5	408·5	454·8	497·9	539·3	579·3	618·2	25
300·9	324·2	366·4	404·6	440·7	475·4	509·0	30
240·4	263·1	303·0	338·0	370·5	401·4	431·1	35
196·8	219·8	255·2	287·8	317·7	345·9	372·8	40
149·3	179·7	217·9	248·9	276·8	302·8	327·5	45
109·8	144·2	188·0	217·8	244·2	268·5	291·4	50
77·6	98·6	143·4	171·6	195·6	217·3	237·5	60
66·6	79·1	112·9	139·3	161·5	181·3	199·4	70
60·5	68·7	93·6	116·6	136·8	154·7	171·3	80
56·8	62·7	80·3	100·2	118·4	134·9	150·0	90
54·2	58·9	72·1	88·2	104·5	119·4	133·3	100
50·8	54·2	63·0	73·8	86·0	97·9	109·4	120
48·5	51·3	57·9	65·8	74·9	84·3	93·9	140
46·9	49·2	54·5	60·7	67·8	75·4	83·3	160
45·7	47·6	52·0	57·2	63·0	69·3	75·9	180
44·7	46·4	50·2	54·5	59·4	64·7	70·4	200
42·7	44·0	46·9	50·0	53·5	57·3	61·3	250
41·3	42·4	44·7	47·2	49·9	52·8	55·9	300
		43·1	45·1	47·4	49·8	52·3	350
		41·8	43·6	45·5	47·5	49·7	400
				44·1	45·9	47·8	450
				42·9	44·5	46·1	500
				41·0	42·3	43·7	600
						41·9	700
							800
							900
							1,000
							1,200

VOLUME, CUBIC CENTIMETRES/MOLE—*cont.*

Pressure atm	Temperature °K							
	210	220	230	240	250	260	270	280
1	17,198	18,023	18,848	19,672	20,495	21,319	22,142	22,965
2	8,582	8,997	9,411	9,825	10,238	10,651	11,064	11,477
3	5,710	5,988	6,265	6,542	6,819	7,096	7,372	7,648
5	3,413	3,581	3,749	3,917	4,084	4,251	4,418	4,584
7	2,428	2,550	2,671	2,791	2,912	3,032	3,152	3,271
10	1,689·6	1,776·0	1,861·9	1,947·4	2,032·6	2,117·5	2,202·1	2,286·5
15	1,115·3	1,174·4	1,233·0	1,291·2	1,349·0	1,406·5	1,463·7	1,520·7
20	828·3	873·8	918·7	963·2	1,007·3	1,051·1	1,094·7	1,138·1
25	656·2	693·5	730·3	766·6	802·5	838·1	873·5	908·7
30	541·6	573·5	604·8	635·6	666·1	696·2	726·1	755·8
35	459·9	487·9	515·3	542·2	568·7	595·0	621·0	646·8
40	398·7	423·8	448·3	472·3	496·0	519·3	542·3	565·2
45	351·2	374·0	396·2	418·0	439·4	460·4	481·2	501·7
50	313·3	334·3	354·7	374·6	394·1	413·3	432·3	451·1
60	256·6	274·9	292·6	309·8	326·6	343·0	359·2	375·2
70	216·5	232·9	248·6	263·8	278·5	293·0	307·2	321·2
80	186·9	210·7	215·9	229·5	242·7	255·7	268·4	280·8
90	164·2	177·7	190·6	203·0	215·0	226·7	238·3	249·6
100	146·3	158·7	170·6	182·0	193·0	203·8	214·4	224·7
120	120·5	131·2	141·4	151·2	160·7	170·0	179·0	187·8
140	103·3	112·5	121·3	129·8	138·1	146·2	154·1	161·8
160	91·3	99·3	107·0	114·4	121·7	128·9	135·9	142·7
180	82·7	89·6	96·3	102·9	109·4	115·8	122·0	128·1
200	76·3	82·2	88·2	94·1	100·0	105·7	111·3	116·8
250	65·6	70·0	74·6	79·2	83·7	88·2	92·6	97·0
300	59·2	62·7	66·3	69·9	73·5	77·2	80·8	84·4
350	55·0	57·8	60·7	63·7	66·7	69·8	72·8	75·8
400	52·0	54·4	56·8	59·3	61·8	64·4	67·0	69·6
450	49·7	51·7	53·8	56·0	58·2	60·4	62·6	64·9
500	47·8	49·6	51·5	53·4	55·3	57·2	59·2	61·2
600	45·1	46·6	48·1	49·6	51·1	52·6	54·2	55·8
700	43·1	44·4	45·6	46·9	48·1	49·4	50·8	52·1
800	41·7	42·7	43·7	44·8	45·9	47·0	48·1	49·3
900		42·3	43·2	44·1	45·1	46·0	47·0
1,000			42·0	42·7	43·5	44·3	45·2
1,200				41·0	41·7	42·5

VOLUME CUBIC CENTIMETRES/MOLE—*cont.*

Temperature °K								Pressure
290	300	320	340	360	380	400	450	atm
23,788	24,610	26,255	27,900	29,543	31,187	32,830	36,937	1
11,889	12,302	13,126	13,949	14,773	15,596	16,418	18,474	2
7,923	8,199	8,749	9,299	9,849	10,398	10,947	12,319	3
4,750	4,916	5,248	5,580	5,911	6,241	6,571	7,396	5
3,391	3,410	3,748	3,986	4,223	4,459	4,695	5,286	7
2,370·7	2,454·8	2,622·6	2,789·8	2,956·6	3,122·9	3,288·8	3,703·2	10
1,577·6	1,634·4	1,747·4	1,859·9	1,972·0	2,083·6	2,194·9	2,472·5	15
1,181·3	1,224·4	1,310·2	1,395·3	1,479·9	1,564·1	1,647·9	1,857·3	20
943·7	978·6	1,047·9	1,116·6	1,184·8	1,252·5	1,319·9	1,488·2	25
785·4	814·8	873·1	930·8	988·1	1,044·9	1,101·2	1,242·1	30
672·5	698·0	748·3	798·2	847·6	896·6	945·2	1,066·5	35
587·9	610·4	654·8	698·8	742·3	785·4	828·2	934·7	40
522·1	542·3	582·2	621·6	660·5	699·0	737·2	832·3	45
469·6	487·9	524·1	559·8	595·1	630·0	664·5	750·4	50
390·9	406·5	437·1	467·3	497·0	526·4	555·4	627·6	60
334·4	348·4	375·2	401·4	427·2	452·6	477·6	540·0	70
293·0	305·0	328·8	352·1	374·9	397·3	419·4	474·4	80
260·6	271·4	292·8	313·7	334·2	354·4	374·2	423·4	90
234·8	244·7	264·2	283·2	301·8	320·1	338·1	382·7	100
196·4	204·8	221·5	237·7	253·4	268·7			120
169·3	176·7	191·2	205·3	219·0	232·2			140
149·4	156·0	168·8	181·2	193·3	205·0			160
134·1	140·0	151·5	162·6	173·4	183·9			180
122·2	127·5	137·9	148·0	157·7	167·1			200
101·3	105·5	113·8	121·9	129·8	137·4			250
87·9	91·4	98·3	105·0	111·6	118·1			300
78·7	81·7	87·5						350
72·1	74·7	79·7						400
67·1	69·3	73·8						450
63·2	65·1	69·1						500
57·4	59·0	62·2						600
53·4	54·8	57·5						700
50·4	51·6	54·0						800
48·1	49·1	51·2						900
46·1	47·0	48·9						1,000
43·2	44·0	45·5						1,200

ENTHALPY, JOULES/MOLE

Pressure atm	Temperature °K										
	90	100	110	120	125	130	135	140	145	150	160
1	6,190	6,493	6,795	7,095	7,245	7,395	7,545	7,695	7,844	7,993	8,290
2	6,147	6,455	6,761	7,065	7,217	7,369	7,520	7,671	7,821	7,971	8,270
3		6,408	6,720	7,031	7,186	7,340	7,493	7,645	7,797	7,948	8,250
5		6,296	6,633	6,959	7,119	7,278	7,435	7,591	7,746	7,901	8,208
7			6,530	6,877	7,045	7,210	7,373	7,534	7,693	7,850	8,164
10			6,353	6,740	6,922	7,098	7,270	7,439	7,606	7,771	8,096
15				6,469	6,684	6,888	7,083	7,271	7,454	7,632	7,978
20					6,392	6,641	6,871	7,086	7,290	7,484	7,856
25				2,475	6,003	6,336	6,624	6,879	7,111	7,326	7,728
30				2,330	2,975	5,946	6,335	6,647	6,916	7,157	7,593
35				2,238	2,808	3,650	5,965	6,380	6,700	6,973	7,450
40				2,178	2,705	3,380	4,682	6,011	6,444	6,767	7,297
45				2,138	2,635	3,240	4,140	5,363	6,046	6,511	7,132
50				2,108	2,586	3,143	3,847	4,698	5,529	6,189	6,952
60				2,066	2,522	3,020	3,575	4,213	4,912	5,566	6,571
70				2,043	2,479	2,943	3,448	4,001	4,586	5,171	6,204
80				2,033	2,451	2,891	3,358	3,854	4,375	4,905	5.901
90				2,028	2,434	2,856	3,297	3,757	4,234	4,719	5,655
100				2,025	2,422	2,832	3,256	3,694	4,143	4,599	5,484
120				2,024	2,406	2,796	3,193	3,598	4,009	4,421	5,224
140				2,030	2,400	2,774	3,152	3,533	3,917	4,302	5,051
160				2,042	2,401	2,763	3,126	3,490	3,854	4,218	4,930
180				2,061	2,411	2,762	3,113	3,463	3,813	4,160	4,842
200				2,086	2,428	2,770	3,111	3,451	3,789	4,123	4,779
250				2,186	2,517	2,844	3,168	3,488	3,804	4,116	4,724
300				2,321	2,644	2,962	3,275	3,582	3,883	4,178	4,749
350											4,831
400											4,944
450											5,078
500											5,217
600											
700											
800											
900											
1,000											
1,200											

ENTHALPY, JOULES/MOLE—*cont.*

170	180	190	200	210	220	230	240	250	260	Pressure atm
					Temperature °K					
8,586	8,882	9,177	9,471	9,764	10,057	10,349	10,641	10,933	11,224	1
8,568	8,865	9,161	9,457	9,752	10,046	10,339	10,632	10,924	11,216	2
8,550	8,849	9,147	9,444	9,740	10,035	10,329	10,622	10,915	11,208	3
8,513	8,816	9,117	9,417	9,715	10,012	10,308	10,603	10,897	11,191	5
8,474	8,781	9,086	9,389	9,690	9,989	10,287	10,584	10,880	11,175	7
8,415	8,729	9,040	9,348	9,653	9,955	10,256	10,555	10,853	11,151	10
8,313	8,640	8,961	9,276	9,588	9,896	10,202	10,506	10,809	11,110	15
8,209	8,549	8,880	9,204	9,523	9,837	10,148	10,457	10,764	11,069	20
8,101	8,456	8,798	9,131	9,467	9,778	10,094	10,408	10,719	11,028	25
7,990	8,361	8,715	9,057	9,391	9,718	10,040	10,358	10,674	10,987	30
7,873	8,263	8,631	8,984	9,326	9,659	9,986	10,309	10,629	10,945	35
7,752	8,163	8,546	8,909	9,259	9,599	9,932	10,260	10,584	10,904	40
7,626	8,061	8,459	8,833	9,191	9,538	9,877	10,210	10,539	10,863	45
7,495	7,957	8,371	8,756	9,123	9,477	9,822	10,160	10,493	10,821	50
7,227	7,743	8,190	8,599	8,984	9,354	9,712	10,061	10,403	10,739	60
6,957	7,525	8,007	8,441	8,846	9,231	9,602	9,962	10,313	10,657	70
6,695	7,307	7,825	8,285	8,709	9,109	9,492	9,863	10,224	10,576	80
6,452	7,097	7,648	8,133	8,576	8,990	9,385	9,766	10,136	10,496	90
6,258	6,915	7,483	7,987	8,446	8,875	9,282	9,673	10,051	10,419	100
5,959	6,615	7,202	7,732	8,216	8,667	9,093	9,501	9,894	10,275	120
5,751	6,394	6,983	7,523	8,021	8,486	8,926	9,347	9,752	10,145	140
5,602	6,229	6,812	7,354	7,859	8,332	8,781	9,211	9,626	10,029	160
5,491	6,103	6,678	7,218	7,724	8,201	8,656	9,093	9,516	9,926	180
5,409	6,006	6,571	7,105	7,610	8,090	8,549	8,991	9,419	9,835	200
5,310	5,872	6,410	6,926	7,422	7,899	8,359	8,805	9,240	9,664	250
5,300	5,832	6,347	6,845	7,328	7,797	8,254	8,700	9,135	9,561	300
5,352	5,858	6,351	6,832	7,302	7,762	8,212	8,653	9,086	9,511	350
5,439	5,923	6,397	6,863	7,321	7,771	8,214	8,650	9,079	9,502	400
5,551	6,017	6,475	6,927	7,373	7,814	8,249	8,679	9,104	9,524	450
5,670	6,119	6,564	7,005	7,442	7,874	8,302	8,726	9,146	9,562	500
	6,334	6,763	7,189	7,611	8,030	8,446	8,859	9,269	9,676	600
		6,977	7,391	7,803	8,213	8,620	9,025	9,427	9,827	700
		7,208	7,613	8,017	8,419	8,819	9,217	9,613	10,008	800
							9,425	9,817	10,208	900
							9,640	10,029	10,416	1,000
										1,200

ENTHALPY, JOULES/MOLE—*cont*.

Pressure atm	Temperature °K									
	270	280	290	300	320	340	360	380	400	450
1	11,515	11,806	12,097	12,388	12,971	13,555	14,139	14,724	15,309	16,775
2	11,508	11,799	12,090	12,382	13,966	13,550	14,135	14,720	15,306	16,773
3	11,500	11,792	12,084	12,376	12,961	13,546	14,132	14,717	15,304	16,772
5	11,485	11,779	12,072	12,365	12,951	13,537	14,124	14,711	15,299	16,769
7	11,470	11,765	12,059	12,353	12,941	13,529	14,117	14,705	15,294	16,766
10	11,448	11,744	12,040	12,335	12,926	13,516	14,106	14,696	15,286	16,762
15	11,410	11,709	12,008	12,306	12,901	13,495	14,088	14,681	15,274	16,756
20	11,373	11,675	11,976	12,277	12,876	13,474	14,070	14,666	15,261	16,749
25	11,335	11,640	11,944	12,247	12,851	13,453	14,052	14,651	15,249	16,743
30	11,297	11,605	11,912	12,218	12,826	13,431	14,034	14,636	15,236	16,736
35	11,259	11,570	11,880	12,188	12,801	13,410	14,016	14,621	15,224	16·729
40	11,221	11,536	11,848	12,159	12,776	13,389	13,999	14,606	15,211	16,722
45	11,183	11,501	11,816	12,129	12,751	13,368	13,981	14,591	15,199	16,715
50	11,145	11,466	11,784	12,100	12,726	13,347	13,963	14,576	15,186	16,708
60	11,070	11,397	11,720	12,041	12,676	13,304	13,927	14,546	15,161	16,694
70	10,995	11,328	11,657	11,983	12,627	13,262	13,891	14,515	15,136	16,680
80	10,921	11,260	11,595	11,926	12,579	13,221	13,856	14,485	15,111	16,666
90	10,848	11,194	11,534	11,871	12,533	13,182	13,822	14,456	15,087	16,652
100	10,778	11,130	11,476	11,818	12,488	13,144	13,790	14,429	15,065	16,639
120	10,647	11,011	11,368	11,719	12,405	13,074	13,731	14,380		
140	10,528	10,902	11,268	11,628	12,329	13,011	13,679	14,337		
160	10,421	10,803	11,177	11,545	12,260	12,954	13,633	14,300		
180	10,325	10,715	11,096	11,470	12,198	12,904	13,593	14,269		
200	10,241	10,637	11,025	11,405	12,144	12,861	13,560	14,244		
250	10,079	10,485	10,883	11,273	12,034	12,772	13,491	14,193		
300	9,979	10,389	10,792	11,189	11,965	12,719	13,453	14,170		
350	9,929	10,341	10,747	11,147	11,933					
400	9,919	10,331	10,738	11,140	11,931					
450	9,939	10,349	10,755	11,157	11,948					
500	9,974	10,382	10,786	11,186	11,976					
600	10,080	10,481	10,880	11,276	12,060					
700	10,224	10,620	11,014	11,406	12,182					
800	10,401	10,792	11,181	11,569	12,339					
900	10,598	10,986	11,372	11,757	12,522					
1,000	10,802	11,187	11,571	11,954	12,715					
1,200	11,209	11,592	11,974	12,355	13,113					

ENTROPY, JOULES/MOLE, °K

Pressure atm	Temperature °K										
	90	100	110	120	125	130	135	140	145	150	160
1	76·90	80·09	82·97	85·60	86·83	88·01	89·14	90·23	91·27	92·28	94·20
2	70·87	74·11	77·03	79·67	80·91	82·10	83·24	84·34	85·39	86·41	88·34
3		70·44	73·41	76·12	77·38	78·59	79·74	80·85	81·92	82·94	84·89
5		65·43	68·64	71·47	72·78	74·03	75·21	76·34	77·43	78·48	80·46
7			65·19	68·21	69·58	70·87	72·10	73·27	74·39	75·45	77·48
10			61·05	64·42	65·91	67·29	68·59	69·82	70·99	72·11	74·21
15				59·38	61·14	62·74	64·21	65·58	66·86	68·07	70·30
20					56·98	58·93	60·66	62·22	63·65	64·97	67·36
25				23·94	52·60	55·21	57·38	59·23	60·86	62·32	64·91
30				22·73	28·00	51·24	54·18	56·45	58·34	59·97	62·78
35				21·88	26·53	33·17 ⊚	50·63	53·65	55·90	57·75	60·83
40				21·27	25·57	30·86	40·68	50·34	53·37	55·56	58·98
45				20·80	24·86	29·60	36·37	45·24	50·02	53·17	57·18
50				20·40	24·30	28·67	33·99	40·19	46·03	50·51	55·43
60				19·72	23·44	27·35	31·54	36·18	41·09	45·52	52·00
70				19·17	22·73	26·37	30·18	34·20	38·31	42·27	48·92
80				18·72	22·13	25·58	29·10	32·71	36·37	39·97	46·40
90				18·33	21·64	24·95	28·28	31·63	34·98	38·27	44·31
100				17·99	21·23	24·45	27·65	30·84	33·99	37·08	42·79
120				17·32	20·44	23·49	26·49	29·44	32·32	35·12	40·30
140				16·72	19·75	22·69	25·55	28·33	31·02	33·61	38·44
160				16·19	19·13	21·97	24·71	27·36	29·92	32·39	36·97
180				15·72	18·59	21·34	23·99	26·54	28·99	31·34	35·74
200				15·30	18·11	20·80	23·38	25·86	28·24	30·51	34·75
250				14·58	17·28	19·84	22·29	24·62	26·84	28·96	32·88
300				14·07	16·71	19·20	21·56	23·79	25·90	27·90	31·58
350											30·66
400											29·98
450											29·41
500											28·93
600											
700											
800											
900											
1,000											
1,200											

ENTROPY, JOULES/MOLE, °K—*cont.*

Pressure atm	Temperature ° K									
	170	180	190	200	210	220	230	240	250	260
1	96.00	97.69	99.28	100.79	102.22	103.58	104.88	106.12	107.31	108.45
2	90.15	91.85	93.45	94.97	96.41	97.78	99.08	100.33	101.52	102.67
3	86.71	88.42	90.03	91.55	92.99	94.36	95.67	96.92	98.12	99.27
5	82.31	84.04	85.67	87.21	88.66	90.04	91.36	92.62	93.82	94.97
7	79.36	81.11	82.76	84.31	85.78	87.17	88.49	89.75	90.96	92.12
10	76.14	77.93	79.61	81.19	82.68	84.08	85.42	86.69	87.91	89.08
15	72.33	74.20	75.94	77.56	79.08	80.51	81.87	83.16	84.40	85.58
20	69.50	71.44	73.23	74.89	76.45	77.91	79.29	80.60	81.85	83.05
25	67.18	69.21	71.06	72.77	74.36	75.85	77.26	78.59	79.86	81.07
30	65.19	67.31	69.22	70.97	72.60	74.12	75.55	76.90	78.19	79.42
35	63.39	65.62	67.61	69.42	71.09	72.64	74.09	75.46	76.77	78.01
40	61.74	64.09	66.16	68.02	69.73	71.31	72.79	74.19	75.51	76.76
45	60.17	62.66	64.81	66.73	68.48	70.09	71.60	73.02	74.36	75.63
50	58.72	61.36	63.60	65.57	67.36	69.01	70.54	71.98	73.34	74.63
60	55.98	58.93	61.35	63.45	65.33	67.05	68.64	70.13	71.53	72.85
70	53.48	56.73	59.34	61.57	63.55	65.34	66.99	68.52	69.95	71.29
80	51.21	54.71	57.51	59.87	61.94	63.80	65.50	67.08	68.55	69.93
90	49.14	52.83	55.81	58.30	60.46	62.39	64.15	65.77	67.28	68.69
100	47.48	51.23	54.30	56.88	59.12	61.12	62.93	64.59	66.13	67.57
120	44.75	48.50	51.67	54.39	56.75	58.85	60.74	62.48	64.08	65.57
140	42.68	46.35	49.53	52.30	54.73	56.89	58.85	60.64	62.29	63.83
160	41.04	44.62	47.77	50.55	53.01	55.21	57.21	59.04	60.73	62.31
180	39.67	43.17	46.28	49.05	51.52	53.74	55.76	57.62	59.35	60.95
200	38.57	41.98	45.03	47.77	50.23	52.46	54.50	56.38	58.13	59.76
250	36.43	39.64	42.55	45.20	47.62	49.84	51.88	53.78	55.56	57.22
300	34.92	37.96	40.74	43.29	45.65	47.83	49.86	51.76	53.54	55.21
350	33.82	36.71	39.37	41.84	44.13	46.27	48.27	50.15	51.92	53.59
400	32.98	35.75	38.31	40.70	42.93	45.02	46.98	48.84	50.59	52.25
450	32.28	34.94	37.42	39.74	41.92	43.97	45.90	47.73	49.46	51.11
500	31.68	34.25	36.66	38.92	41.05	43.06	44.96	46.76	48.47	50.10
600		33.01	35.33	37.51	39.57	41.52	43.37	45.13	46.80	48.40
700			34.22	36.34	38.35	40.26	42.07	43.79	45.43	47.00
800			33.25	35.33	37.30	39.17	40.95	42.64	44.26	45.81
900								41.64	43.24	44.77
1,000								40.73	42.32	43.84
1,200										

ENTROPY, JOULES/MOLE, °K—*cont.*

Temperature °K										Pressure
270	280	290	300	320	340	360	380	400	450	atm
109·55	110·61	111·63	112·62	114·50	116·27	117·94	119·52	121·02	124·47	1
103·77	104·83	105·85	106·84	108·72	110·49	112·16	113·74	115·24	118·69	2
100·37	101·43	102·45	103·44	105·33	107·10	108·77	110·35	111·86	115·31	3
96·08	97·15	98·18	99·17	101·06	102·84	104·52	106·11	107·62	111·08	5
93·23	94·30	95·33	96·33	98·23	100·01	101·69	103·28	104·79	108·25	7
90·20	91·28	92·32	93·32	95·23	97·02	98·71	100·30	101·81	105·28	10
86·71	87·80	88·85	89·86	91·78	93·58	95·27	96·87	98·39	101·88	15
84·20	85·30	86·36	87·38	89·31	91·12	92·82	94·43	95·96	99·46	20
82·23	83·34	84·41	85·44	87·39	89·21	90·92	92·54	94·07	97·59	25
80·59	81·71	82·79	83·83	85·79	87·62	89·34	90·97	92·51	96·04	30
79·19	80·32	81·41	82·45	84·43	86·28	88·01	89·65	91·20	94·74	35
77·96	79·11	80·20	81·25	83·24	85·10	86·84	88·48	90·03	93·58	40
76·84	78·00	79·11	80·17	82·18	84·05	85·80	87·45	89·01	92·58	45
75·85	77·02	78·14	79·21	81·23	83·11	84·87	86·53	88·09	91·67	50
74·10	75·29	76·42	77·51	79·56	81·46	83·24	84·91	86·49	90·09	60
72·57	73·78	74·93	76·04	78·12	80·04	81·84	83·53	85·12	88·75	70
71·23	72·46	73·64	74·76	76·87	78·82	80·63	82·33	83·94	87·60	80
70·02	71·28	72·48	73·62	75·75	77·72	79·55	81·26	82·88	86·56	90
68·92	70·20	71·41	72·57	74·73	76·72	78·57	80·30	81·93	85·63	100
66·97	68·29	69·54	70·73	72·94	74·97	76·85	78·60			120
65·28	66·64	67·92	69·14	71·40	73·47	75·38	77·16			140
63·79	65·18	66·49	67·74	70·05	72·15	74·09	75·89			160
62·46	63·88	65·22	66·49	68·84	70·98	72·95	74·78			180
61·29	62·73	64·09	65·38	67·76	69·93	71·93	73·78			200
58·79	60·27	61·67	62·99	65·44	67·68	69·73	71.63			250
56·79	58·28	59·69	61·04	63·54	65·82	67·92	69·86			300
55·17	56·67	58·09	59·45	61·99						350
53·82	55·32	56·75	58·11	60·66						400
52·68	54·17	55·59	56·95	59·50						450
51·65	53·13	54·55	55·91	58·46						500
49·92	51·38	52·78	54·12	56·65						600
48·50	49·94	51·32	52·65	55·15						700
47·29	48·71	50·07	51·39	53·87						800
46·24	47·65	49·00	50·31	52·78						900
45·30	46·70	48·05	49·35	51·80						1,000
43·59	44·98	46·32	47·61	50·06						1,200

ACETYLENE

F. DIN

The British Oxygen Company Limited,
Research and Development Centre, London

ALTHOUGH acetylene is a most important gas technically the thermo-dynamic data are incomplete and sometimes contradictory. The author has found only one other thermodynamic diagram for acetylene, prepared by FUNK[10], and in this case the diagram was constructed almost entirely on the basis of the Law of Corresponding States, using Edmister's method of approximation for hydrocarbons[9]. Since the present diagram will be later compared with that of Funk, it is desirable to describe his and Edmister's methods in some detail.

Edmister considered first the equation of state for non-ideal gases:

$$r = \frac{RT}{P} - V \qquad \dots \dots (1)$$

where r is a residual of volume. As well as pressure and temperature the term r in this equation can also be put in reduced form, *e.g.*

$$P' = \frac{P}{P_k}; \quad T' = \frac{T}{T_k}; \quad r' = \frac{r}{r_k}$$

where P_k, T_k and r_k refer to the critical state and P', T' and r' the reduced state. The equation of state with reduced terms becomes:

$$r' = \frac{RT_kT'}{r_kP_kP'} - \frac{V}{r_k} \qquad \dots \dots (2)$$

Edmister found that the values of r' in terms of the reduced pressure and reduced temperature for the nine hydrocarbons, methane, ethane, propane, n-pentane, isopentane, n-hexane, n-heptane, ethylene and cyclohexane were in practical agreement, and the mean values were tabulated and plotted as functions of reduced pressure with reduced temperature as parameter. Entropy and enthalpy changes for the

56

general case could be readily calculated from the reduced equation of state by standard methods, the integrals:

$$\int \left(-\frac{\partial r'}{\partial T'} \right)_{P'} \mathrm{d}P' \quad \text{and} \quad \int r' \mathrm{d}P'$$

being determined graphically. For any particular case it was necessary only to insert the appropriate value for the factor $\dfrac{P_k r_k}{T_k}$ to calculate the changes in entropy and enthalpy.

Funk extended this treatment to acetylene. The specific heat at constant pressure was assumed to be a linear function of temperature,

$$C_p = a + bT \qquad \qquad \dots \text{(3)}$$

and for acetylene Funk chose $a = 0 \cdot 2886$, $b = 0 \cdot 000428$, giving C_p in kcal/kg, $^\circ$ K. The factor $\dfrac{P_k r_k}{T_k}$ was taken as $0 \cdot 0558$ kcal/kg, $^\circ$ K and $P_k r_k$ as $17 \cdot 25$ kcal/kg.

In the two-phase region Funk noted that the available experimental values of vapour pressure reported by various authors differed considerably. He established the vapour pressure equation:

$$\mathrm{Log}_{10} P_{\text{atm}} = 4 \cdot 5866 - \frac{860 \cdot 0}{T} \qquad \dots \text{(4)}$$

for the whole of the liquid range up to the critical point. Latent heats were calculated from the Clausius–Clapeyron relationship using the vapour pressure formula and the data for the density of the saturated liquid and vapour determined by MATHIAS[20]. The Mathias data for the volume of the saturated vapour agreed well with those based on Edmister's residual term. For his diagram Funk plotted enthalpy versus the logarithm of the pressure with temperature, entropy and volume as parameters. The pressure range is from $7 \cdot 5$ kg/cm^2 to 70 kg/cm^2 and the temperature range from -30° C to 140° C.

SURVEY OF EXISTING DATA

1. The Compressibility Data

Two accurate compressibility isotherms have been measured at 0° C and 25° C up to 12 atm by SAMESHIMA[25]. Below 1 atm he used a refined Dumas method to measure the density, whilst above 1 atm a standard hydrogen manometer was used to measure the pressure. Sameshima's unsmoothed experimental results are given in Table 1.

There have been no other measurements of the compressibility isotherms of acetylene. The second virial coefficient, however, has been

TABLE 1

COMPRESSIBILITY DATA OF SAMESHIMA[25]

0 °C		25 °C	
Pressure atm	*PV*	*Pressure* atm	*PV*
1·000	1·0000	1·000	1·0937
1·650	0·9919	2·407	1·0808
1·780	0·9907	4·389	1·0655
2·461	0·9846	7·291	1·0436
2·568	0·9837	8·697	1·0333
4·472	0·9671	11·368	1·0180
7·234	0·9425		
10·600	0·9148		
10·798	0·9119		
11·263	0·9095		

measured by Schaefer[26] at temperatures down almost to the triple point using the principle of the Callendar–Barnes constant volume gas thermometer. The apparatus was calibrated at 0° C using Sameshima's results. Schaefer's values are given in Table 2.

TABLE 2

THE SECOND VIRIAL COEFFICIENT (Schaefer[26])

$$PV = RT\,(1 + BP)$$

Tempera-ture °K	*B*	*Tempera-ture* °K	*B*
199·63	− 0·0349	230·57	− 0·0206
205·04	− 0·0316	240·24	− 0·0174
211·71	− 0·0276	248·96	− 0·0156
221·45	− 0·0240	273·15	− 0·0115

Values for the coefficients of expansion and pressure and for the density of gaseous acetylene at N.T.P. have been reported at various times by Leduc[17], Stahrfoss[28] and Bretschger[3] but it is doubtful whether any of these results can compare with those of Sameshima in accuracy. Sameshima's value for the density of the gas at N.T.P. is 1·1747 g/litre.

2. The Density of the Saturated Liquid and Vapour

Mathias[20] has measured the density of the saturated liquid and

TABLE 3

THE DENSITY OF THE SATURATED LIQUID AND VAPOUR (Mathias[20])

$t\ °C$	Density g/cm³		$t\ °C$	Density g/cm³	
	Liquid	Vapour		Liquid	Vapour
−23·75	0·5185	0·02168	24·13	0·3814	0·0958
6·08	0·4474	0·0528	29·02	0·3559	0·1160
6·18	0·4478	0·0529	29·11	0·3556	0·1163
12·04	0·4295	0·0632	31·48	0·3379	0·1305
17·08	0·4120	0·0740	32·14	0·3315	0·1361
20·32	0·3987	0·0831	32·93	0·3282	0·1393
23·43	0·3859	0·0925	35·4	0·2306	0·2306

vapour and determined the rectilinear diameter of acetylene. His results are given in Table 3.

These results are based on Leduc's values for the density of the gas at N.T.P. and the coefficient of expansion between 0° C and 100° C. They can therefore be corrected to allow for the slightly different value of the density at N.T.P. found by Sameshima. At temperatures lower than −23·75° C, the lowest recorded by Mathias, MCINTOSH[21] and MAASS and WRIGHT[19] have measured the density of the saturated liquid and solid in the neighbourhood of the triple point.

3. The Vapour Pressure

For solid acetylene BURRELL and ROBERTSON[4] proposed the vapour pressure formula:

$$\text{Log}_{10}\ P\ _{atm} = 5·95919 - \frac{1127·1}{T} \qquad \dots\ (5)$$

which is in good agreement with the additional results of KLEMENC, BANKOWSKI and VON FRUGNONI[15] and of BURBO[2]. In the case of the liquid, however, some very large discrepancies exist. Plotting the values shows that whilst those of McIntosh[21] and VILLARD[29] agree, those of CAILLETET[5], ANSDELL[1] and HUNTER[13] are widely different, indicating almost certainly a lack of purity of the acetylene used by these investigators.

Triple point temperatures between 189·4° K and 192·2° K with pressures from 895 mm to 950 mm have been variously reported but CLARK and DIN's[7] value of 962 mm at 192·4° K being higher than the the others probably indicates higher purity of the gas used. This value is moreover consistent with the formula of Burrell and Robertson.

59

4. The Critical Constants

In contrast to the discrepancies among the vapour pressure results, the critical constants reported by various authors show remarkably good agreement, as shown in Table 4.

TABLE 4

THE CRITICAL CONSTANTS

t °C	Pressure atm	ϱ g/cm³	Observer
35·25	61·0		Kuenen[16]
36·5	61·6	0·314*	McIntosh[21]
35·4		0·2306	Mathias[20]
35·5	61·65		Cardoso and Baumé[6]
35·9	61·6	0·231	Pickering[24]. (Critical survey)

* McIntosh's value for the critical density is correctly reported here, but is manifestly in error.

For acetylene Edmister selected the following values to be applied with his reduced equation of state: $P_k = 61\cdot7$ atm, $T_k = 309\cdot1°$ K $(35\cdot94°$ C) and $V_k = 113\cdot2$ cm³/mole $(\varrho = 0\cdot2299$ g/cm³).

5. The Latent Heats and Specific Heats

Apart from some simple experiments by McIntosh[21] the latent heats of fusion and vaporization reported for acetylene at pressures around 1 atm have been calculated from the slope of the vapour pressure curve, *i.e.* from the integrated Clausius–Clapeyron equation. HEUSE[12] has measured the specific heat of acetylene at a constant pressure of 1 atm in his glass counter-current flow calorimeter at $-71°$ C and 18° C. The value of the ratio γ was calculated with the aid of the Berthelot equation of state. LEDUC[18] has also reported values for C_p and C_v at 15° C and GIACOMINI[11] for C_v at 13° C. The ratio of the specific heats has also been calculated by SCHWEIKERT[27] and by INGOLD[14] from measurements of the velocity of sound. The various values are given in Table 5.

There has been no determination of the specific heat of the saturated liquid and solid apart from the rough experiments of McIntosh[21].

6. The Spectroscopic Data

The thermodynamic functions of acetylene have been calculated for the ideal gaseous state at 1 atm from spectroscopic and statistical data.

The values at 300° K reported by WAGMAN and others[23] are $S° =$ 48·061 cal/mole, ° K and $H° - H°_0 = 2410·8$ cal/mole. As there have been no calorimetric measurements with condensed acetylene at low temperatures it is not possible to correlate these values with those

TABLE 5

SPECIFIC HEATS

t °C	C_p cal/mole, °C	C_v cal/mole, °C	γ	Observer
– 71	9·13	6·97	1·31	Heuse[12]
18	10·46	8·44	1·24	
15			1·26	Schweikert[27]
13		8·12		Giacomini[11]
0			1·231	
25			1·227	Ingold[14]
100			1·204	
15	9·97	7·91	1·26	Leduc[18]

obtained from the Third Law of Thermodynamics. There is some doubt, however, whether the thermodynamic functions of polyatomic molecules containing hydrogen can be calculated accurately from statistical data.

CALCULATION OF THE THERMODYNAMIC FUNCTIONS AND CONSTRUCTION OF THE THERMODYNAMIC DIAGRAM

7. Units, Constants and Conversion Factors

For the present work the chosen unit of pressure is the international atmosphere, $g = 980·665$, and the unit of volume the cubic centimetre. The Kelvin scale of temperature has been used, related to the Celsius scale by an ice point of 0° C = 273·16° K. For the unit of energy a calorie of 4·1868 J has been used and the quantity unit is the gramme molecule, the molecular weight of acetylene being taken as 26·03. The volume of an ideal gas at N.T.P. has been taken as 22,414·6 cm³ whilst for the molecular volume of acetylene under the same conditions a value of 22,157 cm³ has been derived as will be explained later. Taking the cm³-atm as equivalent to 0·101325 J a factor of 536·22 was obtained to convert Amagat unit-atmospheres to calories per mole.

8. The Equation of State

Owing to the dearth of data it is impossible to use the usual graphical and analytical methods to construct a thermodynamic diagram for acetylene. In these circumstances the methods of Edmister and Funk are justifiable, particularly as good values for the critical constants are available. In the present instance, however, there seemed to be no point in repeating or extending the range of Funk's work, and the alternative of using an equation of state has been adopted. It will subsequently be shown that the agreement between the two diagrams is better than is usually found, and consequently the reliability of both, constructed from entirely different bases, is thereby considerably enhanced.

The choice of a suitable equation of state was dictated by the fact that it was desirable to include the critical region in the thermodynamic diagram and therefore the equation had to be valid at this point. In view of the limited range of the experimental compressibility data, an empirical series equation was ruled out and an equation of the Van der Waals type was indicated. The Van der Waals equation:

$$\left(P+\frac{a}{V^2}\right)(V-b)=RT \qquad \qquad \cdots\cdots (6)$$

although qualitatively of the right form for expressing the behaviour of gases in the critical region fails to predict accurately the values of all three critical constants. Attempts to improve the Van der Waals equation have usually involved an elaboration of the $\frac{a}{V^2}$ term. Berthelot proposed making this term an inverse function of the temperature, i.e. $\frac{a}{TV^2}$, but his equation still fails just as badly as that of Van der Waals at the critical point. Clausius added an additional constant to the volume in the $\frac{a}{V^2}$ term whilst retaining the inverse temperature relationship; so that his equation of state is:

$$\left[P+\frac{a}{T(V+c)^2}\right](V-b)=RT \qquad \qquad \cdots\cdots (7)$$

The equation can be further improved by making a a more complex function of temperature, e.g. a function of the type $\frac{a}{T}+m+nT$. In this way equations of state for gases have been built up which express the observed data over quite large ranges of temperature and pressure with remarkably good accuracy. The simple Clausius equation quoted above is no better than that of Van der Waals over large ranges, but in the present case there was only a limited range of experimental data against which the equation had to be tested, and it has the advantage that, being a three constant equation, besides R, it can be made to express the critical conditions exactly. Such a three constant equation does not imply the validity of the Law of Corresponding States unless a universal mathematical relationship true for all gases exists between two of the constants a, b and c.

To evaluate the constants in the Clausius equation from the critical data the conditions $\left.\dfrac{\partial P}{\partial V}\right)_{Tk} = 0$ and $\left.\dfrac{\partial^2 P}{\partial V^2}\right)_{Tk} = 0$ are applied in the usual manner. It is found that:

$$P_k = \frac{a}{27 T_k (b+c)^2} \qquad \dots\dots (8)$$

$$V_k = 3b + 2c \qquad \dots\dots (9)$$

$$T_k^2 = \frac{8a}{27R(b+c)} \qquad \dots\dots (10)$$

from which a, b and c can be calculated from the known values of P_k, V_k and T_k and an appropriately chosen value of R. For the critical constants the values of CARDOSO and BAUMÉ [6] were chosen for P_k and T_k and for V_k the value of Mathias [20], slightly corrected to conform with Sameshima's value of the density of the gas at N.T.P. The value of R was chosen so that $PV = 1$ at $0°$ C ($273 \cdot 16°$ K) and 1 atm in the equation:

$$PV = RT(1 + BP) \qquad \dots\dots (11)$$

where B is Schaefer's value of the second virial coefficient at $0°$ C based on Sameshima's results. The selected values for the critical constants and R were thus:

$P_k = 61 \cdot 65$ atm
$V_k = 0 \cdot 005095$ Amagat units
$T_k = 308 \cdot 7$ °K
$R = 0 \cdot 0037035$ Amagat unit-atm/mole, °K

from which the values of the constants in the Clausius equation were found to be:

$a = 2 \cdot 7611$
$b = 0 \cdot 000459$
$c = 0 \cdot 001859$

The molar volume of acetylene at $0°$ C and 1 atm, i.e. the Amagat unit of volume per mole is found from the second virial coefficient and an ideal molar volume of 22,414·6 cm³ (0 = 16) to be 22·157 cm³, which with a density of 1·1747 g/litre, as reported by Sameshima, corresponds with a molecular weight of 26·027, in excellent agreement with the chemical figure.

The equation was tested by calculating values of the product PV which were compared with the experimental values of Sameshima, see *Figure 1*. For both the 0° C and 25° C isotherms the agreement is fairly good and the deviations in both isotherms, although outside the limit of the experimental accuracy, appear to be systematic. In this

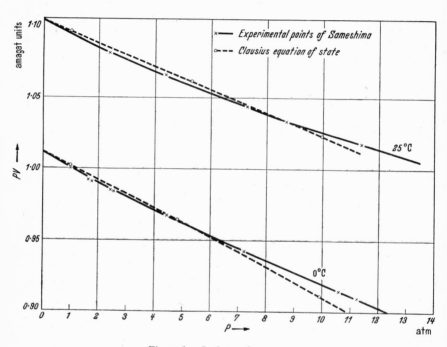

Figure 1.   Isotherms for acetylene

restricted range, therefore, it seems that the equation gives equally good or even better agreement between calculated and experimental values of the derivatives $\left(\dfrac{\partial V}{\partial T}\right)_P$ and $\left(\dfrac{\partial P}{\partial T}\right)_V$ which come into calculations of thermodynamic changes. At low temperatures the equation predicts values for the second virial coefficient which are likewise in good agreement with those reported by Schaefer.

It was decided, therefore, to retain the simple Clausius equation of state and to use it to calculate the changes in the thermodynamic functions over the range for which it could be expected to be reasonably valid, *i.e.* from around the critical pressure and temperature downwards.

It will be shown later that the equation of state is also consistent with the known vapour pressure of acetylene, the Mathias data for the saturated vapour density and the Law of Corresponding States.

9. Calculation of the Thermodynamic Functions

The Clausius equation is implicit in volume and explicit in pressure so that the derivatives $\dfrac{\partial P}{\partial T}\Big)_V$ and $\dfrac{\partial^2 P}{\partial T^2}\Big)_V$ are much more readily obtained than $\dfrac{\partial V}{\partial T}\Big)_P$ and $\dfrac{\partial^2 V}{\partial T^2}\Big)_P$. The isothermal changes in entropy, enthalpy and specific heat at constant volume can thus be calculated with the aid of the following thermodynamic equations:

$$\frac{\partial S}{\partial V}\bigg)_T = \frac{\partial P}{\partial T}\bigg)_V \qquad \dots (12)$$

$$\frac{\partial H}{\partial V}\bigg)_T = V\frac{\partial P}{\partial V}\bigg)_T + T\frac{\partial P}{\partial T}\bigg)_V \qquad \dots (13)$$

$$\frac{\partial C_v}{\partial V}\bigg)_T = T\frac{\partial^2 P}{\partial T^2}\bigg)_V \qquad \dots (14)$$

in which case volume and temperature must be chosen as the independent variables. When applied to the Clausius equation of state the integrated forms of the above equations, giving the isothermal changes in entropy, enthalpy and specific heat at constant volume, are:

$$\Delta S\bigg]_{V_1}^{V_2}{}_T = R\log_e \frac{V_2 - b}{V_1 - b} - \frac{a}{T^2}\left[\frac{1}{V_2 + c} - \frac{1}{V_1 + c}\right] \qquad \dots (15)$$

$$\Delta H\bigg]_{V_1}^{V_2}{}_T = RTb\left[\frac{1}{V_2 - b} - \frac{1}{V_1 - b}\right] - \frac{3a}{T}\left[\frac{1}{V_2 + c} - \frac{1}{V_1 + c}\right]$$
$$+ \frac{ac}{T}\left[\frac{1}{(V_2 + c)^2} - \frac{1}{(V_1 + c)^2}\right] \qquad \dots (16)$$

$$\Delta C_v\bigg]_{V_1}^{V_2}{}_T = \frac{2a}{T^2}\left[\frac{1}{V_2 + c} - \frac{1}{V_1 + c}\right] \qquad \dots (17)$$

Since it is customary to use pressure and temperature as independent variables in thermodynamic tables, values of volume had first to be worked out from the equation for rounded off values of pressure and temperature. As already stated, Amagat units of volume were chosen to conform with the value of the gas constant, R, already given. Solving the equation for volume was done by trial and error to four significant figures. In general not more than two attempts had to be made at each value, but around the critical region, where the volume varies very rapidly with pressure, four or five attempts were sometimes necessary before the correct value of the volume was finally established.

When the volume had thus been established as a function of temperature and pressure the isothermal entropy, enthalpy and specific heat changes between volume limits were calculated from equations (15), (16) and (17). The changes were calculated from 1 atm to 0·1 atm, from 1 atm to 10 atm and from 10 atm to 100 atm until the saturation line for the vapour was reached. The volumes were calculated originally to four significant figures and the other thermodynamic functions to five figures where possible. Only in the case of the enthalpy in the critical region were the final calculated values less precise than the original volumes.

Since the thermodynamic diagram was required to include lines of constant volume, isothermal entropy changes between rounded off values of volume were calculated as the most convenient means of setting up the isochores. The isochores were required for rounded off values of volume in cubic centimetres, and hence these had to be converted to Amagat units for calculation purposes. The base isochore was chosen at 1000 cm^3 and all the others were calculated from it. Finally, the isothermal entropy changes between the 1000 cm^3 isochore and the 1 atm isobar (as a function of volume) had to be calculated.

The changes in the functions thus calculated were given in Amagat unit-atmospheres. A factor of 536·22 was adopted to convert the changes to calories per mole.

To calculate the final values of the functions along both isochores and isobars the values along the 1 atm isobar had to be established. For this purpose the values of C_p and γ at $-71°$ C and $18°$ C reported by Heuse were used, which lead to the following equations for the specific heats:

$$C_v = 3·63 + 0·0165\,T \text{ cal/mole, } °K \qquad \dots \text{(18)}$$

$$C_p = 6·11 + 0·0149\,T \text{ cal/mole, } °K \qquad \dots \text{(19)}$$

From Equation (19) the enthalpy and entropy along the 1 atm isobar could be easily calculated by integration:

$$\Delta H \Big]_{T_1}^{T_2}{}_P = \int_{T_1}^{T_2} C_p \, \mathrm{d}T \qquad \dots \text{(20)}$$

$$\Delta S \Big]_{T_1}^{T_2}{}_P = \int_{T_1}^{T_2} \frac{C_p}{T} \, \mathrm{d}T \qquad \dots \text{(21)}$$

It still remained to fix the reference values of entropy and enthalpy at one point on the 1 atm isobar. In this work purely arbitrary reference values of entropy and enthalpy have been chosen. The entropy at low pressure was set approximately equal to the ideal gaseous state value reported in the *National Bureau of Standards Journal of Research*[23] whilst the ideal gaseous heat content function was increased by 5000 cal/mole to avoid negative values of enthalpy arising in the condensed region.

For the superheated region there remained only the specific heat at constant pressure, C_p, to be calculated. C_p was obtained by evaluating the quotient $\dfrac{\Delta H}{\Delta T}$ along isobars between small temperature intervals and plotting the results against the mean temperature. The final values of C_p were then read off from the graphs. Accurate values could not be obtained around the critical region and have therefore been omitted from the tables.

Since the thermodynamic functions in the superheated region have been calculated from an equation of state, the diagram must be internally consistent and elaborate smoothing of the tables has not been necessary. The tables were, however, checked for smoothness primarily with the object of showing up any errors in calculation. The tables give changes in the functions to four significant figures. The ultimate accuracy depends, however, upon the validity of the Clausius equation of state which cannot be decided.

10. The Two-Phase Boundary

In this work the critical pressure and temperature reported by Cardoso and Baumé and the triple point values of Clark and Din have been adopted. From these two points the simple vapour pressure formula:

$$\text{Log}_{10} P_{\text{atm}} = 4 \cdot 5816 - \frac{861 \cdot 73}{T} \qquad \dots \dots (22)$$

is derived which may be compared with that used by Funk. Plotting the vapour pressure results of Villard and of McIntosh shows that there appears to be a systematic deviation of the true vapour pressures from those given by this simple formula (see *Figure 2*), the true values being less than the calculated ones at high pressures and greater at low pressures. To allow for this deviation the more complex formula:

$$\text{Log}_{10} P_{\text{atm}} = 6 \cdot 7275 - \frac{2445 \cdot 73}{T} + \frac{3 \cdot 8238 \times 10^5}{T^2} - \frac{3 \cdot 0216 \times 10^7}{T^3}$$

$$\dots \dots (23)$$

was derived which fits the results of Villard and of McIntosh within the probable limits of experimental error. With the aid of this vapour pressure formula the saturation line for the vapour was provisionally inserted on the temperature–entropy diagram by marking off the saturation temperatures on the appropriate isobars. The isochores on the diagram then gave values for the saturated vapour volume at various temperatures which could be compared with the experimental data of Mathias. For this purpose the Mathias data were corrected slightly, as described in section 2, and extrapolated down to 200·9° K where the saturation pressure is 2 atm, the volume being determined from equation (11) using Schaefer's second virial coefficient at this temperature.   Below 10 atm the agreement was excellent but from 10 atm to the critical point there were some slight discrepancies.   In no case did these correspond with an entropy difference of more than 0·08 cal/mole, K on the temperature–entropy diagram, but they show up much more distinctly on the *PV* versus *P* diagram as shown in *Figure 3*.   On

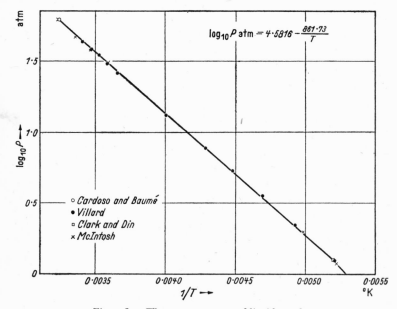

Figure 2.   The vapour pressure of liquid acetylene

this diagram the saturation points can be fixed either from the vapour pressures and the Clausius equation of state or from the vapour pressures and the Mathias data.   In both cases their positions are very sensitive to changes in the vapour pressure.   In the case of the Clausius equation, varying the vapour pressure moves the saturation points along the isotherms whilst for the Mathias data the saturation points are moved along straight lines connecting them to the origin.   The saturation curve on the *PV* versus *P* diagram was drawn as a compromise between the two sets of data, as shown in *Figure 3*, and from it the final saturation values of pressure, volume and temperature were taken.   The effect of this compromise on the vapour pressure values is shown in *Figure 4*, where it is seen to be scarcely greater than the experimental limit of accuracy.   Using the established values of the saturated vapour volume and the Mathias, McIntosh, and Maass and Wright values for the volume of the saturated liquid together with the differentiated vapour pressure formula, latent heats were calculated from the Clausius–Clapeyron relationship. Strictly speaking, the vapour pressure formula should have been re-modified to meet the revised values on the temperature–entropy and PV versus P diagrams

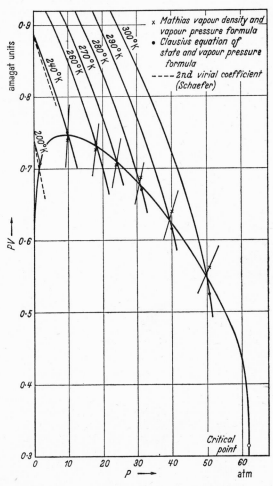

Figure 3. PV versus P diagram for acetylene

but this was not done. For the solid latent heats the vapour pressure formula of Burrell and Robertson was used with the saturated vapour volumes derived directly from the diagram, *i.e.* the Clausius equation of state. A constant volume of 35·7 cm³/mole was assumed for the solid which corresponds with McIntosh's reported value of the density at − 85° C. The values of pressure and temperature given in the table of saturation properties are the fully revised values and not those calculated from the liquid vapour pressure formula The triple point value is that reported by Clark and Din.

Figure 5 shows the densities of the saturated liquid and vapour at various temperatures. The values according to the diagram and to Mathias for the vapour are indistinguishable but a discrepancy is apparent for the liquid. On the temperature–entropy diagram the isochores have been extrapolated into the saturated liquid line and the

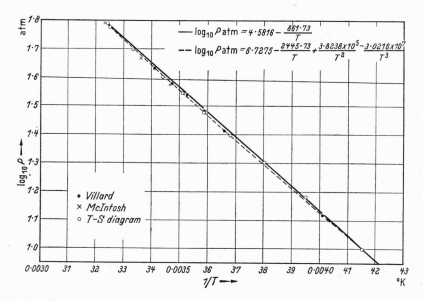

$$\log_{10} P \text{ atm} = 4 \cdot 5816 - \frac{861 \cdot 73}{T}$$

$$\log_{10} P \text{ atm} = 6 \cdot 7275 - \frac{2445 \cdot 73}{T} + \frac{3 \cdot 8238 \times 10^5}{T^2} - \frac{3 \cdot 0218 \times 10^7}{T^3}$$

• *Villard*
× *McIntosh*
○ *T–S diagram*

Figure 4. The vapour pressure of liquid acetylene

oblique intersection does not lead to an accurate assessment of the saturation temperature. The Clausius equation of state is moreover of doubtful validity in this compressed liquid region.

Discussion

Figure 6 shows the present diagram in skeleton form indicating the regions where there are direct experimental data for acetylene which have been considered in this work. Very little need be said about the necessity for further experimental data. Apart from the very limited work of Sameshima and Schaefer there have been no determinations of the compressibility of acetylene. This is possibly due to the hazard involved in working with acetylene at high temperatures and pressures, but unless and until comprehensive compressibility data become available there is no alternative but to accept the indirect methods of evaluating thermodynamic functions. The resulting diagrams must therefore be of uncertain accuracy. Heuse's values for the specific heat at 1 atm are probably reliable but without values at more than two temperatures a linear relationship only between C_p and T can be postulated.

In view of the hazard involved in working with compressed liquid

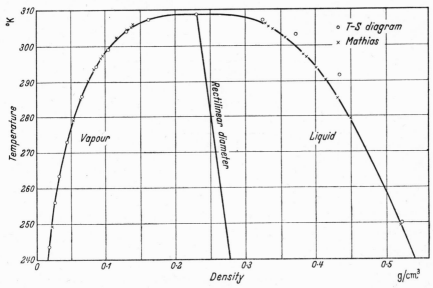

Figure 5. Density of the saturated liquid and vapour for acetylene

acetylene it is remarkable that such good data exist for the two-phase region. The critical constants, vapour pressure data and the data for the density of the saturated liquid and vapour are consistent with the Law of Corresponding States and the Clausius equation to within quite narrow limits, and the two-phase region of the present diagram may well be regarded as its most accurate one.

In Tables 6 and 7 some comparisons are given of the values of the

TABLE 6

COMPARISON OF SATURATION PROPERTIES

F=Funk.   D=This work.

$T°K$	Pressure atm		V_{vap} cm³		H_{vap} cal/mole		S_{vap} cal/mole, °K		Latent heat cal/mole	
	F	D	F	D	F	D	F	D	F	D
243·16	10·85	10·77	1480	1476	6590*	6590	43·66*	43·66	3060	3022
258·16	17·42	17·06	909	944	6603	6605	42·98	43·02	2785	2778
273·16	26·54	25·88	587	599	6588	6594	42·26	42·38	2474	2497
288·16	38·70	38·11	378	374	6496	6510	41·43	41·58	2042	2041
303·16	54·40	53·95	220	208	6218	6252	40·18	40·34	1247	1280

* Adjusted for reference.

71

TABLE 7

COMPARISON OF SUPERHEATED PROPERTIES

F=Funk.   D=This work.

Temperature °K	Pressure atm	Volume cm³		Enthalpy cal/mole		Entropy cal/mole,°K	
		F	D	F	D	F	D
243·16		1758	1748	6632	6617	44·00	43·98
263·16	9·675	1995	1978	6879	6853	44·96	44·91
283·16		2204	2188	7122	7083	45·83	45·77
303·16		2397	2390	7362	7312	46·62	46·57
283·16	29·02	580	545	6717	6665	42·53	42·50
303·16		684	655	7078	7004	43·76	43·66
503·16	48·375	304	269	6613	6475	41·51	41·22

various functions according to Funk's diagram and the present one
in their common range.

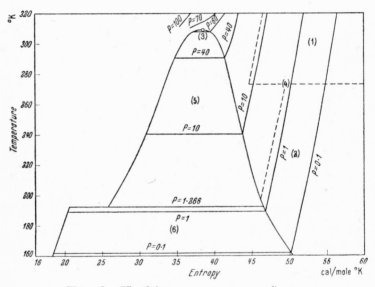

Figure 6.   The skeleton temperature–entropy diagram

(1) Compressibility data—Sameshima.
(2) Second virial coefficient—Schaefer. Specific heat at 1 atm—Heuse.
(3) Critical constants—Cardoso and Baumé.
(4) Clausius equation of state.
(5) Vapour pressure—Villard, McIntosh. Density of saturated liquid and vapour—
Mathias. Latent heats—Clausius–Clapeyron equation.
(6) Vapour pressure—Burrell and Robertson. Triple point—Clark and Din.

Funk's units have been converted to those used in the present diagram. For the two-phase region the agreement is excellent, as might be expected, since similar vapour pressure formulae and the Mathias data were used in both cases. In the superheated region the agreement is very good also, except perhaps when approaching the critical region. It is much better than is generally found between thermodynamic diagrams prepared by different authors using different methods. This agreement between the two diagrams is important, because it means that the general validity of the Clausius equation of state over the range used in this work is borne out by the Law of Corresponding States, besides being consistent with the experimental data.

The isothermal variation of the specific heat at constant volume as derived from the Clausius equation is entirely dependent on the form of the $\frac{a}{V^2}$ term. From the comparatively simple form used here:

$$P = \frac{RT}{V-b} - \frac{a}{T(V+c)^2} \qquad \dots \ (24)$$

there follows:

$$\frac{\partial C_v}{\partial V}\bigg)_T = T\frac{\partial^2 P}{\partial T^2}\bigg)_V = -\frac{2a}{T^2(V+c)^2} \qquad \dots \ (25)$$

from which it is seen that C_v increases progressively as the volume is reduced isothermally. This is in accord with the present author's work on argon[8] but not with the work of MICHELS[22] on the isotherms of carbon dioxide and nitrogen where it appears in both cases that C_v passes through a maximum on isothermal compression in the neighbourhood of the critical density. As mentioned in section 8, the Clausius equation can be improved by making the $\frac{a}{V^2}$ term a complex function of temperature, and by making it more complex in volume it should clearly be possible to derive a form in which the derivative $\frac{\partial C_v}{\partial V}\bigg)_T$ can be equated to zero, giving a maximum value of C_v at the critical density and temperature. In the present case, however, this deviation from what is probably, but not necessarily, the behaviour of most polyatomic gases is not considered a serious discrepancy.

REFERENCES

[1] ANSDELL, Chem. News, 40 (1879) 136.
[2] BURBO, J. phys. U.S.S.R., 7 (1943) 286.
[3] BRETSCHGER, Diss. Zürich (1911).
[4] BURRELL and ROBERTSON, J. Amer. chem. Soc., 37 (1915) 2188.
[5] CAILLETET, C.R. Acad. Sci. Paris, 85 (1877) 851.
[6] CARDOSO and BAUMÉ, J. Chim. phys., 10 (1912) 509.

[7] CLARK and DIN, *Trans. Faraday Soc.*, 46 (1950) 901.

[8] DIN, Thermodynamic Functions of Argon—Page 146.

[9] EDMISTER, *Industr. Engng Chem.*, 30 (1938) 352.

[10] FUNK, *Mitt. Kälte Inst. Karlsruhe*, No. 3 (1948).

[11] GIACOMINI, *Phil. Mag.* (6), 50 (1925) 146.

[12] HEUSE, *Ann. Phys. Lpz.*, (4), 59 (1919) 86.

[13] HUNTER, *J. phys. Chem.*, 10 (1906) 356.

[14] INGOLD, *J. chem. Soc.*, 124 (1924) 1534.

[15] KLEMENC, BANKOWSKI and VON FRUGNONI, *Naturwissenschaften*, 22 (1934) 465.

[16] KUENEN, *Phil. Mag.* (5), 44 (1897) 174.

[17] LEDUC, *Ann. Chim. Phys.*, 13 (1898) 1.

[18] LEDUC, *Chem. Rev.*, 6 (1929) 13.

[19] MAASS and WRIGHT, *J. Amer. chem. Soc.*, 43 (1921) 1104.

[20] MATHIAS, *C.R. Acad. Sci. Paris*, 148 (1909) 1102.

[21] McINTOSH, *J. phys. Chem.*, 11 (1907) 306.

[22] MICHELS and others, *Appl. Sci. Res.*, A 1 (1948) 94; *Physica, 'sGrav.*, 17 (1951) 801.

[23] WAGMAN, KILPATRICK, PITZER and ROSSINI, *J. Res. nat. Bur. Stand.*, 35 (1946) 467.

[24] PICKERING, *J. phys. Chem.*, 28 (1924) 97.

[25] SAMESHIMA, *Bull. chem. Soc. Japan*, 1 (1926) 41.

[26] SCHAEFER, *Z. phys. Chem.*, B36 (1937) 85.

[27] SCHWEIKERT, *Ann. Phys. Lpz.* (4), 48 (1915) 593.

[28] STAHRFOSS, *Arch. Sci. phys.*, 28 (1908) 304.

[29] VILLARD, *C.R. Acad. Sci. Paris*, 120 (1895) 1262.

TABLES OF THERMODYNAMIC FUNCTIONS OF ACETYLENE

The properties are given for 1 gramme mole of acetylene (26·03 g) as functions of the pressure in international atmospheres ($g = 980·665$) and temperature in degrees Kelvin (0° C = 273·16° K). The reference values of entropy and enthalpy are purely arbitrary. One calorie = 4·1868 J.

Molecular weight	$= 26·03$
Density of gas at N.T.P.	$= 0·0011747$ g/cm^3
Molecular volume at N.T.P.	$= 22,157$ cm^3
Normal sublimation point	$= 189·13$ ° K
Triple point: temperature	$= 192·4$ ° K
pressure	$= 962$ mm
Critical constants: temperature	$= 308·7°$ K
pressure	$= 61·65$ atm
volume	$= 112·9$ cm^3

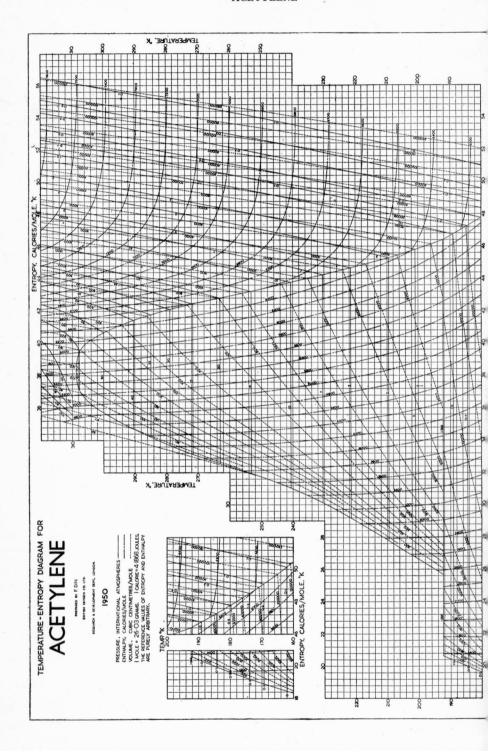

PROPERTIES OF THE SATURATED SOLID AND VAPOUR

Pressure atm	Tempera- ture °K	Entropy cal/mole, °K		Enthalpy cal/mole		Volume cm³	
		Solid	Vapour	Solid	Vapour	Solid	Vapour
0·1	161·96	18·46	50·17	985	6,120	—	132,300
0·2	169·27	18·91	49·09	1,075	6,183	—	68,850
0·3	173·88	19·26	48·52	1,132	6,219	—	46,990
0·5	180·04	19·67	47·74	1,210	6,264	—	29,060
0·7	184·34	20·01	47·27	1,266	6,291	—	21,100
1·0	189·13	20·36	46·74	1,330	6,319	35·7	15,050
1·266 (T.P.)	192·4	20·61	46·39	1,375	6,335	—	12,020

PROPERTIES OF THE SATURATED LIQUID AND VAPOUR

Pressure atm	Tempera- ture °K	Entropy cal/mole, °K		Enthalpy cal/mole		Volume cm³	
		Liquid	Vapour	Liquid	Vapour	Liquid	Vapour
1·266 (T.P.)	192·4	25·68	46·39	2,350	6,335	42·7	12,020
2	200·9	26·73	45·81	2,559	6,392	43·0	7,840
3	209·4	27·76	45·30	2,770	6,443	43·9	5,400
5	221·5	29·15	44·68	3,067	6,507	45·4	3,290
7	230·4	30·10	44·25	3,287	6,547	46·7	2,361
10	240·7	31·05	43·79	3,517	6,584	48·4	1,654
15	253·2	31·94	43·23	3,746	6,605	50·9	1,093
20	263·0	32·55	42·80	3,908	6,604	53·2	804
25	271·6	33·14	42·45	4,067	6,595	55·5	626
30	278·9	33·69	42·11	4,229	6,576	58·0	503
35	284·9	34·19	41·79	4,378	6,543	60·3	414
40	290·4	34·70	41·43	4,525	6,480	62·9	345
50	300·0	35·70	40·66	4,840	6,328	70·2	243
60	307·8	37·12	39·52	5,287	6,025	87·3	159
61·65 (C.P.)	308·7	38·32		5,651		112·9	

ΔH_v
3985
3833

ACETYLENE

ENTHALPY, CALORIES/MOLE

Pressure atm	Temperature °K								
	160	170	180	190	200	210	220	230	240
0·1	6108·0*	6188·2	6270·9	6355·9	6442·9	6531·9	6622·7	6715·3	6809·7
0·2		6184·1	6267·2	6352·5	6439·9	6529·2	6620·2	6713·1	6807·7
0·3			6263·5	6349·2	6436·9	6526·5	6617·8	6710·9	6805·6
0·5			6255·9	6342·5	6430·8	6521·0	6612·8	6706·4	6801·5
0·7				6335·6	6424·7	6515·5	6607·8	6701·8	6797·3
1·0	6063·8*	6149·5*	6236·6*	6325·3	6415·5	6507·1	6600·2	6694·9	6791·0
2					6383·5*	6478·6	6574·5	6671·5	6769·7
3						6448·8	6547·9	6647·4	6747·8
5							6491·2*	6597·0	6702·4
7								6542·6*	6654·1
10									6575·2*
15									
20									
25									
30									
35									
40									
50									
60									
70									
80									
90									
100									

*Supersaturated

ENTHALPY, CALORIES/MOLE

Temperature °K										Pressure atm
250	260	270	280	290	300	305	310	315	320	
05·8	7003·6	7103·0	7204·0	7306·6	7410·8	—	7516·6	—	7623·9	0·1
03·9	7001·8	7101·4	7202·5	7305·2	7409·5	—	7515·3	—	7622·7	0·2
02·0	7000·1	7099·7	7201·0	7303·8	7408·2	—	7514·1	—	7621·6	0·3
98·2	6996·6	7096·5	7198·0	7301·0	7405·6	—	7511·7	—	7619·3	0·5
94·4	6993·0	7093·2	7194·9	7298·1	7402·9	—	7509·2	—	7617·0	0·7
88·6	6987·7	7088·3	7190·3	7293·9	7399·0	7452·0	7505·5	7559·3	7613·5	1·0
69·1	6969·7	7071·7	7175·0	7279·7	7385·7	—	7493·1	—	7602·0	2
49·2	6951·5	7054·9	7159·5	7265·3	7372·3	—	7480·6	—	7590·3	3
07·9	6913·8	7020·4	7127·7	7235·9	7345·1	—	7455·3	—	7566·7	5
64·6	6874·7	6984·7	7095·0	7205·8	7317·3	—	7429·6	—	7542·7	7
95·0	6812·4	6928·6	7044·0	7159·2	7274·4	7332·2	7390·0	7447·9	7506·0	10
61·6*	6696·9	6826·7	6952·9	7076·8	7199·4	—	7321·1	—	7442·6	15
	6558·3*	6710·0	6851·9	6987·5	7119·2	7184·1	7248·5	7312·5	7376·2	20
		6568·9*	6735·6	6888·1	7032·3	7102·2	7171·1	7239·1	7306·4	25
			6596·0	6776·3	6936·8	7013·3	7088·0	7161·0	7232·6	30
			6406·3*	6641·8	6829·8	6915·5	6997·6	7076·8	7153·9	35
				6466·7*	6705·8	6805·5	6897·9	6985·4	7069·7	40
					6327·8	6514·3	6652·9	6770·6	6877·2	50
							6240·0	6473·6	6634·2	60
							⊙ 5166·6	5838·0	6275·1	70
							4976·6	5302·7	5729·9	80
							4863·2	5127·1	5420·4	90
							4767·3	5016·3	5263·3	100

*Supersaturated

79

ACETYLENE

ENTROPY, CALORIES/MOLE, °K

Pressure atm	Temperature °K								
	160	170	180	190	200	210	220	230	240
0·1	50·059*	50·547	51·019	51·477	51·923	52·357	52·780	53·192	53·594
0·2		49·153	49·629	50·090	50·537	50·972	51·396	51·809	52·211
0·3			48·809	49·272	49·722	50·159	50·584	50·998	51·401
0·5			47·768	48·235	48·688	49·127	49·554	49·970	50·375
0·7				47·542	48·000	48·443	48·872	49·289	49·695
1·0	45·299*	45·819*	46·317*	46·796	47·258	47·705	48·138	48·559	48·968
2					45·773*	46·235	46·680	47·112	47·531
3						45·332	45·793	46·236	46·663
5							44·597*	45·068	45·517
7								44·231*	44·706
10									43·764
15									
20									
25									
30									
35									
40									
50									
60									
70									
80									
90									
100									

*Supersaturated

F. DIN

ENTROPY, CALORIES/MOLE, °K

Temperature °K										Pressure atm
250	260	270	280	290	300	305	310	315	320	
53·986	54·369	54·744	55·111	55·471	55·824	—	56·171	—	56·512	0·1
52·604	52·988	53·363	53·730	54·091	54·445	—	54·792	—	55·133	0·2
51·794	52·178	52·553	52·921	53·282	53·636	—	53·984	—	54·325	0·3
50·770	51·156	51·533	51·901	52·262	52·617	—	52·965	—	53·306	0·5
50·091	50·478	50·856	51·225	51·587	51·942	—	52·291	—	52·633	0·7
49·366	49·755	50·135	50·506	50·869	51·225	51·401	51·575	51·747	51·918	1·0
47·937	48·331	48·715	49·090	49·457	49·817	—	50·170	—	50·516	2
47·076	47·477	47·867	48·247	48·618	48·981	—	49·337	—	49·686	3
45·948	46·364	46·766	47·155	47·534	47·904	—	48·266	—	48·620	5
45·158	45·590	46·005	46·405	46·793	47·171	—	47·540	—	47·900	7
44·252	44·713	45·151	45·570	45·973	46·363	46·555	46·742	46·927	47·111	10
43·054*	43·585	44·074	44·532	44·966	45·382	—	45·782	—	46·168	15
	42·610*	43·183	43·698	44·173	44·619	44·834	45·043	45·247	45·449	20
		42·335*	42·942	43·477	43·964	44·195	44·418	44·635	44·848	25
			42·185	42·818	43·363	43·615	43·859	44·091	44·317	30
			41·315*	42·143	42·782	43·065	43·333	43·585	43·829	35
				41·376*	42·189	42·518	42·817	43·098	43·364	40
					40·671	41·289	41·739	42·116	42·452	50
							40·217	40·966	41·472	60
							⊙36·666	38·814	40·194	70
							36·007	37·050	38·395	80
							35·594	36·438	37·362	90
							35·245	36·042	36·820	100

*Supersaturated

ACETYLENE

SPECIFIC HEAT AT CONSTANT VOLUME, CALORIES/MOLE, °K

Pressure atm	Temperature °K									
	160	170	180	190	200	210	220	230	240	250
0·1	6·088*	6·285	6·475	6·660	6·841	7·019	7·195	7·369	7·541	7·712
0·2		6·301	6·489	6·671	6·850	7·027	7·202	7·375	7·547	7·717
0·3			6·503	6·683	6·860	7·036	7·210	7·382	7·553	7·722
0·5			6·531	6·707	6·881	7·053	7·225	7·395	7·564	7·732
0·7				6·731	6·901	7·071	7·241	7·409	7·576	7·743
1·0	6·273*	6·438*	6·603*	6·768	6·933	7·098	7·264	7·429	7·594	7·759
2					7·040*	7·190	7·342	7·497	7·654	7·812
3						7·285	7·425	7·568	7·715	7·865
5							7·600*	7·717	7·843	7·977
7								7·878	7·981	8·095
10									8·205*	8·286
15										8·655*
20										
25										
30										
35										
40										
50										
60										
70										
80										
90										
100										

*Supersaturated

82

SPECIFIC HEAT AT CONSTANT VOLUME, CALORIES/MOLE, °K

Temperature °K									Pressure atm
260	270	280	290	300	305	310	315	320	
7·882	8·052	8·221	8·389	8·557	—	8·725	—	8·893	0·1
7·887	8·056	8·224	8·392	8·560	—	8·728	—	8·895	0·2
7·891	8·060	8·228	8·396	8·563	—	8·731	—	8·898	0·3
7·900	8·068	8·235	8·402	8·569	—	8·736	—	8·903	0·5
7·910	8·076	8·243	8·409	8·575	—	8·742	—	8·908	0·7
7·924	8·089	8·254	8·419	8·584	8·667	8·750	8·832	8·915	1·0
7·970	8·130	8·291	8·452	8·614	—	8·777	—	8·940	2
8·018	8·173	8·329	8·486	8·645	—	8·805	—	8·965	3
8·117	8·260	8·406	8·555	8·706	—	8·859	—	9·015	5
8·219	8·350	8·486	8·626	8·770	—	8·917	—	9·067	7
8·383	8·492	8·611	8·737	8·868	8·936	9·005	9·075	9·146	10
8·690	8·753	8·836	8·933	9·041	—	9·158	—	9·283	15
9·061*	9·053	9·087	9·147	9·227	9·273	9·322	9·373	9·427	20
	9·421*	9·373	9·384	9·430	9·462	9·498	9·538	9·580	25
		9·710	9·663	9·655	9·667	9·687	9·713	9·743	30
		10·225*	9·993	9·912	9·897	9·896	9·904	9·918	35
			10·436*	10·211	10·158	10·127	10·112	10·108	40
				11·151	10·864	10·710	10·611	10·547	50
						11·730	11·327	11·118	60
						14·722	12·957	11·996	70
						15·323	14·480	13·428	80
						15·698	15·027	14·315	90
						16·063	15·381	14·787	100

*Supersaturated

ACETYLENE

SPECIFIC HEAT AT CONSTANT PRESSURE, CALORIES/MOLE, °K

Pressure atm	Temperature °K									
	160	170	180	190	200	210	220	230	240	250
0·1	7·89*	8·16	8·39	8·60	8·80	8·99	9·17	9·35	9·52	9·69
0·2		8·20	8·42	8·63	8·83	9·02	9·20	9·38	9·55	9·72
0·3			8·47	8·67	8·87	9·05	9·23	9·40	9·57	9·74
0·5			8·57	8·75	8·93	9·10	9·27	9·44	9·60	9·76
0·7				8·83	9·00	9·16	9·32	9·48	9·64	9·80
1·0	8·50*	8·65*	8·80*	8·95	9·10	9·25	9·40	9·55	9·70	9·84
2					9·46*	9·55	9·65	9·76	9·88	10·00
3						9·90	9·94	10·00	10·08	10·19
5							10·61*	10·56	10·54	10·57
7								11·23*	11·09	11·03
10									12·14*	11·85
15										13·91*
20										
25										
30										
35										
40										
50										
60										
70										
80										
90										
100										

*Supersaturated

SPECIFIC HEAT AT CONSTANT PRESSURE, CALORIES /MOLE, °K

Temperature °K									Pressure atm
260	270	280	290	300	305	310	315	320	
9·86	10·03	10·19	10·35	10·50	10·58	10·65	10·73	10·80	0·1
9·88	10·05	10·20	10·36	10·51	10·59	10·66	10·74	10·81	0·2
9·90	10·07	10·22	10·38	10·53	10·61	10·68	10·76	10·83	0·3
9·93	10·09	10·24	10·40	10·55	10·63	10·70	10·78	10·85	0·5
9·96	10·11	10·26	10·42	10·57	10·65	10·72	10·80	10·87	0·7
9·99	10·14	10·29	10·44	10·59	10·67	10·74	10·82	10·89	1·0
10·13	10·26	10·40	10·54	10·68	10·75	10·82	10·89	10·96	2
10·29	10·40	10·52	10·64	10·71	10·84	10·90	10·97	11·04	3
10·62	10·69	10·77	10·87	10·97	11·02	11·08	11·13	11·19	5
11·00	11·02	11·06	11·12	11·19	11·23	11·27	11·31	11·36	7
11·67	11·57	11·53	11·51	11·53	11·55	11·58	11·61	11·64	10
13·23	12·79	12·49	12·31	12·22	12·19	12·17	12·15	12·14	15
16·30*	14·61	13·83	13·34	13·04	12·94	12·85	12·77	12·70	20
	16·64*	15·86	14·78	14·12	13·88	13·69	13·53	13·50	25
		—	16·89	15·58	15·13	14·77	14·46	14·20	30
		—	—	17·61	16·74	16·18	15·62	15·25	35
			—	—	19·13	17·95	17·13	16·66	40
				—	—	—	—	—	50
					—	—	—	—	60
						—	—	—	70
						—	—	—	80
						—	—	—	90
						—	—	—	100

*Supersaturated

85

VOLUME, CUBIC CENTIMETRES

Pressure atm	Temperature °K									
	160	170	180	190	200	210	220	230	240	2
0·1	130,700*	139,000	147,200	155,500	163,700	172,000	180,200	188,400	196,700	204
0·2		69,170	73,340	77,500	81,650	85,790	89,930	94,060	98,200	102,
0·3			48,720	51,510	54,290	57,070	59,840	62,610	65,370	68,
0·5			29,050	30,730	32,410	34,100	35,770	37,440	39,110	40,
0·7				21,810	23,040	24,260	25,460	26,660	27,850	29,
1·0	12,460*	13,360*	14,250*	15,130	16,000	16,860	17,720	18,570	19,410	20,
2					7,778*	8,234	8,683	9,126	9,564	9,
3						5,360	5,672	5,978	6,280	6,
5							3,250*	3,452	3,647	3,
7								2,362*	2,513	2,
10									1,657*	1,
15										1,
20										
25										
30										
35										
40										
50										
60										
70										
80										
90										
100										

*Supersaturated

VOLUME, CUBIC CENTIMETRES

	Temperature °K								Pressure atm
	270	280	290	300	305	310	315	320	
•0	221,300	229,500	237,700	245,900	—	254,100	—	262,300	0·1
•0	110,600	114,700	118,800	122,900	—	127,000	—	131,100	0·2
60	73,630	76,390	79,140	81,890	—	84,640	—	87,380	0·3
60	44,090	45,750	47,400	49,050	—	50,700	—	52,350	0·5
-0	31,440	32,630	33,810	35,000	—	36,180	—	37,360	0·7
•0	21,940	22,780	23,620	24,450	24,870	25,280	25,690	26,100	1·0
60	10,860	11,280	11,710	12,130	—	12,560	—	12,980	2
3	7,165	7,455	7,743	8,029	—	8,315	—	8,601	3
4	4,207	4,389	4,569	4,747	—	4,923	—	5,098	5
1	2,939	3,074	3,207	3,339	—	3,469	—	3,598	7
9	1,984	2,086	2,185	2,282	2,330	2,377	2,424	2,470	10
4	1,236	1,313	1,386	1,457	—	1,526	—	1,594	15
9*	853·8	921·5	984·2	1,043	1,071	1,099	1,126	1,153	20
	613·9*	679·5	737·8	791·2	816·4	841·0	864·9	888·2	25
		510·9	569·9	620·8	644·5	667·3	689·2	710·3	30
		376·0*	444·0	496·3	519·6	541·5	562·3	582·3	35
			339·7*	399·0	423·2	445·1	465·5	485·2	40
				239·7	275·8	302·7	325·3	345·4	50
					⊙	185·9	221·3	246·4	60
						72·7	118·1	165·1	70
						62·3	75·3	99·9	80
						56·7	65·1	76·9	90
						53·0	59·4	67·4	100

*Supersaturated

87

ETHYLENE

W. F. L. Dick and A. G. M. Hedley

Imperial Chemical Industries Limited, Northwich, Cheshire

Ethylene is one of the original series of gases for which Keesom and Houthoff[15] prepared thermodynamic diagrams at the University of Leiden in 1926. The authors pointed out at the time that the experimental data available for ethylene were quite insufficient for a direct computation of the thermodynamic functions, and the diagram was accordingly constructed on the basis of the law of corresponding states by comparing ethylene with methane and carbon dioxide for which much more data existed. Even where data for ethylene were available, however, *e.g.* for the vapour pressure and for the densities of the saturated liquid and vapour phases in equilibrium, it was found that there were quite large deviations, in some cases over 10 per cent, between the actual values and those calculated from the law of corresponding states. When constructing the diagram for ethylene Keesom and Houthoff attempted to allow for these deviations. For instance, above the critical pressure the isobars were constructed on the basis of no deviation, since it was found that their positions agreed with calculations based on Amagat's[1] compressibility data. Below $-30°$ C on the other hand, a 4 per cent deviation in the constant volume lines was allowed for, since this was the deviation observed for the saturated liquid and vapour volumes.

This Leiden diagram was revised in 1941 by Keesom, Bijl and Monté for the International Institute of Refrigeration, but the report describing this revised version, although issued privately, has not been published. Above $0°$ C the authors were able to make use of the precise P-V-T measurements of Michels and his co-workers[22, 24], but below $0°$ C the methods adopted were, in principle, precisely the same as for the earlier diagram, although with considerable improvements in the technique of calculation. Values of the product pressure times volume, PV, were calculated from an empirical equation of state of the form:

$$\frac{\varDelta}{\varrho} = \frac{PV - f(\varrho T)}{\varrho}$$

where ϱ is the Amagat density and $\varDelta$ a residual term. It was found that the $\dfrac{\varDelta}{\varrho}$ terms for ethylene and methane were not identical, as they should have been if the law of corresponding states were followed exactly. The differences between these residual functions for ethylene and methane were plotted as functions of the temperature and the necessary allowances made when computing the final PV values for ethylene below 0° C. For the isothermal entropy and enthalpy changes Keesom, Bijl and Monté claim an accuracy of 2 per cent in the regions where experimental data are available, but elsewhere, which includes the region below 0° C, they state that the precision is impossible to assess.

As far as the present authors are aware no other thermodynamic diagram for ethylene has been published, although MICHELS and his co-workers[23] have computed the thermodynamic functions from their own P-V-T measurements according to their usual practice.

It is clear that the position with regard to calculating the thermodynamic functions of ethylene, at any rate below 0° C, is far from satisfactory, and there seems little point in repeating the work from Leiden. It was decided therefore in the present instance to limit the diagram to temperatures above 0° C, covered by the excellent data of Michels, and to omit the regions below 0° C entirely. The calculation of the thermodynamic functions below 0° C is best left until such time as experimental data of the necessary precision become available.

SURVEY OF EXISTING DATA

1. The Compressibility Data

The isotherms of ethylene have been determined up to pressures of 3000 atm over the temperature range 0° C to 150° C by Michels and his co-workers[22, 24]. The most recent data in this work, by Michels and Geldermans[22], were obtained with extreme care and an accuracy of 1 part in 10,000 is claimed. The calculations of this survey are based very largely upon these later data, after applying the correction suggested by Michels[23] which involved multiplying all values of the Amagat density by a factor of 0·9999.

P-V-T data over more restricted fields have been reported by Amagat[1], MASSON and DOLLEY[20], CROMMELIN and WATTS[6] and DANNEEL and STOLTZENBERG[8], but the data are of a lower order of accuracy than those of Michels and have not been given further attention.

2. The Specific Heat of the Gas

Values for $C_p{}^\circ$, the specific heat at constant pressure corrected to zero pressure, have been reported by several workers over a wide range of temperature. Calorimetric measurements have been made by Heuse[13] over the temperature range – 91° C to 18° C; HAAS and STEGEMAN[12], 2° C to 67° C; EUCKEN and PARTS[10], – 95° C to 191° C and by BURCIK, EYSTER and YOST[4] over the range – 3° C to 48° C. These authors[4] have also calculated $C_p°$ from spectroscopic data over the range – 100° C to 300° C. Other spectroscopic calculations have been made by BEECK[2] from 0° C to 3000° C whilst KILPATRICK and PITZER[16] and BRICKWEDDE, MOSKOW and ASTON[3] used the spectroscopic data of GALLAWAY and BARKER[11] to calculate $C_p°$ from 0° K to 1500° K.

The data from the direct calorimetric measurements are consistent except for those of Haas and Stegeman which are not very accurate. The spectroscopic data are less consistent but those of Beeck agree well with the calorimetric values. Greater reliance has therefore been placed on the calorimetric data, and in particular the results of Heuse, Eucken and Parts, and Burcik, Eyster and Yost, which together with the spectrographic data of Beeck, have been fitted to a cubic equation to represent the variation of C_p^0 with temperature over the range – 91° C to 191° C.

$$C_p^0 = 8 \cdot 022 - 1 \cdot 3158 \times 10^{-2} T + 0 \cdot 93617 \times 10^{-4} T^2$$
$$- 0 \cdot 07943 \times 10^{-6} T^3 \text{ cal/mole, }°K$$

3. The Vapour Pressure

Several reliable determinations of the saturated vapour pressure of ethylene have been made over wide ranges of temperature. Among these are the measurements of MATHIAS, CROMMELIN and WATTS[21] over the range – 141° C to 7·9° C, MICHELS and WASSENAAR[25], – 124° C to 7·39° C, EGAN and KEMP[9], – 150° C to – 103° C, and LAMB and ROPER[17], – 125·27° C to 99·91° C.

Since the calculations of the thermodynamic properties for this survey are mainly for temperatures above 0° C the choice rests between the data of Mathias, Crommelin and Watts and those of Michels and Wassenaar. The latter have been accepted since they appear to be more accurate.

4. The Critical Pressure and Temperature

The values given in Table 1 have been reported for the critical pressure and temperature of ethylene.

The values of MAASS and GEDDES[18] are closely consistent with the vapour pressure data of Michels and Wassenaar[25] and have been accepted for this survey.

5. The Density of the Saturated Liquid and Vapour Phases in Equilibrium: the Critical Density

Mathias, Crommelin and Watts[21] measured the density of the saturated liquid and vapour phases in equilibrium over the temperature range − 145° C to 7·98° C whilst MAASS and WRIGHT[19] measured liquid densities only over the range − 112·4° C to − 69·5° C. The former work was carried out very carefully and is probably accurate to 1 part in 10,000. These data have therefore been used for this survey after

TABLE 1

THE CRITICAL PRESSURE AND TEMPERATURE

Observer	P_k atm	T_k °C
Maass and Wright[19] . .	—	9·9
Dacey, McIntosh and Maass[7] .	50·50	9·9
Kay[14]	50·05	9·25
Maass and Geddes[18] . .	49·98	9·5

adjustment of the temperature scale. Mathias, Crommelin and Watts took an ice point of 0° C = 273·06° K which differs by 0·1° from that used here. Their results have been extrapolated to 9·5° C to obtain the critical density, namely 0·2198 g/cm³.

6. *The Specific Heat of the Condensed Phases and the Latent Heats*

From 15° K to the normal boiling point of liquid ethylene the low temperature calorimetric data of Egan and Kemp[9] are by far the best available. Besides measuring the specific heat of the solid and liquid in equilibrium with the saturated vapour, these authors have also measured the latent heats of fusion and of vaporization at the normal boiling point, which they give as − 103·70° C, in close agreement with that given by Michels and Wassenaar. Egan and Kemp have also shown that the entropy of the gas in the ideal gaseous state at the normal boiling point, calculated from spectroscopic and statistical data is in excellent agreement with the value calculated from their calorimetric measurements after allowing for gas imperfections in the usual way. Their results have been used in this survey for calculating the absolute values of the thermodynamic functions.

CALCULATION OF THE THERMODYNAMIC FUNCTIONS AND
CONSTRUCTION OF THE THERMODYNAMIC DIAGRAM

7. *Units, Constants and Conversion Factors*

The pressure unit chosen for the present work is the bar or 10^6 dyn/cm². To relate this unit to the international atmosphere ($g = 980·665$) as used by Michels for his *P-V-T* data, a factor of 1 atm = 1·013250 bars has been used. The unit of volume is the cubic centimetre. The Celsius scale of temperature has been chosen related

91

to the absolute Kelvin scale by an ice point of $0°$ C $=273\cdot16°$ K. For the energy unit the Joule has been chosen, and where experimental data are given in calories a factor of 1 cal $=4\cdot1840$ J has been adopted. The cubic centimetre-atmosphere unit of energy is thus equivalent to $0\cdot101325$ J and the cubic centimetre-bar to $0\cdot1$ J. The unit of quantity is the gramme.

The ideal gas constant, R, has been taken as $8\cdot31439$ J/mole, degree, and since the chosen unit of quantity is the gramme it was necessary to divide this value by the molecular weight of ethylene to convert it to J/gramme, degree. The international molecular weight of ethylene is $28\cdot052$ based on the limiting density measurements of CAWOOD and PATTERSON[5] and MOLES, TORAL and ESCRIBANO[26]. This leads to a value of $0\cdot29639$ J/gramme, degree for the ideal gas constant for ethylene.

On the basis of the above figures the ideal gas volume of ethylene at $0°$ C and 1 international atmosphere pressure is $799\cdot037$ cm^3/g. To calculate the real volume of 1 gramme of ethylene under these conditions it is necessary to use the P-V-T data. Michels[22] gives a series of the form:

$$\frac{P}{\varrho} = A + B\varrho + C\varrho^2 + D\varrho^4$$

which has been fitted to the experimental points between 19 atm and 53 atm. ϱ is the Amagat density or V_N/V, the normal volume—at $0°$ C and 1 atm—divided by the actual volume. The value of the coefficient A at $0°$ C corrected by Michels[23] is $1\cdot007582$ atm. When the density is zero the gas can be considered perfect so that:

$$\frac{P}{\varrho} = \frac{PV}{V_N} = \frac{RT}{V_N} = A$$

Using this relationship V_N, or the volume occupied by 1 gramme of ethylene at $0°$ C and 1 atm is found to be $793\cdot025$ cm^3.

The enthalpy has been set at zero for the ideal gas at $0°$ C. This is equivalent to identifying the zero condition with that of infinite attenuation of the real gas at $0°$ C. The entropy has been taken as zero for the ideal gas at $0°$ C and 1 bar pressure.

8. Calculation of the Thermodynamic Functions from the P-V-T Data in the Homogeneous Region

The source of data for the calculation of the thermodynamic functions of ethylene in the homogeneous region has been the precise P-V-T measurements of Michels and his co-workers[22, 24]. These data cover the range from $0°$ C to $150°$ C and 0 atm to 2500 atm. The calculations have been limited to this range.

The most convenient numerical computation for determining the various derivatives and integrals that arise depends on a combination of algebraic and graphical methods. The usual first step is to express the function which is being considered as the sum of an algebraic polynomial, usually in terms of ϱ, the Amagat density, and a residual function which is merely the difference between the algebraic and experimental values. The processes of differentiation or integration can be carried out algebraically on the polynomial and graphically on the residual function. For the success of this method it is important that the residual function should be small, say 1 per cent, compared with the main variation expressed by the polynomial. For the present work, in regions where the thermodynamic functions vary smoothly and regularly, e.g. at high temperatures and low densities, very simple algebraic functions were sufficient, but in the lower temperature regions where the data change very rapidly more elaborate polynomials had to be used to keep the residual function small.

In certain areas, particularly near the critical region, use has been made of Michels' sextic polynomial expression for the product pressure times volume, PV, with its accompanying residual function which is always less, sometimes much less, than 1 per cent of the PV value. Despite the apparent tedium of handling a seven term polynomial and powers of ϱ up to the sixth, this method was not too slow and guaranteed approximately the accuracy of Michels' original P-V-T values. In every case the calculations were carried out for the isotherms 0° C to 150° C by steps of 25°.

The first step was to calculate the entropy of the real gas at 1 bar pressure at various temperatures. The equation for the ideal specific heat, which is not a function of pressure, given in section 2, was integrated to give the entropy of the ideal gas at 1 bar as a function of temperature, and since the reference zero has been chosen for the ideal gas at 1 bar and 0° C the ideal entropy is given by the equation:

$$S_{\text{ideal}} = \int_{273 \cdot 16}^{T} \frac{C_p^\circ}{T} \, dT \bigg]_{P=1}$$

After the integration the values had to be converted from cal/mole, °K to J/g, °K.

The ideal entropy values at 1 bar were converted to real entropies by using the volume residual, r, defined by:

$$r = \frac{RT}{P} - V$$

The isothermal entropy change with pressure is given by the thermodynamic equation:

$$\frac{\partial S}{\partial P}\bigg)_T = -\frac{\partial V}{\partial T}\bigg)_P$$

93

which in its integrated form becomes:

$$\Delta S\Big]_T = \int -\frac{\partial V}{\partial T}\Big)_P \mathrm{d}P\Big]_T = \int \frac{\partial r}{\partial T}\Big)_P \mathrm{d}P\Big]_T - \int \frac{R}{P}\mathrm{d}P\Big]_T$$

The term $\int \frac{R}{P}\,\mathrm{d}P$ represents the ideal isothermal entropy change with

pressure, the $\int \frac{\partial r}{\partial T}\Big)_P \mathrm{d}P$ term the change due solely to departure from

ideal behaviour. The real entropies at 1 bar were therefore found from the ideal values from the expression:

$$S_{\text{real}} - S_{\text{ideal}} = \int_0^1 \frac{\partial r}{\partial T}\Big)_P \mathrm{d}P\Big]_T$$

It was found by calculating r from Michels' experimental results[22] that r was constant over the pressure range from 0 bar to 1 bar and the dependence of r on the absolute temperature was given, within the limits of experimental error, by the equation:

$$r = 1 \cdot 2305 \times 10^5 T^{-1 \cdot 73425} - 1 \cdot 163 \ (\text{cm}^3/\text{g}) \qquad \ldots \ (1)$$

which, with the previous equation, leads to:

$$S_{\text{real}} - S_{\text{ideal}} = 2 \cdot 1340 \times 10^4 T^{-2 \cdot 73425} \ (\text{J/g, degree})$$

The next step was to calculate the isothermal entropy changes over the whole of the homogeneous area, and for this purpose it was decided to use the volume as the other independent variable besides the temperature, *i.e.* the isothermal entropy change with volume was calculated. The thermodynamic equation expressing this change is:

$$\frac{\partial S}{\partial V}\Big)_T = \frac{\partial P}{\partial T}\Big)_V$$

which in its integrated form becomes:

$$\Delta S\Big]_T = \int \frac{\partial P}{\partial T}\Big)_V \mathrm{d}V\Big]_T$$

The calculation of the integral was effected in terms of ϱ, the Amagat density, where $\varrho = V_N/V$, V_N being the normal volume. The pressure P_t at temperature t was expressed as the sum of a graphical term and an algebraic expression. By a study of Michels' P-V-T data it was possible to find an algebraic expression in terms of ϱ and t which represented P_t sufficiently closely for the graphical term to be 1 per cent to 3 per cent of P_t. The differentiation and integration could be performed to any required numerical accuracy on the algebraic term whilst the numerical differentiation and integration by graphical means could be carried out within the experimental accuracy in most cases. Algebraically this method consisted of writing:

$$P_t = P_{25} + (t - 25) \left.\frac{\partial P}{\partial T}\right)_V' + \pi_t$$

where P_t = the experimental pressure of the gas at $t°$ C, P_{25} = the pressure of the same volume of gas at 25° C, $\left.\dfrac{\partial P}{\partial T}\right)_V'$ = an algebraic function of ϱ, the Amagat density, independent of temperature and π_t = the residual pressure at $t°$ C.

$\left.\dfrac{\partial P}{\partial T}\right)_V'$ was calculated as an empirical function of ϱ, using Michels' experimental results to calculate P_t and P_{25}. Different functions of ϱ were found, which will be denoted generally as $f(\varrho)$, for different ranges of values of V (and therefore of ϱ) so that:

$$\left.\frac{\partial P}{\partial T}\right)_V = \left.\frac{\partial P}{\partial T}\right)_V' + \left.\frac{\partial \pi}{\partial T}\right)_V = f(\varrho) + \left.\frac{\partial \pi}{\partial T}\right)_V$$

Since:
$$V = \frac{V_N}{\varrho}, \quad dV = -\frac{V_N d\varrho}{\varrho^2}$$

therefore:
$$\Delta S \Big]_{V_1}^{V_2} = \int_{V_1}^{V_2} \left.\frac{\partial P}{\partial T}\right)_V dV \Big]_T$$

$$= -V_N \int_{\varrho_1}^{\varrho_2} \frac{f(\varrho)}{\varrho^2} d\varrho \Big]_T + \int_{V_1}^{V_2} \left.\frac{\partial \pi}{\partial T}\right)_V dV \Big]_T \qquad \dots (2)$$

For convenience of computation the first step was to calculate the entropies at $\varrho = 1$ for various temperatures. The entropies at 1 bar had already been worked out and it was next necessary to find the entropy difference for each temperature between the point where the pressure was 1 bar and the point where the density was 1 Amagat unit. The density at 1 bar pressure was readily calculated from the expression for r in equation (1) and the relationship:

$$\varrho = \frac{V_N}{RT - r}$$

In this region the function:

$$f(\varrho) = 0·0036886\varrho + 1·90 \times 10^{-5}\varrho^2$$

was used, and for each temperature the required entropy change was calculated by integrating equation (2) numerically and graphically from $\varrho = 1$ to the value of ϱ corresponding with 1 bar.

Then, using $\varrho = 1$ as a fixed limit in the integral of equation (2), other entropies at round value volumes were calculated for all temperatures by integrating to the appropriate values of ϱ. Different forms of $f(\varrho)$ were used in the higher density ranges.

After the entropies had been calculated as functions of volume and temperature, it was necessary to interpolate to obtain the values for rounded off pressures. The method used was to find the value of the density corresponding with a round value pressure and then to find the corresponding value of the entropy by using the algebraic and grapical methods already formulated for the calculation of entropies at round value volumes. Two methods were used for the calculation of the density. In the low pressure region use was made of the fact that the residual r is a fairly slowly varying function of pressure. The residual can be calculated from the original data of Michels[22] and plotted as a function of the pressure in bars for each temperature. Generally r was not plotted directly but was expressed as a simple function of the pressure together with a residual δ:

$$r = AP + B + \delta$$

The residual function δ was plotted against the pressure and by this combination of algebraic and graphical methods δ could be interpolated to round values of the pressure with satisfactory accuracy. From r the density was readily calculated.

As the pressure increases the residual r begins to vary rapidly with pressure, and graphical interpolation, even when assisted by auxiliary algebraic expressions, becomes increasingly difficult. In this region, therefore, it was decided to make the determination of the density depend as much as possible on the fundamental power series calculated by Michels.

Michels expresses his experimental results by the series:

$$\frac{P}{\varrho} = A + B\varrho + C\varrho^2 + Z\varrho^3 + D\varrho^4 + Y\varrho^5 + E\varrho^6 + \Delta(\varrho)$$

and, since he provides tables of $\Delta(\varrho)$ for all experimental temperatures and densities, algebraic interpolation in these tables is simple. Since the power series is explicit in pressure and implicit in density, the calculation of the latter for round values of the pressure was carried out by a trial and error process. This was not as difficult as it might at first appear, since after the initial values had been calculated it was possible to make informed guesses for trial by extrapolating the already calculated values.

The above calculations not only enabled the isobars on the temperature–entropy diagram to be drawn but also provided the values of volume at round values of temperature and pressure for the tables. For the two methods described the specific volumes were obtained respectively from the expressions:

$$V = \frac{RT}{P} - r \ (\text{cm}^3/\text{g})$$

and :

$$V = \frac{V_N}{\varrho} = \frac{793 \cdot 025}{\varrho} \ (\text{cm}^3/\text{g})$$

After the entropy had been calculated at rounded off pressures and temperatures, calculation of the enthalpy followed. The method used was to calculate first the enthalpies of the gas at zero pressure for various temperatures, which is equivalent to calculating the enthalpies of the ideal gas. The enthalpies of the real gas at 1 bar pressure were next found by applying the necessary correction and then, by using the 1 bar values as starting points, the enthalpy increments for other round pressures were found for each isotherm.

A reference point of zero enthalpy for the ideal gas at 0° C has been chosen, and consequently the ideal enthalpies were calculated by integrating the specific heat equation and converting to J/g in a similar manner as for the ideal entropy calculation:

$$H° = \int_{273 \cdot 16}^{T} C_p° \, \mathrm{d}T$$

The enthalpy values for the real gas at 1 bar pressure were obtained by means of the relationship:

$$\frac{\partial H}{\partial P}\bigg)_T = V - T \frac{\partial V}{\partial T}\bigg)_P = T \frac{\partial r}{\partial T}\bigg)_P - r$$

By using the empirical relationship between r and temperature given in equation (1) and integrating the above equation between zero pressure and 1 bar there followed:

$$H_{\text{real}} - H_{\text{ideal}} = 3 \cdot 3645 \times 10^4 T^{-1 \cdot 73425} - 1 \cdot 163 \ (\text{J}/\text{g})$$

Adding these corrections to the ideal enthalpy gave the enthalpies at 1 bar pressure for various temperatures.

The isothermal enthalpy differences from 1 bar pressure to other pressures then followed from the equation:

$$\Delta H \bigg]_{P=1}^{P=P} = \int_1^P V \mathrm{d}P + T\Delta S \bigg]_{P=1}^{P=P}$$

$$= RT \log_e P - \int_1^P r\mathrm{d}P + T\Delta S \bigg]_{P=1}^{P=P}$$

The $\int r\mathrm{d}P$ term had to be multiplied by a factor of $0 \cdot 1$ to convert the values from cm³-bars/g to J/g. Since the ΔS values had already been calculated and the logarithmic term was easily computed, the ΔH

values followed after evaluating the $\int r \mathrm{d}P$ term. In the low pressure region, where r varies slowly with the pressure, the integral was easily evaluated since the residual had already been expressed as the sum of an algebraic expression and another residual, δ, when carrying out the corresponding entropy calculation. At higher pressures where r begins to vary rapidly with pressure, an alternative method using Michels' power series was used in the same manner as for the entropy.

The equation:

$$\Delta H \Big]_{P=1}^{P=P} = \int_1^P V\mathrm{d}P + T\Delta S \Big]_{P=1}^{P=P}$$

can be put in the form:

$$\Delta H \Big]_{P=1}^{P=P} = \Delta PV \Big]_{P=1}^{P=P} - \int_{V_1}^{V_2} P\mathrm{d}V + T\Delta S \Big]_{P=1}^{P=P}$$

V_1 and V_2 being the limits corresponding with $P=1$ and $P=P$ respectively.

In this equation the ΔS and ΔPV terms were known from the entropy and volume calculations at rounded off pressures which had already been carried out, and it was necessary only to evaluate the $\int P\mathrm{d}V$ term from the Michels' power series.

Since:
$$\frac{P}{\varrho} = A + B\varrho + C\varrho^2 + Z\varrho^3 + D\varrho^4 + \Upsilon\varrho^5 + E\varrho^6 + \Delta(\varrho)$$

and:
$$V = \frac{V_N}{\varrho}$$

$$\mathrm{d}V = -\frac{V_N}{\varrho^2}\,\mathrm{d}\varrho$$

$$-\int_{V_1}^{V_2} P\mathrm{d}V = \frac{V_N}{\varrho}\int_{\varrho_1}^{\varrho_2} [A + B\varrho + C\varrho^2 + Z\varrho^3 + D\varrho^4 + \Upsilon\varrho^5 + E\varrho^6 + \Delta(\varrho)]\mathrm{d}\varrho$$

$$= V_N\Big[A \ln \varrho + B\varrho + \ldots\ldots + \tfrac{1}{6}E\varrho^6\Big]_{\varrho_1}^{\varrho_2} + V_N\int_{\varrho_1}^{\varrho_2}\frac{\Delta(\varrho)}{\varrho}\mathrm{d}\varrho$$

The calculation of the algebraic expression was simplified by the fact that the powers of ϱ had already been computed for the entropy calculations. The numerical integration of the small $\dfrac{\Delta(\varrho)}{\varrho}$ term was estimated by a simple mean ordinate formula:

$$\int_{\varrho_1}^{\varrho_2}\frac{\Delta(\varrho)}{\varrho}\mathrm{d}\varrho = \tfrac{1}{2}(\varrho_2 - \varrho_1)\left[\frac{\Delta(\varrho_1)}{\varrho_1} + \frac{\Delta(\varrho_2)}{\varrho_2}\right]$$

As in the case of the entropy calculations, care had to be taken with the units so that the final result was given in $\mathrm{J/g}$.

98

9. *The Specific Heats*

The specific heat at constant pressure was calculated from the tabulated enthalpy values from the expression:

$$C_p = \frac{\Delta H}{\Delta T}\bigg)_P$$

The enthalpy increments along the isobars were divided by the temperature intervals, 25°, to give the specific heat at the intermediate temperatures, 12·5° C, 37·5° C, *etc.* The values at 0° C, 25° C, *etc.*, were then found by graphical interpolation and extrapolation and these values were smoothed by plotting both as isotherms and isobars. The process of smoothing the specific heat values also called for some slight adjustments to the enthalpy values, mostly in the high pressure region, to preserve the consistency. At 25° C it was impossible to interpolate with accuracy in the critical region and at 0° C to extrapolate with accuracy above 25 bars. These values have therefore been omitted from the tables.

The specific heat at constant volume was calculated from the original table of entropy values as functions of volume and temperature from the expression:

$$C_v = T\frac{\Delta S}{\Delta T}\bigg)_V$$

where T is the mean absolute temperature of the temperature interval ΔT. In this way values of C_v along the isochores were found at temperatures 12·5° C, 37·5° C, *etc.* These values were first interpolated and extrapolated along the isochores in a similar manner to the C_p values to give the values at 0° C, 25° C, *etc.* This was followed by interpolation along the isotherms at the same values of volume as those tabulated for the rounded off pressures, thus giving the values of C_v at the tabulated rounded off pressures and temperatures.

The C_v values do not vary over the pressure–temperature plane nearly so much as the C_p values, and interpolation and extrapolation were much easier and more certain than in the latter case. Even so, the values at 25° C in the critical region and at 0° C at pressures above 40 bars have been omitted.

It will be seen that along the isotherms in the critical region C_v rises to a maximum around the critical density followed by a fall to a minimum and then a subsequent rise at the highest pressures. Above 100° C, however, these maxima and minima become smoothed out into an inflexion and there is a continuous increase in C_v on isothermal compression.

10. Calculation of the Two-Phase Boundary

After a careful assessment of the work of Dacey, McIntosh and Maass[7] and Maass and Geddes[18], the critical temperature and pressure determined by Maass and Geddes were taken, namely:

$$P_k = 49.98 \text{ atm} = 50.6 \text{ bars}$$

$$t_k = 9.5° \text{ C}$$

To determine ϱ_k, the critical density, the data of Mathias, Crommelin and Watts[21] were used. They determined the gas and liquid densities ϱ_g and ϱ_l from experimental results in the temperature range $-145°$ C to $8°$ C and the mean density $\bar{\varrho}$ was expressed by the relationship:

$$\bar{\varrho} = \tfrac{1}{2}(\varrho_g + \varrho_l) = 0.22179 - 0.00061277t + \text{residual}$$

To determine $\bar{\varrho}$ at $9.5°$ C, *i.e.* ϱ_k, it was necessary to extrapolate the residual function to $9.5°$ C. Within the accuracy of the extrapolation this gave:

$$\varrho_k = 0.2160 + 0.0038 = 0.2198 \pm 0.0003 \text{ (g/cm}^3)$$

and $\qquad V_k = 4.550 \pm 0.006 \text{ (cm}^3\text{/g)}$

In order to calculate the actual volumes of the saturated liquid and vapour phases in equilibrium on the two-phase boundary it was necessary to use the function:

$$\Delta\bar{\varrho} = \tfrac{1}{2}(\varrho_g - \varrho_l)$$

i.e. half the difference between the densities, as well as the expression for the mean density $\bar{\varrho}$ calculated by Mathias, Crommelin and Watts, given above. $\Delta\bar{\varrho}$ varies rather rapidly with temperature, but by using the expression:

$$\Delta\bar{\varrho} = 0.0260 + 0.0294(10.28 - t)^{\frac{1}{2}} + \text{residual}$$

it was possible to calculate $\Delta\bar{\varrho}$ for the required temperatures with reasonable accuracy. The densities and volumes of the liquid and vapour phases followed from the expressions:

$$\varrho_l = \bar{\varrho} - \Delta\bar{\varrho} \qquad\qquad V_l = \frac{1}{\varrho_l}$$

$$\varrho_g = \bar{\varrho} + \Delta\bar{\varrho} \qquad\qquad V_g = \frac{1}{\varrho_g}$$

To determine the entropy values round the two-phase boundary, the isochores on the temperature–entropy diagram were extrapolated to the appropriate temperatures on the boundary. First the temperatures on the boundary for round values of the saturated volume were found by interpolation from the saturated liquid and vapour volumes already derived. The appropriate isochores for the same round values of volume were then extrapolated to these temperatures, thereby giving the entropy values. At $0°$ C the volumes were extrapolated isothermally to the saturated vapour volume to give the saturated vapour entropy. The liquid entropy at $0°$ C was then found by subtracting the entropy of vaporization which was calculated from the Clausius–Clapeyron equation in the form:

$$\Delta S = \frac{dP}{dT}(V_g - V_l)$$

the derivative $\dfrac{dP}{dT}$ being the differential coefficient of the vapour pressure relationship. The enthalpy of vaporization, *i.e.* the ordinary latent heat, followed from the expression:

$$\Delta H = T \Delta S$$

Michels and Wassenaar[25] give an equation for calculating the vapour pressure of ethylene in conjunction with a graphical residual term expressing the difference between the calculated pressure and the true pressure. The derivatives $\dfrac{dP}{dT}$ were calculated by algebraic differentiation of the equation, with the appropriate correction for pressure in bars instead of atmospheres, and numerical differentiation of the residual term. Use of these values with the saturated liquid and vapour volumes enabled the entropy and enthalpy of vaporization to be calculated from the Clausius–Clapeyron equation.

The processes described above were carried out for rounded off values of the temperature and the volume. After the latent heats had been calculated for rounded off temperatures, interpolation was possible to obtain values for rounded off pressures with the aid of the vapour pressure relationship. The rounded off isobars on the temperature–entropy diagram could then be extrapolated to give additional points on the saturation boundary in the same manner as for the isochores.

11. Drawing the Diagram

The methods of deriving the thermodynamic functions that have been described enabled the isochores and isobars and the two-phase boundary to be drawn on the temperature–entropy diagram directly. The plotting of the isenthalps was based on interpolation from the table giving isothermal enthalpies at round value pressures. The diagram shows that in some regions the isenthalps rise steeply so that the derivative $\left(\dfrac{\partial T}{\partial S}\right)_H$ is large. In these regions the co-ordinates of the isenthalps were calculated by interpolating at a constant temperature for the value of

101

the entropy corresponding with a selected round value of the enthalpy. This was done in two stages; by backwards interpolation to give the value of the pressure corresponding with the given round value enthalpy, followed by forward interpolation in the pressure–entropy table to give the value of entropy corresponding with this value of the pressure and therefore with the selected round value enthalpy. Where the isenthalp is fairly flat, so that $\left. \dfrac{\partial T}{\partial S} \right)_H$ is small, this method would yield only a sparse number of points. For these regions co-ordinates of the isenthalps were found by backward interpolation at a constant pressure for the temperature corresponding with the selected round value. This gave the temperature co-ordinate of the isenthalp on the given pressure line which had already been drawn on the diagram.

The method described in section 8 for finding entropies corresponding with round value pressures was to calculate the Amagat densities, ϱ, for these pressures and then calculate the entropy changes from equation (2). Along the 0° C isotherm the two-phase boundary created a discontinuity above 40 bars pressure. However, after the saturated vapour and liquid densities at 0° C had been calculated there was no difficulty in continuing the calculations and finding the entropy co-ordinates on the high pressure side of the boundary.

12. The Absolute Values of the Entropy and Enthalpy

The reference zero of entropy for this survey is for the ideal gas at 0° C and 1 bar pressure. In order to correlate this value with the absolute value required by the Third Law of Thermodynamics, *i.e.* entropy zero for the perfect crystal at the absolute zero of temperature, use had to be made of the low temperature calorimetric specific and latent heat data of Egan and Kemp[9]. From 15° K to the absolute zero the Debye relationship was used to calculate the entropy change for the solid. Elsewhere the entropy changes of the saturated solid and liquid were calculated by integrating Egan and Kemp's specific heat data in the usual manner, and the entropies of fusion and vaporization were calculated by dividing the experimental latent heat by the absolute temperatures of the triple point and normal boiling point respectively. The following values were found:

	ΔS cal/mole, °K
0° K to 15° K (Debye extrapolation) . . .	0·25
15° K to 103·95° K (experimental specific heats) .	12·226
Fusion at 103·95° K	7·704
103·95° K to 169·40° K (experimental specific heats)	7·924
Vaporization at 1 atm and 169·40° K . . .	19·11
	47·214

The figure 47·214 cal/mole, °K is for the real gas at 169·40° K and 1 atm, the normal boiling point. To correct this value to the ideal gas state, the experimentally based equation of Eucken and Parts[10] for the second virial coefficient, B, was used which agrees well with values calculated from the Berthelot equation of state:

$$B = 50·3 - \frac{1·95 \times 10^6}{T^{1·62}} - \frac{2·83 \times 10^{13}}{T^{5·2}} \ (cm^3/mole)$$

and

$$B = V - \frac{RT}{P} = -r$$

$$S_{real} - S_{ideal} = \int_0^1 \frac{\partial r}{\partial T}\bigg)_P \ dP = -\frac{dB}{dT}$$

$$= -0·165 \ cal/mole, °K \ at \ 169·40° \ K \ and \ 1 \ atm$$

Therefore

$$S_{ideal} = 47·214 + 0·165$$

$$= 47·379 \ cal/mole, °K \ at \ 169·40° \ K \ and \ 1 \ atm$$

The ideal entropy change from 169·40° K to 273·16° K was found by integrating the ideal gaseous specific heat values in the usual way. This gave:

$$\Delta S_{ideal} \Bigg]_{T=169·40°K}^{T=273·16°K} = 4·207 \ cal/mole, °K$$

If the integration is carried on to 25° C, a value of 5·09 cal/mole, °K is obtained, in excellent agreement with the values 5·11 and 5·12 obtained by Egan and Kemp on the basis of spectroscopic calculations and their own calorimetric measurements respectively.

For the ideal gas entropy at 0° C and 1 atm we have therefore:

$$S_{ideal \ 0° \ C, \ 1 \ atm} = 47·379 + 4·207$$

$$= 51·586 \ cal/mole, °K$$

The ideal gas at 0° C and 1 atm has now to be expanded to 1 bar pressure resulting in a further small increase of entropy amounting to $R \log_e 1·01325 = 0·0259$ cal/mole, °K, so that for the ideal gas at 0° C and 1 bar a value 51·612 cal/mole, °K = 7·698 J/g, °K is finally obtained. With the reference point adopted for this survey, therefore, the entropy at the absolute zero becomes $-7·698$ J/g, °K.

DISCUSSION

It is considered that the methods of calculating the thermodynamic functions that have been adopted for this survey have done justice to the extremely precise P-V-T measurements of Michels. Michels claims an accuracy of 1 part in 10,000 for his P-V-T data and it is impossible, therefore, for the derived thermodynamic functions to exceed this precision. In the present calculations the accuracy of the graphical differentiation and integration is estimated to have been about 1 per cent and, since the graphical term represented in general 1 per cent or less of the total function under consideration, an accuracy of the order of 1 in 10,000 was maintained. Interpolation for rounded off values of pressure and volume involved a slight loss of accuracy so that the final accuracy is assessed at 1 part in 1000 over most of the range of the diagram falling to 1 part in 100 in the critical region and in the vicinity of the two-phase boundary. In the tables the last figures of the values are not significant but are included to assist in taking differences.

The accuracy of the thermodynamic functions can also be judged by comparing the values evaluated for this survey with those computed by Michels, Geldermans and de Groot[23] from the same original data. In Table 2 entropy and enthalpy values are compared at 1 atm, 100 atm, 400 atm and 2000 atm and at 25° C, 75° C and 150° C. For purposes of comparison the values given in the tables of this survey were interpolated for the appropriate pressures in atmospheres instead of bars and converted to calories per mole instead of joules per gramme. The values were then adjusted so as to agree exactly with those of Michels at 1 atm and 25° C.

TABLE 2

COMPARISON OF ENTROPY AND ENTHALPY VALUES

M= Michels, Geldermans and de Groot.   DH= this work.

Pressure atm		Entropy, cal/mole, °K			Enthalpy, cal/mole		
		25° C	75° C	150° C	25° C	75° C	150° C
1	M	+0·892	+2·591	+4·995	+792·5	+1340·1	+2265·0
	DH	+0·892*	+2·583	+4·919	+792·5*	+1338·7	+2265·1
100	M	−13·417	−8·805	−5·177	−1175·8	+303·9	+1688·5
	DH	−13·425	−8·807	−5·173	−1181·0	+304·7	+1695·0
400	M	−15·596	−12·953	−9·429	−1330·5	−479·6	+873·7
	DH	−15·610	−12·956	−9·437	−1336·9	−478·8	+877·2
2000	M	−18·473	−16·109	−12·980	−159·5	+601·4	+1801·7
	DH	−18·491	−16·114	−12·970	−167·7	+601·0	+1803·5

* Adjusted for reference.

The agreement between the values is considered to be excellent. The discrepancies at 1 atm arise from the different data for the specific heat at constant pressure that have been adopted, Michels, Geldermans and de Groot relying exclusively on the results of Eucken and Parts. Elsewhere the discrepancies appear to be more or less random and they arise from the different methods of calculation that have been adopted. The present values have been calculated over much smaller pressure intervals than those of Michels and are therefore believed to be more accurate.

The excellent agreement between the present work and that of Michels, Geldermans and de Groot can also be judged from a comparison of the specific heat values as shown in Table 3.

TABLE 3

COMPARISON OF SPECIFIC HEAT VALUES

M = Michels, Geldermans and de Groot. DH = this work.

Pressure atm		C_p cal/mole, °C			C_v cal/mole, °C		
		25° C	75° C	150°C	25° C	75° C	150°C
1	M	1·556	1·718	1·972	1·252	1·415	1·671
	DH	1·549	1·713	1·974	1·245	1·413	1·676
100	M	4·86	3·60	2·49	1·40	1·635	1·730
	DH	4·1	3·53	2·52	1·39	1·616	1·822
400	M	2·33	2·67	2·74	1·371	1·656	1·775
	DH	2·34	2·635	2·78	1·344	1·624	1·84
2000	M	2·06	2·39	2·44	1·47	1·813	1·841
	DH	2·06	2·352	2·44	1·47	1·781	1·92

When it is borne in mind that the specific heats are calculated in effect by taking the second derivative of the P-V-T data, the agreement is excellent. The only serious discrepancy in the above table is in the C_p values at 100 atm and 25° C, and here the influence of the critical region is still dominant.

There is still plenty of scope for further experimental work on the thermodynamic properties of ethylene. First and foremost, extensive P-V-T data are needed below 0° C down to the normal boiling point at least, and up to the saturated vapour pressure. Until such data become available it appears that no really reliable thermodynamic diagram for ethylene covering this region can be constructed. P-V-T data at high pressures and low temperatures, *i.e.* for the compressed liquid and for the solid–liquid equilibrium, though less important technologically, would also provide a welcome addition to the knowledge of ethylene. Reliable measurements of the vapour pressure have already been made and the calorimetric measurements of Egan and Kemp leave little to be desired. The work from Leiden University on the density of the saturated liquid and vapour phases in equilibrium is of high accuracy; consequently, reliable latent heat values can be calculated from the Clausius–Clapeyron equation. Determinations of the Joule–Thomson effect at high and low temperatures would also provide an additional check on the values of the thermodynamic functions computed from the P-V-T data. Meanwhile, the authors are confident that in confining themselves to the region above 0° C where excellent original data are available, they have produced a diagram of indisputable accuracy.

REFERENCES

[1] AMAGAT, *Ann. Chim. Phys.*, 29 (1893) 68.
[2] BEECK, *J. chem. Phys.*, 4 (1936) 680.
[3] BRICKWEDDE, MOSKOW and ASTON, *J. Res. nat. Bur. Stand.*, 37 (1946) 263.
[4] BURCIK, EYSTER and YOST, *J. chem. Phys.*, 9 (1941) 118.
[5] CAWOOD and PATTERSON, *Phil. Trans.* A, 236 (1936) 77 .
[6] CROMMELIN and WATTS, *Commun. phys. Lab. Univ. Leiden*, 189c (1927).
[7] DACEY, McINTOSH and MAASS, *Canad. J. Res.*, 17B (1939) 241.
[8] DANEEL and STOLTZENBERG, *Z. angew. Chem.*, 42 (1929) 1121.
[9] EGAN and KEMP., *J. Amer. chem. Soc.*, 59 (1937) 1264.
[10] EUCKEN and PARTS, *Z. phys. Chem.*, 20B (1933) 184.
[11] GALLAWAY and BARKER, *J. chem. Phys.*, 10 (1942) 88.
[12] HAAS and STEGEMAN, *J. phys. chem.*, 36 (1932) 2127.
[13] HEUSE, *Ann. Phys. Lpz.*, 59 (1919) 86.
[14] KAY, *Industr. Engng Chem.*, 40 (1948) 1459.
[15] KEESOM and HOUTHOFF, *Commun. phys. Lab. Univ. Leiden Suppl.*, 65b (1926).
[16] KILPATRICK and PITZER, *J. Res. nat. Bur. Stand.*, 37 (1946) 163.
[17] LAMB and ROPER, *J. Amer. chem. Soc.*, 62 (1940) 806.
[18] MAASS and GEDDES, *Phil. Trans.* A, 236 (1937) 303.
[19] MAASS and WRIGHT, *J. Amer. chem. Soc.*, 43 (1921) 1098.
[20] MASSON and DOLLEY, *Proc. roy. Soc.* A, 103 (1923) 524.
[21] MATHIAS, CROMMELIN and WATTS, *Ann. Phys. Paris*, 11 (1929) 343.
[22] MICHELS and GELDERMANS, *Physica, 'sGrav.*, 9 (1942) 967.
[23] MICHELS, GELDERMANS and DE GROOT, *Physica, 'sGrav.*, 12 (1946) 105; *Appl. Sci. Res.* A, 1 (1947) 55.
[24] MICHELS, DE GRUYTER and NIESEN, *Physica, 'sGrav.*, 3 (1936) 346.
[25] MICHELS and WASSENAAR, *Physica, 'sGrav.*, 16 (1950) 221.
[26] MOLES, TORAL and ESCRIBANO, *Trans. Faraday Soc.*, 35 (1939) 1439.

TABLES OF THERMODYNAMIC FUNCTIONS OF ETHYLENE

The properties are given for 1 gramme of ethylene as functions of the pressure in bars and the temperature in degrees Celsius. Entropy and enthalpy are zero for the gas in the ideal gaseous state at $0°$ C and 1 bar pressure.

Molecular weight	$= 28 \cdot 052$
Density of the gas at N.T.P. (International atm $g = 980 \cdot 665$)	$= 0 \cdot 00126099$ g/cm^3
Molecular volume at N.T.P. (International atm $g = 980 \cdot 665$)	$= 22{,}245 \cdot 9$ cm^3
Triple point	$= -169 \cdot 15°$ C
Normal boiling point	$= -103 \cdot 78°$ C
Critical constants: temperature	$= 9 \cdot 5°$ C
pressure	$= 49 \cdot 98$ atm $= 50 \cdot 6$ bars
volume	$= 4 \cdot 550$ cm^3/g

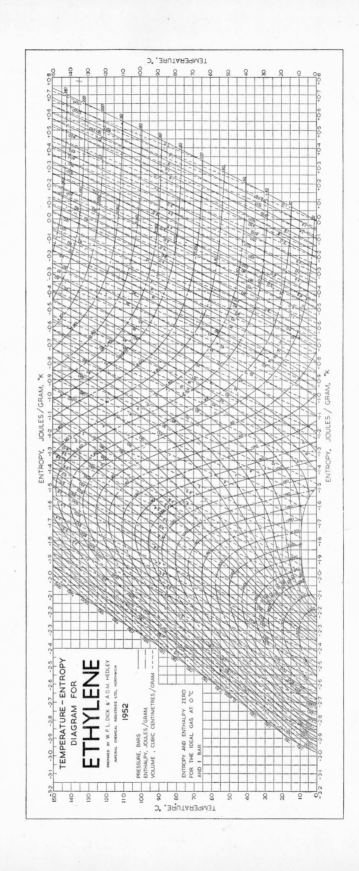

TEMPERATURE - ENTROPY
DIAGRAM FOR
ETHYLENE

PREPARED BY W. F. L. DICK & A. G. M. HEDLEY

IMPERIAL CHEMICAL INDUSTRIES LTD, NORTHWICH

1952

PRESSURE, BARS
ENTHALPY, JOULES / GRAM
VOLUME , CUBIC CENTIMETRES / GRAM

ENTROPY AND ENTHALPY ZERO
FOR THE IDEAL GAS AT 0°C
AND 1 BAR

TEMPERATURE, °C.

ENTROPY, JOULES / GRAM, °K

_.9869 ATM

VOLUME, CUBIC CENTIMETRES/GRAMME

Pressure Bars	Temperature °C						
	0	25	50	75	100	125	150
1·0	803·61	878·71	953·61	1028·4	1103·0	1177·6	1252·0
1·2	668·67	731·41	793·97	856·38	918·66	980·86	1043·0
1·4	572·28	626·21	679·94	733·53	786·99	840·37	893·66
1·6	499·98	547·30	594·42	641·39	688·24	735·00	781·68
1·8	443·75	485·92	527·90	569·73	611·43	653·05	694·58
2·0	398·77	436·83	474·69	512·40	549·98	587·48	624·90
2·5	317·79	348·44	378·90	409·20	439·38	469·47	499·48
3·0	263·79	289·52	315·04	340·41	365·64	390·80	415·86
3·5	225·22	247·43	269·43	291·26	312·97	334·60	356·14
4·0	196·29	215·86	235·21	254·41	273·47	292·45	311·34
4·5	173·78	191·30	208·60	225·74	242·75	259·67	276·50
5·0	155·77	171·65	187·31	202·81	218·17	233·44	248·63
6	128·75	142·18	155·37	168·40	181·30	194·11	206·82
7	109·44	121·11	132·56	143·83	154·96	166·01	176·96
8	94·94	105·31	115·44	125·39	135·21	144·93	154·57
9	83·66	93·02	102·13	111·06	119·85	128·54	137·15
10	74·62	83·18	91·48	99·59	107·55	115·42	123·21
12	61·04	68·41	75·49	82·38	89·12	95·76	102·31
14	51·31	57·84	64·07	70·08	75·95	81·71	87·38
16	43·99	49·91	55·49	60·86	66·07	71·17	76·19
18	38·26	43·72	48·82	53·68	58·38	62·98	67·48
20	33·65	38·76	43·47	47·94	52·23	56·42	60·51
25	25·23	29·79	33·84	37·59	41·16	44·62	47·98
30	19·42	23·75	27·39	30·68	33·78	36·75	39·63
35	14·97	19·37	22·76	25·74	28·51	31·13	33·66
40	11·27	16·02	19·27	22·03	24·55	26·92	29·20
45	2·842 ⊙	13·33	16·53	19·14	21·47	23·65	25·72
50	2·777	11·08	14·33	16·82	19·01	21·04	22·95
60	2·670	7·323	10·97	13·34	15·33	17·12	18·79
70	2·601	4·401	8·535	10·85	12·71	14·34	15·84
80	2·547	3·500	6·717	9·000	10·75	12·26	13·64
90	2·504	3,195	5·402	7·586	9·248	10·66	11·94
100	2,467	3,026	4·541	6·501	8·071	9·398	10·59
120	2·407	2·826	3·682	5·048	6·389	7·558	8·604
140	2·358	2·702	3·293	4·229	5·304	6·317	7·241
160	2·318	2·613	3·069	3·754	4·598	5·455	6·266
180	2·283	2·544	2·919	3·453	4·123	4·834	5·552
200	2·253	2·488	2·810	3·246	3·793	4·400	5·018
250	2·190	2·381	2·623	2·927	3·294	3·711	4·157
300	2·140	2·303	2·500	2·736	3·013	3·324	3·662
350	2·098	2·242	2·410	2·606	2·828	3·076	3·345
400	2·063	2·192	2·340	2·507	2·695	2·902	3·125
450	2·032	2·150	2·282	2·430	2·593	2·770	2·961
500	2·004	2·113	2·234	2·366	2·511	2·667	2·833
600	1·957	2·052	2·155	2·266	2·385	2·512	2·646
700	1·917	2,002	2·093	2·190	2·292	2·399	2·512
800	1·884	1·961	2·042	2·128	2·218	2·312	2·410
900	1·854	1·925	1·999	2·077	2·158	2·241	2·328
1000	1·828	1·893	1·962	2·033	2·107	2·182	2·261
1200	1·783	1·840	1·900	1·962	2·024	2·089	2·155
1400	1·745	1·797	1·850	1·905	1·959	2·016	2·073
1600	1·712	1·760	1·808	1·857	1·906	1·957	2·008
1800	1·684	1·727	1·772	1·817	1·862	1·907	1·954
2000	1·659	1·699	1·740	1·782	1·823	1·865	1·907
2500	1·605	1·640	1·675	1·711	1·745	1·780	1·816

ENTHALPY, JOULES/GRAMME

Pressure Bars	Temperature °C						
	0	25	50	75	100	125	150
1·0	− 1·89	+ 35·88	+ 75·60	+ 117·36	+ 161·25	+ 207·30	+ 255·53
1·2	− 2·25	+ 35·57	+ 75·33	+ 117·13	+ 161·04	+ 207·12	+ 255·38
1·4	− 2·61	+ 35·26	+ 75·06	+ 116·89	+ 160·84	+ 206·94	+ 255·23
1·6	− 2·98	+ 34·94	+ 74·78	+ 116·66	+ 160·63	+ 206·76	+ 255·07
1·8	− 3·34	+ 34·63	+ 74·51	+ 116·42	+ 160·42	+ 206·58	+ 254·92
2·0	− 3·71	+ 34·31	+ 74·24	+ 116·18	+ 160·22	+ 206·40	+ 254·76
2·5	− 4·63	+ 33·52	+ 73·55	+ 115·59	+ 159·70	+ 205·95	+ 254·38
3·0	− 5·56	+ 32·72	+ 72·86	+ 114·99	+ 159·18	+ 205·50	+ 254·00
3·5	− 6·49	+ 31·92	+ 72·17	+ 114·40	+ 158·66	+ 205·04	+ 253·61
4·0	− 7·43	+ 31·12	+ 71·48	+ 113·80	+ 158·14	+ 204·59	+ 253·22
4·5	− 8·39	+ 30·31	+ 70·79	+ 113·20	+ 157·62	+ 204·14	+ 252·83
5·0	− 9·34	+ 29·50	+ 70·09	+ 112·60	+ 157·10	+ 203·68	+ 252·44
6	− 11·27	+ 27·86	+ 68·69	+ 111·40	+ 156·05	+ 202·77	+ 251·66
7	− 13·23	+ 26·21	+ 67·29	+ 110·19	+ 155·00	+ 201·86	+ 250·88
8	− 15·22	+ 24·54	+ 65·87	+ 108·98	+ 153·95	+ 200·95	+ 250·10
9	− 17·24	+ 22·85	+ 64·44	+ 107·76	+ 152·90	+ 200·03	+ 249·31
10	− 19·30	+ 21·14	+ 63·00	+ 106·53	+ 151·84	+ 199·11	+ 248·53
12	− 23·51	+ 17·68	+ 60·09	+ 104·03	+ 149·71	+ 197·26	+ 246·95
14	− 27·88	+ 14·13	+ 57·14	+ 101·57	+ 147·57	+ 195·40	+ 245·36
16	− 32·42	+ 10·50	+ 54·14	+ 99·05	+ 145·41	+ 193·53	+ 243·76
18	− 37·16	+ 6·78	+ 51·09	+ 96·51	+ 143·23	+ 191·65	+ 242·15
20	− 42·12	+ 2·96	+ 48·00	+ 93·94	+ 141·04	+ 189·77	+ 240·53
25	− 55·69	− 7·05	+ 40·03	+ 87·39	+ 135·49	+ 184·98	+ 236·44
30	− 71·63	− 17·87	+ 31·70	+ 80·65	+ 129·84	+ 180·12	+ 232·31
35	− 91·64	− 29·70	+ 22·98	+ 73·72	+ 124·09	+ 175·19	+ 228·13
40	−118·76	− 42·82	+ 13·81	+ 66·59	+ 118·23	+ 170·20	+ 223·91
45	−312·67	− 57·70	+ 4·13	+ 59·24	+ 112·27	+ 165·16	+ 219·66
50	− 317·21	− 74·92	− 6·12	+ 51·68	+ 106·22	+ 160·07	+ 215·38
60	− 323·17	− 122·66	− 28·76	+ 35·86	+ 93·82	+ 149·76	+ 206·72
70	− 327·28	− 195·64	− 54·12	+ 19·09	+ 81·07	+ 139·31	+ 197·97
80	− 330·25	− 233·10	− 82·65	+ 1·48	+ 68·03	+ 128·78	+ 189·17
90	− 332·50	− 248·51	− 111·86	− 16·61	+ 54·74	+ 118·23	+ 180·37
100	− 334·25	− 257·77	− 137·16	− 34·70	+ 41·24	+ 107·72	+ 171·62
120	− 336·73	− 268·57	− 169·56	− 67·70	+ 15·73	+ 87·25	+ 154·46
140	− 338·29	− 274·95	− 187·19	− 92·91	− 7·12	+ 68·23	+ 138·27
160	− 339·20	− 279·09	− 197·92	− 110·48	− 25·89	+ 51·26	+ 123·42
180	− 339·63	− 281·87	− 204·92	− 122·64	− 40·70	+ 36·66	+ 110·20
200	− 339·68	− 283·75	− 209·80	− 131·30	− 52·08	+ 24·66	+ 98·71
250	− 338·68	− 285·91	− 216·83	− 144·21	− 70·32	+ 3·41	+ 76·84
300	− 336·53	− 285·85	− 219·62	− 150·46	− 80·04	− 9·02	+ 62·74
350	− 333·62	− 284·41	− 220·12	− 153·19	− 85·12	− 16·25	+ 53·92
400	− 330·16	− 282·08	− 219·20	− 153·85	− 87·41	− 20·05	+ 48·80
450	− 326·26	− 279·07	− 217·31	− 153·15	− 87·98	− 21·86	+ 45·91
500	− 322·01	− 275·54	− 214·59	− 151·30	− 87·05	− 21·86	+ 45·11
600	− 312·72	− 267·58	− 207·71	− 145·70	− 82·83	− 19·07	+ 46·51
700	− 302·73	− 258·58	− 199·45	− 138·29	− 76·36	− 13·61	+ 50·92
800	− 292·19	− 248·82	− 190·27	− 129·71	− 68·45	− 6·43	+ 57·26
900	− 281·25	− 238·50	− 180·40	− 120·31	− 59·55	+ 1·91	+ 64·97
1000	− 270·07	− 227·75	− 170·01	− 110·27	− 49·93	+ 11·07	+ 73·60
1200	− 247·06	− 205·39	− 148·18	− 88·95	− 29·14	+ 31·27	+ 93·07
1400	− 223·63	− 182·36	− 125·50	− 66·49	− 6·94	+ 53·15	+ 114·47
1600	− 199·83	− 158·83	− 102·23	− 43·43	+ 15·95	+ 75·89	+ 136·87
1800	− 175·70	− 134·90	− 78·50	− 19·90	+ 39·36	+ 99·19	+ 159·94
2000	− 151·29	− 110·62	− 54·38	+ 4·05	+ 63·17	+ 122·88	+ 183·47
2500	− 89·92	− 49·42	+ 6·60	+ 64·79	+ 123·68	+ 183·17	+ 243·57

110

ENTROPY, JOULES/GRAMME, °K

Pressure Bars	Temperature °C						
	0	25	50	75	100	125	150
1·0	− 0·00465	+ 0·12760	+ 0·25546	+ 0·37991	+ 0·50161	+ 0·62104	+ 0·73850
1·2	− 0·05957	+ 0·07284	+ 0·20083	+ 0·32540	+ 0·44719	+ 0·56668	+ 0·68420
1·4	− 0·10615	+ 0·02644	+ 0·15457	+ 0·27924	+ 0·40111	+ 0·52067	+ 0·63826
1·6	− 0·14662	− 0·01385	+ 0·11441	+ 0·23918	+ 0·36114	+ 0·48077	+ 0·59842
1·8	− 0·18243	+ 0·04949	+ 0·07891	+ 0·20380	+ 0·32483	+ 0·44553	+ 0·56325
2·0	− 0·21455	− 0·08144	+ 0·04710	+ 0·17209	+ 0·29421	+ 0·41398	+ 0·53176
2·5	− 0·28295	− 0·14938	− 0·02050	+ 0·10476	+ 0·22709	+ 0·34703	+ 0·46497
3·0	− 0·33928	− 0·20525	− 0·07601	+ 0·04953	+ 0·17207	+ 0·29218	+ 0·41028
3·5	− 0·38727	− 0·25277	− 0·12318	+ 0·00264	+ 0·12540	+ 0·24568	+ 0·36394
4·0	− 0·42918	− 0·29419	− 0·16424	− 0·03814	+ 0·08483	+ 0·20528	+ 0·32370
4·5	− 0·46644	− 0·33096	− 0·20064	− 0·07425	+ 0·04893	+ 0·16956	+ 0·28814
5·0	− 0·50004	− 0·36406	− 0·23336	− 0·10669	+ 0·01671	+ 0·13752	+ 0·25625
6	− 0·55890	− 0·42188	− 0·29041	− 0·16315	− 0·03931	+ 0·08184	+ 0·20090
7	− 0·60950	− 0·47139	− 0·33914	− 0·21128	− 0·08700	+ 0·03451	+ 0·15389
8	− 0·65409	− 0·51484	− 0·38178	− 0·25331	− 0·12858	− 0·00671	+ 0·11298
9	− 0·69409	− 0·55368	− 0·41979	− 0·29069	− 0·16551	− 0·04327	+ 0·07674
10	− 0·73052	− 0·58889	− 0·45417	− 0·32440	− 0·19875	− 0·07616	+ 0·04418
12	− 0·79531	− 0·65106	− 0·51450	− 0·38346	− 0·25686	− 0·13354	− 0·01255
14	− 0·85227	− 0·70512	− 0·56665	− 0·43422	− 0·30666	− 0·18261	− 0·06096
16	− 0·90367	− 0·75335	− 0·61281	− 0·47895	− 0·35038	− 0·22559	− 0·10325
18	− 0·95103	− 0·79713	− 0·65442	− 0·51907	− 0·38948	− 0·26393	− 0·14091
20	− 0·99546	− 0·83755	− 0·69250	− 0·55559	− 0·42494	− 0·29862	− 0·17491
25	− 1·0985	−·0·92806	− 0·77641	− 0·63528	− 0·50183	− 0·37353	− 0·24809
30	− 1·1975	− 1·0090	− 0·84924	− 0·70335	− 0·56688	− 0·43648	− 0·30933
35	− 1·3020	− 1·0846	− 0·91485	− 0·76359	− 0·62385	− 0·49130	− 0·36236
40	−1·4253	− 1·1581	− 0·97565	− 0·81825	− 0·67498	− 0·54016	− 0·40937
45	−2·1458 ⊚	− 1·2326	− 1·0332	− 0·86883	− 0·72170	− 0·58448	− 0·45181
50	− 2·1676	− 1·3107	− 1·0887	− 0·91634	− 0·76498	− 0·62527	− 0·49065
60	− 2·1993	− 1·5016	− 1·1976	− 1·0048	− 0·84391	− 0·69880	− 0·56015
70	− 2·2240	− 1·7657	− 1·3061	− 1·0875	− 0·91555	− 0·76438	− 0·62156
80	− 2·2443	− 1·9042	− 1·4180	− 1·1665	− 0·98192	− 0·82413	− 0·67707
90	− 2·2618	− 1·9671	− 1·5269	− 1·2423	− 1·0442	− 0·87938	− 0·72800
100	− 2·2773	− 2·0079	− 1·6204	− 1·3144	− 1·1029	− 0·93086	− 0·77520
120	− 2·3042	− 2·0637	− 1·7457	− 1·4420	− 1·2099	− 1·0245	− 0·86081
140	− 2·3274	− 2·1036	− 1·8218	− 1·5408	− 1·3022	− 1·1069	− 0·93632
160	− 2·3478	− 2·1353	− 1·8746	− 1·6141	− 1·3790	− 1·1790	− 1·0032
180	− 2·3662	− 2·1619	− 1·9147	− 1·6697	− 1·4419	− 1·2415	− 1·0622
200	− 2·3830	− 2·1851	− 1·9476	− 1·7138	− 1·4936	− 1·2947	− 1·1143
250	− 2·4200	− 2·2331	− 2·0112	− 1·7949	− 1·5896	− 1·3986	− 1·2196
300	− 2·4517	− 2·2721	− 2·0594	− 1·8534	− 1·6577	− 1·4738	− 1·2989
350	− 2·4798	− 2·3054	− 2·0989	− 1·8996	− 1·7104	− 1·5320	− 1·3608
400	− 2·5051	− 2·3347	− 2·1327	− 1·9381	− 1·7535	− 1·5790	− 1·4111
450	− 2·5283	− 2·3609	− 2·1625	− 1·9713	− 1·7901	− 1·6188	− 1·4537
500	− 2·5495	− 2·3847	− 2·1891	− 2·0006	− 1·8221	− 1·6533	− 1·4903
600	− 2·5882	− 2·4280	− 2·2358	− 2·0511	− 1·8764	− 1·7112	− 1·5514
700	− 2·6226	− 2·4658	− 2·2759	− 2·0938	− 1·9216	− 1·7591	− 1·6015
800	− 2·6537	− 2·4996	− 2·3115	− 2·1312	− 1·9608	− 1·8002	− 1·6442
900	− 2·6823	− 2·5302	− 2·3436	− 2·1644	− 1·9955	− 1·8363	− 1·6815
1000	− 2·7088	− 2·5584	− 2·3728	− 2·1946	− 2·0269	− 1·8688	− 1·7150
1200	− 2·7569	− 2·6088	− 2·4249	− 2·2481	− 2·0815	− 1·9250	− 1·7731
1400	− 2·8000	− 2·6532	− 2·4706	− 2·2947	− 2·1290	− 1·9734	− 1·8225
1600	− 2·8390	− 2·6932	− 2·5114	− 2·3363	− 2·1711	− 2·0160	− 1·8655
1800	− 2·8747	− 2·7297	− 2·5486	− 2·3740	− 2·2093	− 2·0545	− 1·9043
2000	− 2·9078	− 2·7632	− 2·5826	− 2·4086	− 2·2442	− 2·0897	− 1·9397
2500	− 2·9820	− 2·8378	− 2·6579	− 2·4845	− 2·3208	− 2·1669	− 2·0173

ETHYLENE

PROPERTIES OF THE SATURATED LIQUID AND VAPOUR

Temperature °C	Pressure Bars	Entropy, J/g, °K		Enthalpy, J/g		Volume, cm³/g	
		Liquid	Vapour	Liquid	Vapour	Liquid	Vapour
0	40·94	−2·127	−1·493	−307·6	−134·4	2·914	9·728
1	41·88	−2·113	−1·509	−303·7	−137·9	2·959	9·342
2	42·84	−2·099	−1·525	−299·5	−141·7	3·007	8·965
3	43·81	−2·084	−1·542	−295·2	−145·6	3·059	8·591
4	44·79	−2·068	−1·560	−290·6	−149·8	3·117	8·220
5	45·80	−2·052	−1·579	−285·8	−154·2	3·182	7·851
6	46·82	−2·034	−1·598	−280·5	−159·1	3·255	7·482
7	47·86	−2·015	−1·618	−275·2	−164·0	3·336	7·111
8	48·92	−1·981	−1·655	−265·2	−173·6	3·487	6·532
9	50·00	−1·892	−1·746	−239·8	−198·6	3·975	5·317
9·5 (C.P.)	50·6	−1·820		−219·1		4·550	

SPECIFIC HEAT AT CONSTANT PRESSURE, JOULES/GRAMME, °C

Pressure Bars	Temperature °C						
	0	25	50	75	100	125	150
0	1·461	1·539	1·621	1·706	1·793	1·881	1·969
1	1·472	1·549	1·629	1·713	1·798	1·886	1·974
2	1·483	1·558	1·637	1·720	1·804	1·891	1·980
3	1·495	1·568	1·645	1·727	1·810	1·896	1·985
5	1·521	1·588	1·662	1·740	1·821	1·906	1·995
7	1·550	1·609	1·679	1·754	1·833	1·917	2·005
10	1·594	1·644	1·707	1·776	1·851	1·933	2·021
15	1·69	1·714	1·759	1·816	1·882	1·960	2·047
20	1·82	1·800	1·819	1·859	1·914	1·988	2·074
25	2·00	1·905	1·887	1·907	1·948	2·016	2·102
30		2·034	1·964	1·960	1·985	2·045	2·130
35		2·21	2·055	2·017	2·024	2·075	2·159
40		2·48	2·169	2·079	2·066	2·106	2·190
45			2·300	2·149	2·110	2·140	2·21
50			2·461	2·228	2·156	2·175	2·24
60			2·95	2·417	2·260	2·247	2·29
70			3·8	2·640	2·378	2·324	2·35
80		5·4	4·3	2·921	2·508	2·406	2·41
90		4·7	4·6	3·23	2·648	2·494	2·46
100		4·1	4·6	3·52	2·798	2·590	2·52
120		3·43	4·1	3·704	3·047	2·760	2·63
140		3·13	3·71	3·630	3·212	2·889	2·73
160		2·92	3·43	3·469	3·240	2·976	2·82
180		2·78	3·23	3·308	3·196	3·010	2·88
200		2·70	3·071	3·172	3·129	3·010	2·92
250		2·54	2·853	2·937	2·956	2·942	2·94
300		2·45	2·726	2·796	2·829	2·854	2·89
350		2·39	2·644	2·703	2·738	2·775	2·83
400		2·34	2·585	2·639	2·674	2·718	2·78
450		2·30	2·538	2·589	2·624	2·671	2·74
500		2·26	2·505	2·553	2·587	2·636	2·71
600		2·22	2·456	2·499	2·530	2·579	2·66
700		2·18	2·424	2·463	2·491	2·538	2·62
800		2·16	2·401	2·437	2·463	2·507	2·59
900		2·14	2·383	2·418	2·442	2·483	2·56
1000		2·12	2·369	2·403	2·425	2·464	2·54
1200		2·10	2·348	2·383	2·402	2·438	2·50
1400		2·09	2·336	2·372	2·391	2·425	2·48
1600		2·08	2·328	2·365	2·385	2·416	2·46
1800		2·07	2·321	2·359	2·380	2·409	2·45
2000		2·06	2·315	2·353	2·375	2·404	2·44
2500		2·05	2·306	2·344	2·367	2·396	2·43

ETHYLENE

SPECIFIC HEAT AT CONSTANT VOLUME, JOULES/GRAMME, °C

Pressure Bars	Temperature, °C						
	0	25	50	75	100	125	150
0	1·167	1·244	1·327	1·412	1·499	1·587	1·675
1	1·168	1·245	1·328	1·413	1·500	1·588	1·676
2	1·169	1·246	1·329	1·414	1·501	1·589	1·678
3	1·171	1·248	1·331	1·416	1·502	1·591	1·680
5	1·174	1·251	1·334	1·419	1·505	1·594	1·684
7	1·178	1·255	1·338	1·422	1·508	1·598	1·688
10	1·185	1·261	1·344	1·427	1·512	1·603	1·695
15	1·199	1·273	1·355	1·436	1·519	1·610	1·705
20	1·216	1·286	1·367	1·446	1·527	1·618	1·716
25	1·238	1·302	1·380	1·457	1·534	1·626	1·727
30	1·266	1·320	1·394	1·468	1·542	1·634	1·739
35	1·303	1·341	1·408	1·478	1·549	1·641	1·750
40	1·354	1·367	1·423	1·489	1·557	1·648	1·761
45		1·398	1·440	1·500	1·564	1·655	1·771
50		1·438	1·458	1·511	1·571	1·661	1·779
60		1·530	1·500	1·534	1·585	1·672	1·792
70		1·559	1·543	1·557	1·598	1·681	1·803
80			1·582	1·579	1·610	1·689	1·812
90			1·601	1·600	1·621	1·696	1·818
100		1·39	1·603	1·615	1·632	1·702	1·822
120		1·36	1·582	1·630	1·650	1·713	1·827
140		1·35	1·565	1·628	1·660	1·721	1·828
160		1·344	1·554	1·622	1·662	1·726	1·829
180		1·342	1·548	1·617	1·663	1·729	1·829
200		1·341	1·545	1·615	1·663	1·731	1·830
250		1·339	1·543	1·614	1·662	1·732	1·830
300		1·339	1·544	1·615	1·663	1·733	1·83
350		1·340	1·548	1·619	1·666	1·735	1·83
400		1·344	1·553	1·624	1·670	1·738	1·84
450		1·352	1·559	1·630	1·674	1·741	1·84
500		1·362	1·566	1·636	1·679	1·745	1·85
600		1·378	1·580	1·649	1·688	1·752	1·86
700		1·389	1·593	1·662	1·698	1·761	1·87
800		1·397	1·605	1·674	1·707	1·769	1·88
900		1·404	1·615	1·686	1·716	1·777	1·89
1000		1·411	1·624	1·697	1·724	1·783	1·89
1200		1·424	1·641	1·716	1·740	1·796	1·90
1400		1·436	1·657	1·733	1·754	1·807	1·91
1600		1·447	1·673	1·749	1·767	1·817	1·91
1800		1·46	1·688	1·765	1·779	1·827	1·92
2000		1·47	1·703	1·780	1·791	1·836	1·92
2500			1·733	1·811	1·819	1·858	1·93

PROPANE

N. R. Kuloor and D. M. Newitt

Imperial College of Science and Technology

and

J. S. Bateman

Mechanical Engineering Research Laboratory,
Department of Scientific and Industrial Research

THERMODYNAMIC charts and compilations of the thermodynamic properties of propane have been published by a number of authors, namely by the National Bureau of Standards of the U.S.A.[1], by BUR-GOYNE[5], DANA and his co-workers[11]; HANSON[16], JUSTI[20], RAGATZ[29], SAGE, SCHAAFSMA and LACEY[31], and STEARNS and GEORGE[36]. The most recent of these, which give the thermodynamic properties of propane for the homogeneous region and for the liquid–vapour phase boundary, are those of Burgoyne and of Stearns and George. Burgoyne's survey gives data for the two-phase region from 189° K to the critical temperature, 370° K. In the compressed liquid region the data are given up to 60 atm for temperatures below 273° K and up to 200 atm at higher temperatures. In the superheated vapour region the pressure range is 1 atm to 200 atm up to a temperature of 473° K. Stearns and George do not cover so wide a pressure range as Burgoyne, the maximum pressure in their case being only 20 atm in the superheated vapour region. However, they made use of the P-V-T data of DESCHNER and BROWN[13] in this region which are believed to be more accurate than those of Sage, Schaafsma and Lacey[31] as used by Burgoyne.

So far as is known, however, the P-V-T data of Deschner and Brown have not yet been used over their full range in a general survey of thermodynamic properties. Moreover a considerable amount of new P-V-T data in the superheated and compressed liquid regions, as well as for the saturation boundary, has recently been published by REAMER, SAGE and LACEY[30]. These data extend up to 680 atm for the temperature range from 311° K to 511° K and permit a substantial increase in the range of thermodynamic calculations over those previously published, as well as considerable improvement in the accuracy in those regions previously covered.

Survey of Existing Data

1. The Compressibility Data

Cope, Lewis and Weber[8] and Brown, Souders and Smith[4] have given estimated values for the P-V-T data of propane. Values are also reported by Sage, Schaafsma and Lacey[31], Beattie and his co-workers[2, 3], Deschner and Brown[13], Reamer, Sage and Lacey[30], Cherney, Marchman and York[7] and in the compressed liquid region Burgoyne[5] reports values obtained by Lu.

The values of Sage, Schaafsma and Lacey cover the temperature range from 294° K to 378° K and for pressures up to 204 atm. Beattie and his co-workers covered a higher range of temperature, namely from 370° K to 548° K and a specific volume range from 0·1 to 1 litre/mole. They give also the constants of the Beattie–Bridgeman equation of state, which for specific volumes greater than 0·2 litres/mole represents the experimental P-V-T data within an average pressure deviation of less than 0·6 per cent. Deschner and Brown quote values for the compressibility factor, PV/RT, over the temperature range 303° K to 609° K and for pressures up to 140 atm. Comparison of their data with those of Beattie and his co-workers shows a difference in pressure of about 0·2 per cent except in the critical region where the difference is between 1 per cent and 2 per cent. The data of Sage, Schaafsma and Lacey show marked deviations from those of Beattie and his co-workers and likewise from those of Deschner and Brown. The later data of Reamer, Sage and Lacey cover the temperature range from 311° K to 511° K and pressures up to 680 atm. These authors state that on comparing their results with those of Beattie and his co-workers for about 50 points remote from the critical region, the average deviation is 0·22 per cent and the maximum deviation less than 0·4 per cent. The work of Cherney, Marchman and York is for regions already covered by other authors and is not very extensive. Their data agree with those of Beattie and his co-workers within 0·33 per cent in pressure at 373° K and within 0·1 per cent at 398° K.

For the present work the data of Beattie and his co-workers, Deschner and Brown and of Reamer, Sage and Lacey have been used for the superheated vapour region. The data of Beattie and his co-workers required a slight adjustment to allow for the slightly different molecular weight which has been adopted in this work from that assumed by them. In the compressed liquid region the data of Lu, as reported by Burgoyne, and those of Reamer, Sage and Lacey have been preferred. The data of the latter workers are believed to be more accurate than the earlier values of Sage, Schaafsma and Lacey and of Deschner and Brown because they are in better agreement with the saturated liquid data and because their gas isotherms in the critical region, determined with the same apparatus as for those in the compressed liquid region, agree much better with the work of Beattie and his co-workers.

2. The Specific Heat of the Superheated Vapour

The specific heat of propane at a constant pressure of one atmosphere has been determined by SAGE, WEBSTER and LACEY[34], by KISTIAKOWSKY and RICE[22] and by DAILEY and FELSING[10]. The values of Dailey and Felsing agree with those calculated from spectroscopic data and with the experimental values of Kistiakowsky and Rice, but show a deviation from those of Sage, Webster and Lacey. After due consideration it was decided to omit these latter values from the present work since in other instances also they are somewhat anomalous, showing a lack of conformity with the published specific heat data of other closely related hydrocarbons. The values selected for this work at a constant pressure of 1 atm can be represented by the equation:

$$C_p = 12 \cdot 981 - 3 \cdot 22234 \times 10^{-2}T + 2 \cdot 15036 \times 10^{-4}T^2 - 1 \cdot 86935 \\ \times 10^{-7}T^3 \ (\text{cal/mole}, °K)$$

3. The Joule–Thomson Expansion

Joule–Thomson coefficients for propane have been determined by SAGE, KENNEDY and LACEY[33]. The data do not extend to the inversion points however.

4. The Vapour Pressure, Triple Point and Normal Boiling Point

Table 1 gives the values of the normal boiling point and the melting point under a pressure of one atmosphere that have been reported at various times.

TABLE 1

THE NORMAL BOILING POINT AND MELTING POINT

Observer	Boiling point °K	Melting point °K
Olszewski[27] (1889) . . .	228	
Meyer[26] (1894)	236	
Hainlen[15] (1894)	236	
Lebeau[23] (1905)	228·7	
Burrell and Robertson[6] (1915) .	229·1	
Maass and Wright[25] (1921) . .	228·7	83·2
Dana and co-workers[11] (1926) .	231·1	
Young[37] (1928)	230·7	
Francis and Robins[14] (1933) . .	230·9	
Sage, Schaafsma and Lacey[31] (1934)*	230·6	
Hicks-Bruun and Bruun[18] (1936) .	230·99 ±0·05	86·0
Kemp and Egan[21] (1938) . .	231·10 ±0·05	85·45
Hartneck and Edse[17] (1938) . .	231·02 ±0·01	

* Calculated by Cox[9].

117

The earlier determinations of the boiling point are in disagreement and cannot be considered at all reliable, presumably on account of the presence of impurities in the propane used. The more recent values appear to be much more concordant and for this work Kemp and Egan's value of $231 \cdot 1°$ K has been adopted.

Data for the saturated vapour pressure of liquid propane are available from most of the sources quoted in Table 1 and are given also by Reamer, Sage and Lacey[30]. The values given by the various authors were plotted on a large scale and a smooth curve was drawn through those of Dana and his co-workers; Sage, Schaafsma and Lacey; Kemp and Egan and finally Deschner and Brown. This curve was used as the basis of the vapour–pressure relationship throughout the present work, since all the data mentioned above are the results of recent and accurate work and can be given equal weight.

5. The Specific Volumes of the Saturated Liquid and Vapour Phases in Equilibrium and the Critical Constants

Data for the specific volumes of the saturated liquid and vapour phases in equilibrium are available from the work of Dana and his co-workers[11], Sage, Schaafsma and Lacey[31], Deschner and Brown[13] and Reamer, Sage and Lacey[30]. For the saturated liquid alone there are some recent data by LEGATSKI and others[24] and earlier values by MEYER[26], LEBEAU[23] and MAASS and WRIGHT[25]. Before the data of Reamer, Sage and Lacey appeared, values for the present work had already been established for the vapour by drawing a smooth curve through the data of Dana, of Sage, Schaasfma and Lacey, and Deschner and Brown. The curve was extrapolated down to $0 \cdot 1$ atm but no weight was given to the values of Sage, Schaafsma and Lacey near the critical point where later work has shown them to be in error. The newer data of Reamer, Sage and Lacey agreed well with these established values except near the critical point where the new volumes were somewhat greater than those taken from the original curve. Reamer, Sage and Lacey's estimate of the critical volume was derived from the law of the rectilinear diameter just as that of Deschner and Brown whose values for the critical constants have been adopted for this work since they are in close agreement with the work of Beattie, Poffenberger and Hadlock[2]. It was decided, therefore, to retain the values adopted before the publication of Reamer, Sage and Lacey's work. In the case of the liquid volumes, however, the values of Reamer, Sage and Lacey have been included with those of Maass and Wright, Deschner and Brown and Legatski, a smooth curve being drawn through the values of all these authors. The law of the rectilinear diameter is followed by the finally adopted values for the liquid and vapour.

The following values for the critical constants given in Table 2 have been reported.

TABLE 2

THE CRITICAL CONSTANTS

Observer	Crit. Temp. °K	Crit. Press. atm	Crit. Vol. cm³/mole
Olszewski[27] (1889) . .	370	44·0	
Meyer[26] (1894) . . .	375	48·5	
Hainlen[15] (1894) . . .	375	48·5	
Lebeau[23] (1905) . . .	370·7	45·0	
Maass and Wright[25] (1921) .	368·8		
Sage, Schaafsma and Lacey[31] (1934)	373·3	43·77	189·2
Beattie, Poffenberger and Hadlock[2] (1935) . . .	369·96 ±0·01	42·01 +0·02	195·0
Deschner and Brown[13] (1940) .	370·0	42·10	195·7
Ipatieff and Munroe[19] (1942) .	369–371		
Reamer, Sage and Lacey[30] (1949)			199·9

As already mentioned, the values of Deschner and Brown have been adopted in the present work since they are in close agreement with those of Beattie, Poffenberger and Hadlock, leaving the higher value for the critical volume of Reamer, Sage and Lacey in some doubt.

6. The Latent Heat of Vaporization

The latent heat of vaporization of propane has been determined by Dana and his associates[11], Kemp and Egan[21] and SAGE, EVANS and LACEY[35]. The results are all reasonably concordant and the general empirical relationship proposed originally by OSBORNE and VAN DUSEN[28] represents them quite well. The exact form of the equation for propane was found to be:

$$L = 532·2 \, (T_k - T)^{\frac{1}{3}} - 12·92 \, (T_k - T)$$

L being the latent heat in cal/mole and T and T_k the temperature and critical temperature in degrees Kelvin. Values have been calculated from this equation for the present work.

7. The Specific Heat of the Saturated Liquid

Experimental values for the specific heat of saturated liquid propane are available from the work of Dana and his co-workers[11], SAGE and LACEY[32] and Kemp and Egan[21]. The values of all these observers were plotted and a smooth curve drawn representing all the data fairly well. This curve was used in the subsequent calculations of the entropy and enthalpy of the saturated liquid.

119

It may be mentioned here that Kemp and Egan have used the calorimetric data to calculate the entropy of the real gas at the normal boiling point whilst the enthalpy of the boiling liquid at 1 atm has been calculated by Stearns and George[36] by graphical integration of the specific heat values of Kemp and Egan. In both these calculations the entropy and enthalpy were set at zero at the absolute zero of temperature and both calculated values have been accepted for the present work.

Calculation of the Thermodynamic Functions and Construction of the Thermodynamic Diagram

8. Units, Constants and Conversion Factors

The pressure unit used in the present survey is the international atmosphere equal to 1,013,250 dyn/cm². The volume unit is the cubic centimetre and the Kelvin temperature scale with an ice point of 273·16° has been adopted. The quantity unit is the gramme molecule, the molecular weight of propane, 44·094, being based on the 1943 international chemical values. For the energy unit a calorie of 4·1868 J has been used. The ideal gas constant R has been taken as 82·05 cm³-atm/mole, ° K. This value is the same to four significant figures whether the mole is taken from the 1943 atomic weights or Birge's 1941 values. The difference between the exact value of R and 82·05 is not significant for present purposes.

9. Calculation of the Thermodynamic Functions in the Homogeneous region from the P-V-T Data

The entropy and enthalpy along the 1 atm isobar were first calculated by integrating the equation for the specific heat at constant pressure given in section 2.

$$\Delta S \left.\right]_{T_1}^{T_2}{}_{P} = \int_{T_1}^{T_2} \frac{C_p}{T}\, dT \left.\right]_{P}$$

$$\Delta H \left.\right]_{T_1}^{T_2}{}_{P} = \int_{T_1}^{T_2} C_p\, dT \left.\right]_{P}$$

The reference values for the entropy and enthalpy of the real gas at the normal boiling point, 231·1° K, were taken as 60·23 cal/mole, °K and 8925 cal/mole respectively.

Having evaluated the entropies and enthalpies for 1 atm pressure at various temperatures, the functions at higher pressures were calculated by integrating the appropriate derivatives of the P-V-T data along isotherms according to the following thermodynamic equations.

120

$$\frac{\partial S}{\partial P}\bigg)_T = -\frac{\partial V}{\partial T}\bigg)_P$$

$$\Delta S \bigg]_{P_1}^{P_2}{}_T = \int_{P_1}^{P_2} -\frac{\partial V}{\partial T}\bigg)_P dP\bigg]_T$$

$$\frac{\partial H}{\partial P}\bigg)_T = V - T\frac{\partial V}{\partial T}\bigg)_P$$

$$\Delta H \bigg]_{P_1}^{P_2}{}_T = \int_{P_1}^{P_2} VdP\bigg]_T - \int_{P_1}^{P_2} T\frac{\partial V}{\partial T}\bigg)_P dP\bigg]_T = \int_{P_1}^{P_2} VdP\bigg]_T + T\Delta S \bigg]_{P_1}^{P_2}{}_T$$

These equations were applied in the higher pressure ranges. In the lower pressure ranges where the specific volume is greater than 200 cm³/ mole, equations derived from the Beattie–Bridgeman equation were used. The thermodynamic equation:

$$\frac{\partial P}{\partial T}\bigg)_V = \frac{\partial S}{\partial V}\bigg)_T$$

may be put in the integrated form as follows:

$$S\bigg]_T = \int \frac{\partial P}{\partial T}\bigg)_V dV\bigg]_T + \text{integration constant}$$

The Beattie–Bridgeman equation may be written:

$$P = \frac{RT}{V^2}\left(1 - \frac{c}{VT^3}\right)\left[V + B_0\left(1 - \frac{b}{V}\right)\right] - \frac{A_0}{V^2}\left(1 - \frac{a}{V}\right)$$

The values of the constants R, A_0, a, B_0, b and c (given by Beattie) for the system of units chosen here are as follows:

$$R = 82 \cdot 06$$
$$A_0 = 1 \cdot 19200 \times 10^7$$
$$a = 73 \cdot 21$$
$$B_0 = 181 \cdot 00$$
$$b = 42 \cdot 93$$
$$c = 1 \cdot 2000 \times 10^9$$

After differentiating to find $\frac{\partial P}{\partial T}\bigg)_V$ and subsequent integration along the isotherm it is found that:

$$S\bigg]_T = R \log_e V - \left(\frac{2c}{T^3} + B_0\right)\frac{R}{V} + \left(\frac{b}{2} - \frac{c}{T^3}\right)\frac{RB_0}{V^2} + \frac{2RB_0bc}{3\,T^3V^3}$$

$$+ \text{integration constant}$$

Similarly the thermodynamic equation:

$$\left(\frac{\partial H}{\partial V}\right)_T = T\left(\frac{\partial S}{\partial V}\right)_T + V\left(\frac{\partial P}{\partial V}\right)_T = T\left(\frac{\partial P}{\partial T}\right)_V + V\left(\frac{\partial P}{\partial V}\right)_T$$

in the isothermal integrated form becomes:

$$H\Big]_T = TS\Big]_T + \int V\left(\frac{\partial P}{\partial V}\right)_T dV\Big]_T + \text{integration constant}$$

By finding $\left(\dfrac{\partial P}{\partial V}\right)_T$ from the Beattie–Bridgeman equation, integration along the isotherm and incorporation of the expression for $S]_T$ there follows:

$$H\Big]_T = \left(RTB_0 - \frac{4Rc}{T^2} - 2A_0\right)\frac{1}{V} - \left(RTB_0b + \frac{5RB_0c}{2T^2} - \frac{3A_0a}{2}\right)\frac{1}{V^2} + \frac{2RB_0bc}{T^2V^3}$$
$$+ \text{constant}$$

The integration constants in the expressions for the entropy and enthalpy are functions of the temperature only and incorporate the values of the entropy or enthalpy and the volume at 1 atm.

In using these equations adjustments were made for the slightly different molecular weight and Kelvin ice point taken by Beattie in deducing the constants of the equation of state.

Where necessary the selected P-V-T data were interpolated for integral pressures in atmospheres. In the region not covered by the Beattie–Bridgeman equation, i.e. for specific volumes less than 200 cm^3/ mole, this was achieved with the aid of the second of the two residuals used by Deming and Shupe[12] namely:

$$r' = V\left(\frac{PV}{RT} - 1\right)$$

In the compressed liquid region the data were interpolated directly from large scale graphs of pressure–volume isotherms.

The graphical method of Deming and Shupe was used to determine the values of the derivative $\left(\dfrac{\partial V}{\partial T}\right)_P$. The values of r' were plotted against the pressure as isotherms and then cross-plotted against the temperature as isobars. From these latter curves values of the derivative $\left(\dfrac{\partial r'}{\partial T}\right)_P$ were found by drawing tangents and the values of $\left(\dfrac{\partial V}{\partial T}\right)_P$ then calculated. In the critical and compressed liquid regions, however, $\left(\dfrac{\partial V}{\partial T}\right)_P$ was obtained directly as accurately as possible from the volume versus temperature isobars. The values of $\dfrac{\partial V}{\partial T}\Big)_P$ were then integrated to give the entropy and enthalpy in the usual manner.

The entropy values were tested by plotting isobars on the temperature–entropy diagram and also isotherms on an entropy–pressure diagram. The enthalpy values were tested as isotherms on an enthalpy–pressure diagram. Where the Beattie–Bridgeman equation has been used the entropy and enthalpy values are naturally consistent with each other.

10. The Two-Phase Boundary

The entropy changes along the saturated liquid line were calculated by graphical integration of the values of the specific heat of the saturated liquid according to the equation:

$$\Delta S \left.\right]_{T_1}^{T_2}{}_{\sigma} = \int_{T_1}^{T_2} \frac{C_\sigma}{T} \mathrm{d}T$$

The values of the specific heat were taken from the smooth curve drawn through the experimental values as mentioned in section 7.

Similarly the enthalpy changes along the saturated liquid boundary were calculated by integrating the expression:

$$\Delta H \left.\right]_{T_1}^{T_2}{}_{\sigma} = \int_{T_1}^{T_2} C_\sigma \mathrm{d}T + \int_{P_1}^{P_2} V \mathrm{d}P$$

where P_1 and P_2 are the vapour pressures at temperatures T_1 and T_2 respectively and V is the volume of the saturated liquid. The $V\mathrm{d}P$ term had to be converted from cm^3-atm/mole to cal/mole.

The latent heats of vaporization, i.e. the enthalpy differences between saturated liquid and vapour phases at the same temperature and pressure were calculated from the equation given in section 6. The entropy changes on vaporization followed from the relationship:

$$\Delta H = T\Delta S$$

The enthalpy and entropy of the saturated vapour branch of the two-phase boundary were thus calculated.

The boiling points at different pressures were read of from the large scale vapour pressure curve.

11. Preparation of the Final Tables. Calculation of the Specific Heats

The calculations of the thermodynamic functions described in the preceding sections did not yield values at rounded off temperatures in degrees Kelvin but at temperatures dictated by convenience in handling the original data. It was necessary, therefore, to interpolate from these values to obtain the required values at rounded off Kelvin degrees. Round the saturation boundary values were interpolated for rounded off selected pressures also, keeping the quantities consistent with the Clausius–Clapeyron equation. In this process the latent heats calculated from the equation given in section 6 were modified slightly, becoming numerically smoothed values believed to be the best representation of the experimental results.

In the homogeneous region the gas volumes were interpolated graphically and smoothed with the aid of Deming and Shupe's first residual, namely: $r = \dfrac{RT}{P} - V$. In the compressed liquid region, however, a direct interpolation of the volume was used.

Entropy and enthalphy values were interpolated with the aid of tables of isothermal and isobaric differences and the values along the 1 atm isobar which could readily be obtained for rounded off Kelvin degrees by integrating the specific heat equation given in section 2.

The specific heat at constant pressure was calculated from the final table of entropy values from the relation:

$$C_p = T \left. \frac{\varDelta S}{\varDelta T} \right)_P$$

i.e. by numerical differentiation. The values were then re-interpolated for the same rounded off Kelvin degrees as for the entropy values. No values are given in the critical region since these were impossible to obtain with any degree of accuracy.

To calculate the specific heat at constant volume, the difference in the specific heats, $C_p - C_v$, was first obtained from the following thermodynamic expressions:

$$C_p - C_v = - T \frac{\left. \dfrac{\partial V}{\partial T} \right)_P^2}{\left. \dfrac{\partial V}{\partial P} \right)_T}$$

$$= \frac{T \left[\dfrac{R}{P} - \left. \dfrac{\partial r}{\partial T} \right)_P \right]^2}{\dfrac{RT}{P^2} + \left. \dfrac{\partial r}{\partial P} \right)_T}$$

The differential coefficients were determined by numerical differentiation as before. The first expression was used in the compressed liquid region and the second in the gas region. After subtracting the re-interpolated values from C_p, the values C_v so obtained were smoothed along isotherms and isobars. The accuracy obtained is probably not better than 5 per cent, except at low pressures in the gas region, and it may increase to 10 per cent as the critical region is approached.

12. The Joule–Thomson Inversion Curve

The pressures at points on the isotherms on the enthalpy–pressure diagram at which the derivative $\dfrac{\partial H}{\partial P}\Big)_T$ was equal to zero were estimated and smoothed graphically. The values are given in Table 3.

TABLE 3

THE JOULE–THOMSON INVERSION POINTS

Temperature °K	Pressure atm	Temperature °K	Pressure atm
300	37	420	286
320	85	440	320
340	131	460	350
360	174	480	378
380	214	500	402
400	251		

DISCUSSION

The errors in the calculated entropy values arise from a number of causes, namely, the errors in the integration of the specific heats of solid and liquid propane up to the normal boiling point, the error in the value of the latent heat of vaporization at 1 atm, the errors in the specific heat of the superheated vapour at a constant pressure of 1 atm and finally from the inevitable errors in the isothermal integration of the P-V-T data to yield the thermodynamic functions. The latter errors arise from poor or insufficient original P-V-T data and from failure to interpret the data accurately when deducing the values of the derivative $\dfrac{\partial V}{\partial T}\Big)_P$.

After much consideration Tables 4 and 5 were drawn up showing the estimated maximum possible errors in the entropy values in the superheated region and round the two-phase boundary.

The errors in the enthalpy are given by the relation:

$$\delta H \simeq T \delta S$$

where δH and δS are the corresponding errors in enthalpy and entropy respectively.

PROPANE

TABLE 4

ESTIMATED MAXIMUM ERRORS IN ENTROPY IN THE HOMOGENEOUS REGION
cal/mole, °K

Pressure atm	Temperature °K					
	300	350	400	450	500	600
1	±0·1	±0·1	±0·1	±0·1	±0·1	±0·1
10	±0·5	±0·2	±0·2	±0·1	±0·1	±0·1
50			±0·9	±0·2	±0·1	±0·1
100		±0·6	±0·5	±0·4	±0·2	±0·2
200		±0·6	±0·6	±0·6	±0·4	±0·2
600	±0·5	±0·7	±0·7	±0·6	±0·4	

In general the absolute errors for two states which are adjacent, or nearly so, will be about the same, so that the error in the difference of the values will be much less than the absolute errors of either of them. For this reason the tabulated values are given to more significant figures than their absolute accuracy warrants.

TABLE 5

ESTIMATED MAXIMUM ERRORS IN ENTROPY ON THE TWO-PHASE BOUNDARY
cal/mole, °K

Pressure atm	Temperature °K	Liquid	Vapour
2	249·5	±0·2	±0·3
10	300·8	±0·4	±0·5
35	360·0	±0·5	±0·7
42·1	370·0 (C.P.)	±0·6	

The estimated errors in the volume follow from consideration of the original P-V-T data. The accuracy of these data can sometimes be judged from the statements of the authors themselves in the published papers, from their descriptions of their apparatus and methods and by comparing the results of different workers. Often, however, the original sources do not give sufficient details for an adequate analysis, and the practice of giving smoothed out results makes the investigation of the possible errors even more difficult. An attempt has been made, however, to deduce the errors which are unlikely to be exceeded at various points of the pressure–volume plane. The estimates are given

126

in Tables 6, 7 and 8. They are given as volume errors in the compressed liquid region and on the two-phase boundary in Tables 6 and 7 and as pressure errors in the superheated region in Table 8. These different forms were adopted as a consequence of the manner in which the data are given in the literature.

Figure 1 shows the temperature–entropy diagram in skeleton form. The sources of the data in the different regions are indicated and also those regions where the data are poor, scanty or non-existent.

TABLE 6

POSSIBLE VOLUME ERRORS IN THE COMPRESSED LIQUID REGION
$cm^3/mole$

Pressure atm	Temperature °K		
	250	300	350
10	1·2	0·9	
100		0·9	0·21
200		0·8	0·19
300			0·18
400			0·17
600			0·16

TABLE 7

POSSIBLE VOLUME ERRORS ON THE TWO-PHASE BOUNDARY, $cm^3/mole$

Pressure atm	Temperature °K	Liquid	Vapour
2	249·5	0·08	50
10	360·8	0·18	10
35	360·0	0·25	13
42·1 (C.P.)	370·0	4·0	

There is still plenty of scope for future experimental work on propane. In particular further data on the specific heat of the saturated liquid above the normal boiling point are required, especially at temperatures close to the critical point. New values for the latent heats of vaporization under similar conditions are also needed. There are also various ranges where additional or more accurate *P-V-T* data would be particularly welcome, namely, in the compressed liquid region below 311° K and up to higher pressures than those hitherto measured, in the critical

TABLE 8

POSSIBLE PRESSURE ERRORS IN THE SUPERHEATED REGION, atm

Pressure atm	Temperature °K					
	250	300	350	400	500	600
1	0·001	0·001	0·001	0·001	0·001	0·001
10		0·02	0·01	0·01	0·01	0·01
50			0·25	0·05	0·05	0·05
100			0·5	0·1	0·1	0·1
200			0·4	0·2	0·2	0·2
300			0·6	0·6	0·3	
400			0·8	0·8	0·4	
600			1·2	1·2	0·6	

region and in the gaseous region above 100 atm where the present data are rather scanty. An extension of the pressure range above 250 atm for the temperature range 511° K to 609° K is also desirable.

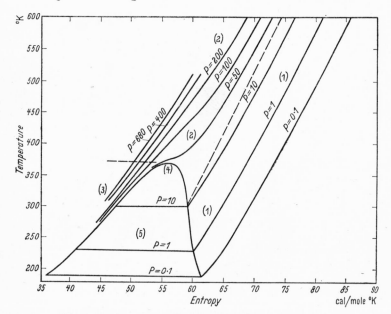

Figure 1. Skeleton temperature–entropy diagram for propane

(1) Beattie–Bridgeman equation of State. C_p at 1 atm—Dailey and Felsing; Kistiakowsky and Rice.
(2) *P-V-T* data—Deschner and Brown; Reamer, Sage and Lacey.
(3) *P-V-T* data—Burgoyne; Reamer, Sage and Lacey.
(4) Critical constants—Deschner and Brown.
(5) Vapour pressure, density of saturated liquid and vapour—various authors. Specific heat of saturated liquid—Dana and others; Sage and Lacey; Kemp and Egan. Latent heat of vaporization at 1 atm—Dana and others; Kemp and Egan; Sage, Evans and Lacey.

In the two-phase regions the present specific volumes of the saturated vapour near the critical point are uncertain. Triple point values and other data for the solid–liquid equilibrium under high pressure would also provide a further extension of the temperature–entropy diagram. Below 189° K the physical properties of propane are almost completely unexplored.

REFERENCES

1 A.P.I. Res. Proj. 44, *Nat. Bur. Standards, Tables of Physical and Thermo-dynamic Properties of Hydrocarbons.*
2 BEATTIE, POFFENBERGER and HADLOCK, *J. chem. Phys.*, 3 (1935) 96.
3 BEATTIE, KAY and KAMINSKY, *J. Amer. chem. Soc.*, 59 (1937) 1589.
4 BROWN, SOUDERS and SMITH, *Industr. Engng Chem.*, 24 (1932) 513.
5 BURGOYNE, *Proc. roy. Soc.* A, 176 (1940) 280.
6 BURRELL and ROBERTSON, *J. Amer. chem. Soc.*, 37 (1915) 2188.
7 CHERNEY, MARCHMAN and YORK, *Industr. Engng Chem.*, 41 (1949) 2653.
8 COPE, LEWIS and WEBER, *Industr. Engng Chem.*, 23 (1931) 887.
9 COX, *Petrol. World*, 31 (1934) 44.
10 DAILEY and FELSING, *J. Amer. chem. Soc.*, 65 (1943) 42.
11 DANA, JENKINS, BURDICK and TIMM, *Refrig. Engng*, 12 (1926) 387.
12 DEMING and SHUPE, *Phys. Rev.*, 34 (1929) 527; 37 (1931) 638; 38 (1931) 2245; 40 (1932) 848.
13 DESCHNER and BROWN, *Industr. Engng Chem.*, 32 (1940) 836.
14 FRANCIS and ROBBINS, *J. Amer. chem. Soc.*, 55 (1933) 4339.
15 HAINLEN, *Liebigs Ann.*, 282 (1894) 229.
16 HANSON, *Trans. Amer. Inst. chem. Engrs*, 42 (1946) 959.
17 HARTNECK and EDSE, *Z. phys. Chem.*, 182 (1938) 220.
18 HICKS-BRUUN and BRUUN, *J. Amer. chem. Soc.*, 58 (1936) 810.
19 IPATIEFF and MUNROE, *Industr. Engng Chem. Anal.*, 14 (1942) 171.
20 JUSTI, *Z. Ver. dtsch. Ing.*, 80 (1936) 103.
21 KEMP and EGAN, *J. Amer. chem. Soc.*, 60 (1938) 1521.
22 KISTIAKOWSKY and RICE, *J. chem. Phys.*, 8 (1940) 616.
23 LEBEAU, *C.R. Acad. Sci. Paris*, 140 (1905) 1454.
24 LEGATSKI and others, *Industr. Engng Chem.*, 34 (1942) 1240.
25 MAASS and WRIGHT, *J. Amer. chem. Soc.*, 43 (1921) 1098.
26 MEYER, *Ber. dtsch. chem. Ges.*, 27 (1894) 2767.
27 OLSZEWSKI, *Abh. Krakau. Akad.* (1889).
28 OSBORNE and VAN DUSEN, *Bull. U.S. Bur. Stand.*, 14 (1918) 439.
29 RAGATZ, *Petrol. World*, 31 (1934) 43.
30 REAMER, SAGE and LACEY, *Industr. Engng Chem.*, 41 (1949) 482.
31 SAGE, SCHAAFSMA and LACEY, *Industr. Engng Chem.*, 26 (1934) 1218.
32 SAGE and LACEY, *Industr. Engng Chem.*, 27 (1935) 1484.
33 SAGE, KENNEDY and LACEY, *Industr. Engng Chem.*, 28 (1936) 601.
34 SAGE, WEBSTER and LACEY, *Industr. Engng Chem.*, 29 (1937) 1309.
35 SAGE, EVANS and LACEY, *Industr. Engng Chem.*, 31 (1939) 763.
36 STEARNS and GEORGE, *Industr. Engng Chem.*, 35 (1943) 602.
37 YOUNG, *Proc. Irish Acad.*, 38 (1928) 65.

TABLES OF THERMODYNAMIC FUNCTIONS OF PROPANE

The properties are given for 1 gramme mole of propane (44·094 gramme) as functions of the pressure in international atmospheres ($g = 980 \cdot 665$) and temperature in degrees Kelvin (0° C = 273·16° K). One calorie = 4·1868 J. Entropy and enthalpy are zero for the perfect crystal at the absolute zero of temperature.

Molecular weight	= 44·094
Density of the gas at N.T.P. (international atm, $g = 980 \cdot 665$)	= 0·002005 g/cm³
Molecular volume at N.T.P. (international atm, $g = 980 \cdot 665$)	= 21,990 cm³
Normal boiling point	= 231·10° K
Triple point	= 85·45° K
Critical constants: temperature	= 370·0° K
pressure	= 42·10 atm
volume	= 195·7 cm³/mole

PROPERTIES OF THE SATURATED LIQUID AND VAPOUR

Pressure atm	Tempera-ture °K	Entropy cal/mole, °K		Enthalpy cal/mole		Volume cm³/mole	
		Liquid	Vapour	Liquid	Vapour	Liquid	Vapour
0·1	189·50	35·91	61·77	3,418	8,320	70·0	154,600
0·5	216·54	39·30	60·75	4,101	8,744	73·6	34,690
1	231·10	40·81	60·23	4,438	8,925	75·7	18,200
2	248·06	42·48	59·77	4,840	9,129	78·4	9,530
3	259·33	43·54	59·54	5,111	9,260	80·3	6,513
4	268·05	44·35	59·39	5,326	9,358	82·0	4,957
5	275·24	45·01	59·28	5,505	9,434	83·5	4,000
6	281·44	45·58	59·20	5,664	9,498	84·9	3,348
7	286·90	46·08	59·13	5,805	9,550	86·2	2,875
8	291·83	46·51	59·06	5,933	9,595	87·5	2,516
9	296·30	46·92	59·01	6,054	9,635	88·7	2,231
10	300·44	47·31	58·96	6,169	9,669	89·9	2,003
15	317·42	48·88	58·76	6,655	9,790	95·8	1,301
20	330·70	50·14	58·57	7,086	9,873	101·6	936·0
25	341·71	51·25	58·40	7,477	9,920	107·8	708·7
30	351·23	52·29	58·18	7,856	9,925	115·6	548·7
35	359·61	53·36	57·85	8,234	9,849	126·9	421·8
40	367·18	54·71	57·19	8,732	9,644	146·8	294·7
42·10 (C.P.)	370·0	56·14		9,227		195·7	

PROPANE

SPECIFIC HEAT AT CONSTANT VOLUME, CALORIES/MOLE, °K

Pressure Atm	Temperature °K													
	230	240	250	260	270	280	290	300	310	320	330	340	350	360
0.1	12.0	12.5	13.0	13.5	14.0	14.5	15.0	15.5	16.0	16.5	17.0	17.5	18.0	18.5
0.5	12.1	12.6	13.1	13.6	14.0	14.5	15.0	15.5	16.0	16.5	17.0	17.5	18.0	18.5
1	21.3	12.7	13.2	13.7	14.1	14.6	15.1	15.5	16.0	16.5	17.0	17.5	18.0	18.5
2	21.2	20.6	13.4	13.9	14.3	14.8	15.2	15.7	16.1	16.6	17.1	17.5	18.0	18.5
3	21.2	20.6	20.0	14.2	14.6	15.0	15.4	15.8	16.2	16.6	17.1	17.5	18.0	18.5
4	21.1	20.5	19.9	19.4	15.0	15.3	15.6	15.9	16.3	16.7	17.2	17.6	18.1	18.6
5	21.1	20.5	19.9	19.4	19.0	15.7	15.9	16.2	16.5	16.9	17.2	17.6	18.1	18.6
6	21.0	20.4	19.8	19.3	18.9	18.5	16.2	16.4	16.7	17.0	17.3	17.7	18.2	18.7
7	21.0	20.4	19.8	19.3	18.9	18.5	16.5	16.6	16.8	17.1	17.4	17.8	18.3	18.7
8	20.9	20.3	19.7	19.2	18.8	18.4	18.0	16.9	17.0	17.2	17.5	17.9	18.3	18.7
9	20.9	20.3	19.7	19.2	18.8	18.4	18.0	17.2	17.3	17.5	17.7	18.0	18.4	18.8
10	20.8	20.2	19.6	19.1	18.7	18.3	18.0	17.8	17.6	17.7	17.9	18.2	18.5	18.9
15	20.4	19.8	19.3	18.8	18.4	18.1	17.8	17.6	17.4	18.6	18.7	18.8	19.0	19.3
20	20.0	19.5	19.0	18.5	18.1	17.8	17.6	17.4	17.3	17.3	17.3	19.5	19.6	19.7
25	19.7	19.2	18.7	18.2	17.8	17.5	17.4	17.3	17.3	17.3	17.4	17.6	20.3	20.2
30	19.4	18.9	18.4	17.9	17.6	17.4	17.3	17.2	17.3	17.4	17.6	17.9	18.4	20.7
35	19.1	18.6	18.1	17.7	17.4	17.2	17.1	17.1	17.2	17.4	17.7	18.2	18.8	21.2
40	18.9	18.4	17.9	17.5	17.2	17.1	17.0	17.0	17.2	17.5	17.9	18.5	19.2	—
50	18.4	18.0	17.5	17.2	17.0	16.9	16.9	16.9	17.1	17.6	18.2	19.0	20.0	—
60	18.0	17.6	17.2	16.9	16.8	16.7	16.7	16.8	17.1	17.6	18.4	19.4	20.6	—
70						16.3	16.4	16.6	17.0	17.7	18.7	19.8	21.0	22.0
80						15.9	16.1	16.4	16.9	17.7	18.7	20.0	21.3	22.4
90						15.6	15.9	16.3	16.9	17.8	18.9	20.2	21.5	22.6
100						15.3	15.7	16.2	16.9	17.8	19.0	20.3	21.6	22.8
150						14.8	15.3	15.9	16.8	17.7	18.8	19.9	21.0	22.1
200						14.3	15.0	15.8	16.7	17.6	18.5	19.3	20.1	20.9
250									16.5	17.4	18.2	19.0	19.8	20.5
300									16.3	17.1	17.9	18.7	19.4	20.1
350									16.2	16.9	17.7	18.5	19.2	19.8
400									16.1	16.8	17.6	18.3	19.0	19.6
500									16.1	16.8	17.5	18.2	18.9	19.5
600									16.1	16.8	17.5	18.2	18.9	19.5

SPECIFIC HEAT AT CONSTANT VOLUME, CALORIES/MOLE, °K—*cont.*

Pressure atm	Temperature °K													
	370	380	390	400	420	440	460	480	500	520	540	560	580	600
0·1	19·0	19·5	20·0	20·5	21·5	22·5	23·5	24·4	25·3	26·1	26·9	27·6	28·2	28·7
0·5	19·0	19·5	20·0	20·5	21·5	22·5	23·5	24·4	25·3	26·1	26·9	27·6	28·2	28·7
1	19·0	19·5	20·0	20·5	21·5	22·5	23·5	24·4	25·3	26·1	26·9	27·6	28·2	28·7
2	19·0	19·5	20·0	20·5	21·5	22·5	23·5	24·4	25·3	26·1	26·9	27·6	28·2	28·7
3	19·0	19·5	20·0	20·5	21·5	22·5	23·5	24·4	25·3	26·1	26·9	27·6	28·2	28·7
4	19·1	19·5	20·0	20·5	21·5	22·5	23·5	24·4	25·3	26·1	26·9	27·6	28·2	28·7
5	19·1	19·5	20·0	20·5	21·5	22·5	23·5	24·4	25·3	26·1	26·9	27·6	28·2	28·7
6	19·1	19·6	20·0	20·5	21·5	22·5	23·5	24·4	25·3	26·1	26·9	27·6	28·2	28·7
7	19·2	19·6	20·1	20·6	21·5	22·5	23·5	24·4	25·3	26·1	26·9	27·6	28·2	28·7
8	19·2	19·6	20·1	20·6	21·5	22·5	23·5	24·4	25·3	26·1	26·9	27·6	28·2	28·8
9	19·3	19·7	20·2	20·7	21·6	22·5	23·5	24·4	25·3	26·1	26·9	27·6	28·2	28·8
10	19·3	19·8	20·2	20·7	21·6	22·5	23·5	24·4	25·3	26·1	26·9	27·6	28·2	28·8
15	19·7	20·0	20·4	20·8	21·7	22·6	23·5	24·4	25·3	26·1	26·9	27·6	28·2	28·8
20	19·9	20·2	20·5	20·9	21·8	22·7	23·6	24·5	25·4	26·2	27·0	27·7	28·3	28·8
25	20·2	20·4	20·7	21·0	21·8	22·7	23·6	24·5	25·4	26·2	27·0	27·7	28·3	28·8
30	20·6	20·7	20·9	21·1	21·9	22·8	23·7	24·5	25·4	26·2	27·0	27·7	28·3	28·9
35	20·9	21·0	21·2	21·3	22·1	22·9	23·7	24·6	25·5	26·3	27·0	27·7	28·3	28·9
40	21·3	21·3	21·4	21·5	22·2	23·0	23·8	24·7	25·5	26·3	27·0	27·7	28·3	28·9
50	—	—	—	—	22·5	23·2	24·0	24·8	25·6	26·4	27·1	27·8	28·4	28·9
60	—	—	—	—	22·9	23·5	24·2	25·0	25·8	26·5	27·2	27·8	28·4	28·9
70	22·9	23·6	24·3	—	—	23·9	24·5	25·2	25·9	26·6	27·3	27·9	28·4	28·9
80	23·3	24·1	24·9	—	—	—	24·8	25·4	26·0	26·7	27·3	27·9	28·4	28·9
90	23·6	24·5	25·3	—	—	—	25·1	25·6	26·2	26·8	27·4	27·9	28·4	28·8
100	23·8	24·6	25·4	25·9	26·2	25·7	25·5	25·9	26·4	27·0	27·5	28·0	28·4	28·8
150	23·1	23·9	24·6	25·1	25·9	26·3	26·6	26·7	26·9	27·1	27·4	27·7	28·0	28·3
200	21·6	22·3	22·9	23·4	24·4	25·2	25·8	26·2	26·6	26·9	27·2	27·4	27·5	27·7
250	21·1	21·7	22·3	22·8	23·7	24·4	25·0	25·6	26·0	26·3	26·6	26·9	27·1	27·3
300	20·7	21·3	21·9	22·4	23·3	24·1	24·6	25·3	25·8					
350	20·4	21·0	21·6	22·1	23·0	23·8	24·4	25·1	25·6					
400	20·2	20·8	21·3	21·8	22·8	23·7	24·3	25·0	25·5					
500	20·1	20·7	21·2	21·7	22·7	23·6	24·3	24·9	25·4					
600	20·1	20·7	21·2	21·7	22·7	23·6	24·3	24·8	25·3					

133

PROPANE

SPECIFIC HEAT AT CONSTANT PRESSURE, CALORIES/MOLE, °K

Pressure Atm	Temperature °K													
	230	240	250	260	270	280	290	300	310	320	330	340	350	360
0·1	14·2	14·7	15·1	15·6	16·1	16·5	17·0	17·5	17·9	18·4	18·9	19·4	19·9	20·4
0·5	14·3	14·8	15·2	15·7	16·2	16·6	17·1	17·6	18·0	18·5	19·0	19·5	20·0	20·5
1	23·7	15·0	15·4	15·9	16·4	16·8	17·2	17·7	18·2	18·7	19·1	19·6	20·1	20·5
2	23·7	23·8	16·1	16·3	16·8	17·1	17·5	18·0	18·4	18·9	19·3	19·8	20·2	20·6
3	23·7	23·8	23·9	17·5	17·6	17·7	17·9	18·3	18·7	19·1	19·5	19·9	20·3	20·7
4	23·7	23·8	23·9	24·1	19·2	18·6	18·4	18·6	19·0	19·3	19·7	20·1	20·5	20·9
5	23·7	23·8	23·9	24·1	24·6	19·8	19·2	19·0	19·3	19·6	19·9	20·3	20·6	21·0
6	23·7	23·8	23·9	24·1	24·6	25·5	20·4	19·6	19·7	19·9	20·1	20·4	20·8	21·2
7	23·7	23·8	23·9	24·1	24·5	25·4	22·1	20·8	20·2	20·3	20·4	20·6	20·9	21·3
8	23·7	23·8	23·9	24·1	24·5	25·3	26·7	23·1	20·9	20·8	20·7	20·8	21·1	21·4
9	23·7	23·8	23·9	24·1	24·5	25·3	26·6	27·1	21·7	21·3	21·1	21·0	21·2	21·5
10	23·7	23·8	23·9	24·1	24·5	25·3	26·5	28·1	22·8	22·0	21·5	21·3	21·4	21·7
15	23·7	23·8	23·9	24·1	24·5	25·2	26·4	27·8	29·6	34·0	26·3	23·8	22·8	22·6
20	23·7	23·8	23·9	24·1	24·4	25·1	26·2	27·6	29·3	31·5	34·4	32·6	25·7	23·9
25	23·6	23·7	23·8	24·0	24·3	24·9	26·0	27·3	29·0	31·1	33·7	38·7	32·8	27·6
30	23·5	23·6	23·7	23·9	24·2	24·7	25·7	27·0	28·7	30·8	33·2	37·6	45·0	38·0
35	23·5	23·5	23·6	23·8	24·1	24·6	25·5	26·8	28·4	30·4	32·7	36·7	42·7	73·0
40	23·4	23·4	23·5	23·7	24·0	24·5	25·4	26·6	28·2	30·1	32·3	36·0	41·3	—.
50	23·3	23·3	23·4	23·6	23·9	24·4	25·3	26·4	27·8	29·5	31·6	34·7	38·8	—
60	23·3	23·3	23·4	23·6	23·9	24·4	25·2	26·2	27·5	29·1	31·1	33·6	36·8	—
70						24·3	25·1	26·1	27·3	28·8	30·6	32·7	35·2	38·3
80						24·3	25·1	26·1	27·2	28·6	30·2	32·0	33·9	35·9
90						24·2	25·0	26·0	27·1	28·4	29·8	31·3	32·9	34·6
100						24·2	25·0	26·0	27·1	28·3	29·5	30·8	32·2	33·7
150						24·2	24·9	25·8	26·7	27·5	28·3	29·1	29·9	30·7
200									26·2	26·8	27·4	28·1	28·7	29·4
250									25·8	26·3	26·8	27·4	28·0	28·6
300									25·4	25·9	26·4	26·9	27·4	28·0
350									25·1	25·6	26·1	26·6	27·0	27·5
400									24·8	25·3	25·8	26·3	26·7	27·2
500									24·4	24·9	25·4	25·9	26·3	26·8
600									24·1	24·6	25·1	25·6	26·0	26·5

SPECIFIC HEAT AT CONSTANT PRESSURE, CALORIES/MOLE, °K—*cont.*

						Temperature °K								Pressure atm
370	380	390	400	420	440	460	480	500	520	540	560	580	600	
20·9	21·4	21·9	22·4	23·4	24·4	25·4	26·3	27·2	28·1	28·8	29·5	30·1	30·7	0·1
21·0	21·5	22·0	22·5	23·4	24·4	25·4	26·3	27·2	28·1	28·8	29·5	30·1	30·7	0·5
21·0	21·5	22·0	22·5	23·5	24·5	25·5	26·4	27·2	28·1	28·8	29·5	30·1	30·7	1
21·1	21·6	22·1	22·6	23·6	24·5	25·5	26·4	27·3	28·2	28·9	29·6	30·1	30·7	2
21·2	21·7	22·2	22·7	23·7	24·6	25·6	26·5	27·3	28·2	28·9	29·6	30·2	30·8	3
21·3	21·8	22·3	22·8	23·8	24·6	25·6	26·5	27·4	28·3	28·9	29·6	30·2	30·8	4
21·5	21·9	22·3	22·8	23·8	24·7	25·7	26·6	27·4	28·3	28·9	29·6	30·2	30·8	5
21·6	22·0	22·4	22·9	23·9	24·8	25·7	26·6	27·4	28·3	29·0	29·7	30·2	30·8	6
21·7	22·1	22·5	23·0	23·9	24·8	25·8	26·7	27·5	28·4	29·0	29·7	30·2	30·8	7
21·8	22·2	22·6	23·1	24·0	24·9	25·8	26·7	27·5	28·4	29·0	29·7	30·3	30·9	8
21·9	22·3	22·7	23·2	24·0	24·9	25·9	26·8	27·6	28·5	29·1	29·8	30·3	30·9	9
22·0	22·4	22·8	23·2	24·1	25·0	25·9	26·8	27·6	28·5	29·1	29·8	30·3	30·9	10
22·7	23·0	23·3	23·7	24·5	25·3	26·1	27·0	27·8	28·6	29·3	29·9	30·4	31·0	15
23·9	23·9	24·0	24·2	24·9	25·6	26·4	27·2	28·0	28·8	29·4	30·0	30·5	31·1	20
26·0	25·2	25·0	24·9	25·4	26·0	26·8	27·5	28·2	28·9	29·5	30·2	30·6	31·2	25
30·3	27·1	26·4	25·9	26·1	26·6	27·2	27·8	28·4	29·1	29·7	30·3	30·7	31·3	30
38·2	30·2	28·3	27·4	27·0	27·3	27·7	28·2	28·7	29·3	29·9	30·4	30·8	31·4	35
64·4	40·0	31·8	29·7	28·3	28·1	28·2	28·5	29·0	29·5	30·1	30·6	31·0	31·5	40
—	—	—	—	32·5	29·9	29·4	29·3	29·6	30·0	30·5	30·9	31·3	31·7	50
—	—	—	—	37·2	32·1	30·8	30·4	30·4	30·6	30·9	31·2	31·5	31·9	60
42·2	57·0	51·9	—	—	34·9	32·4	31·8	31·5	31·5	31·5	31·7	31·9	32·1	70
38·0	40·6	43·6	—	—	—	34·3	33·5	32·8	32·6	32·4	32·3	32·3	32·4	80
36·3	38·2	40·3	—	—	—	36·5	35·4	34·3	33·5	33·1	32·8	32·7	32·7	90
35·2	36·7	38·3	39·9	41·3	40·6	38·6	36·8	35·4	34·3	33·7	33·3	33·1	33·1	100
31·5	32·3	33·1	33·9	35·4	36·5	37·2	37·4	37·0	36·2	35·6	35·1	34·9	34·8	150
30·1	30·7	31·3	31·9	33·0	34·1	35·0	35·7	36·0	36·0	35·9	35·6	35·4	35·2	200
29·2	29·7	30·2	30·7	31·7	32·6	33·5	34·3	34·9	35·2	35·1	34·8	34·6	34·5	250
28·5	28·9	29·4	29·9	30·8	31·7	32·6	33·5	34·2						300
28·0	28·4	28·9	29·4	30·3	31·2	32·1	32·9	33·7						350
27·7	28·1	28·6	29·1	30·0	30·9	31·8	32·6	33·3						400
27·3	27·7	28·2	28·7	29·6	30·5	31·4	32·2	32·9						500
27·0	27·4	27·9	28·4	29·3	30·2	31·1	31·9	32·6						600

135

PROPANE

VOLUME, CUBIC CENTIMETRES/MOLE

Pressure atm	Temperature °K							
	230	240	250	260	270	280	290	300
0·1	188,200	196,400	204,700	212,900	221,100	229,400	237,600	245,800
0·5	37,130	38,830	40,520	42,200	43,870	45,540	47,210	48,870
1	75·5	19,090	19,970	20,840	21,710	22,570	23,420	24,260
2	75·5	77·1	9,670	10,150	10,610	11,060	11,500	11,940
3	75·5	77·0	78·7	6,538	6,875	7,199	7,512	7,819
4	75·4	77·0	78·6	80·4	5,008	5,264	5,511	5,752
5	75·4	76·9	78·6	80·4	82·3	4,103	4,311	4,513
6	75·4	76·9	78·5	80·3	82·3	84·5	3,508	3,685
7	75·3	76·9	78·5	80·3	82·2	84·5	2,928	3,086
8	75·3	76·8	78·4	80·2	82·2	84·4	87·0	2,635
9	75·3	76·8	78·4	80·2	82·2	84·4	86·9	2,281
10	75·2	76·8	78·4	80·1	82·1	84·3	86·8	89·8
15	75·1	76·6	78·2	79·9	81·8	84·0	86·5	89·4
20	74·9	76·4	78·0	79·7	81·5	83·8	86·2	89·1
25	74·8	76·3	77·9	79·6	81·4	83·5	85·9	88·7
30	74·7	76·1	77·7	79·4	81·2	83·3	85·7	88·4
35	74·6	76·0	77·6	79·2	81·0	83·1	85·5	88·2
40	74·4	75·9	77·4	79·1	80·9	83·0	85·3	87·9
50	74·3	75·7	77·2	78·8	80·5	82·5	84·8	87·4
60	74·1	75·5	77·0	78·6	80·3	82·2	84·4	86·9
70						81·8	84·0	86·4
80						81·5	83·7	86·1
90						81·2	83·3	85·6
100						81·0	83·0	85·3
150						80·0	81·8	83·8
200						79·2	80·9	82·6
250								
300								
350								
400								
500								
600								

VOLUME, CUBIC CENTIMETRES/MOLE—*cont.*

Temperature °K							Pressure atm
310	320	330	340	350	360	370	
254,000	262,300	270,500	278,700	286,900	295,100	303,400	0·1
50,530	52,200	53,860	55,510	57,170	58,820	60,480	0·5
25,100	25,940	26,770	27,610	28,450	29,280	30,110	1
12,370	12,800	13,230	13,660	14,080	14,510	14,930	2
8,121	8,418	8,712	9,004	9,295	9,584	9,872	3
5,989	6,221	6,449	6,675	6,899	7,120	7,339	4
4,710	4,902	5,090	5,276	5,460	5,641	5,820	5
3,855	4,021	4,183	4,342	4,498	4,653	4,806	6
3,239	3,388	3,532	3,673	3,812	3,949	4,083	7
2,776	2,912	3,043	3,171	3,296	3,418	3,538	8
2,414	2,541	2,663	2,780	2,893	3,004	3,113	9
2,121	2,241	2,355	2,464	2,570	2,673	2,774	10
92·8	1,328	1,422	1,510	1,594	1,674	1,750	15
92·3	96·3	101·2	1,014	1,093	1,165	1,232	20
91·9	95·7	100·4	106·4	777·6	849·8	914·4	25
91·6	95·3	99·7	105·4	114·1	624·0	694·0	30
91·3	94·8	99·0	104·3	111·9	427·4	523·6	35
90·9	94·4	98·5	103·5	110·3	122·4	361·0 ⊙	40
90·3	93·6	97·4	102·0	107·7	115·4	129·6	50
89·7	92·9	96·5	100·7	105·7	112·0	121·6	60
89·1	92·2	95·6	99·5	104·0	109·7	116·5	70
88·7	91·6	94·8	98·4	102·6	107·5	113·3	80
88·2	91·0	94·0	97·4	101·3	105·9	111·3	90
87·8	90·5	93·4	96·6	100·2	104·3	109·0	100
85·9	88·1	90·5	93·1	95·9	98·9	102·1	150
84·4	86·3	88·3	90·4	92·7	95·1	97·6	200
83·2	84·9	86·7	88·5	90·4	92·4	94·5	250
82·1	83·6	85·2	86·9	88·6	90·4	92·3	300
81·1	82·5	84·0	85·5	87·1	88·8	90·5	350
80·2	81·5	82·9	84·3	85·8	87·3	88·8	400
78·7	79·9	81·1	82·3	83·6	84·9	86·3	500
77·4	78·4	79·5	80·6	81·7	82·9	84·2	600

VOLUME, CUBIC CENTIMETRES/MOLE—*cont.*

Pressure atm	Temperature °K						
	380	390	400	420	440	460	480
0·1	311,600	319,800	328,000	344,400	360·900	377,300	393,700
0·5	62,130	63,780	65,430	68,740	72,040	75,340	78,630
1	30,950	31,780	32,610	34,270	35,930	37,590	39,250
2	15,360	15,780	16,200	17,040	17,880	18,720	19,550
3	10,160	10,450	10,730	11,300	11,860	12,430	12,990
4	7,558	7,776	7,992	8,424	8,853	9,280	9,705
5	5,998	6,175	6,351	6,700	7,047	7,393	7,738
6	4,958	5,108	5,256	5,551	5,844	6,135	6,425
7	4,214	4,344	4,473	4,730	4,984	5,236	5,487
8	3,657	3,773	3,887	4,114	4,339	4,562	4,784
9	3,221	3,327	3,430	3,635	3,837	4,037	4,236
10	2,873	2,970	3,064	3,251	3,436	3,619	3,800
15	1,824	1,896	1,966	2,099	2,230	2,359	2,486
20	1,296	1,357	1,416	1,524	1,628	1,730	1,830
25	973·9	1,029	1,081	1,176	1,266	1,352	1,436
30	754·4	807·8	857·1	944·7	1,025	1,101	1,174
35	590·9	645·9	693·8	776·5	851·0	920·0	986·0
40	457·1	518·2	568·0	649·0	721·3	785·1	845·7
50	177·8	329·0	383·1	470·0	538·3	596·4	650·4
60	140·3	190·3	248·2	348·0	415·0	470·7	520·3
70	128·0	146·7	176·9	261·6	328·4	382·8	428·5
80	122·0	134·5	150·5	205·5	266·9	316·6	359·5
90	117·8	125·8	138·7	172·9	219·6	268·7	308·5
100	114·6	121·4	130·1	156·6	194·2	233·3	269·8
150	105·6	109·4	113·8	124·8	139·0	156·1	175·1
200	100·2	102·9	105·9	113·4	122·4	132·7	143·8
250	96·7	99·0	101·4	107·0	113·6	121·1	129·3
300	94·3	96·4	98·6	103·3	108·6	114·3	120·3
350	92·3	94·2	96·1	100·2	104·6	109·3	114·2
400	90·4	92·2	94·0	97·6	101·4	105·4	109·6
500	87·7	89·1	90·5	93·4	96·5	99·8	103·2
600	85·4	86·7	87·9	90·4	93·0	95·7	98·6

VOLUME, CUBIC CENTIMETRES/MOLE—*cont.*

Temperature °K						Pressure atm
500	520	540	560	580	600	
410,200	426,600	443,000	459,400	475,800	492,300	0·1
81,930	85,230	88,520	91,810	95,100	98,380	0·5
40,910	42,560	44,210	45,860	47,500	49,150	1
20,390	21,230	22,060	22,890	23,710	24,540	2
13,550	14,110	14,670	15,230	15,780	16,330	3
10,130	10,560	10,980	11,400	11,810	12,230	4
8,081	8,423	8,763	9,100	9,435	9,768	5
6,713	7,000	7,285	7,568	7,849	8,128	6
5,736	5,984	6,230	6,474	6,716	6,956	7
5,004	5,223	5,440	5,655	5,867	6,077	8
4,434	4,630	4,824	5,016	5,206	5,393	9
3,979	4,156	4,331	4,504	4,675	4,845	10
2,611	2,734	2,855	2,974	3,091	3,206	15
1,928	2,024	2,118	2,210	2,299	2,387	20
1,518	1,598	1,676	1,751	1,824	1,895	25
1,245	1,314	1,381	1,445	1,507	1,568	30
1,050	1,111	1,169	1,225	1,280	1,334	35
903·7	959·6	1,013	1,063	1,112	1,159	40
700·8	748·1	792·8	835·3	876·1	915·5	50
565·6	607·7	647·1	684·3	719·7	753·6	60
469·9	508·0	543·6	577·1	608·8	639·0	70
398·2	433·8	466·9	497·7	526·5	553·8	80
344·2	377·2	407·9	436·6	463·4	488·4	90
303·0	333·7	362·2	388·8	413·7	436·9	100
194·7	214·4	233·8	252·9	271·8	290·5	150
155·7	168·3	181·6	195·6	209·8	224·1	200
137·9	146·9	156·2	165·7	175·4	185·4	250
126·7						300
119·4						350
114·1						400
106·6						500
101·5						600

PROPANE

ENTROPY, CALORIES/MOLE, °K

Pressure atm	Temperature °K												
	230	240	250	260	270	280	290	300	310	320	330	340	350
0·1	64·86	65·48	66·09	66·70	67·30	67·89	68·48	69·06	69·64	70·22	70·79	71·37	71·94
0·5	61·63	62·25	62·86	63·47	64·07	64·66	65·25	65·83	66·41	66·99	67·57	68·15	68·72
1	40·72	60·80	61·42	62·04	62·65	63·25	63·84	64·43	65·01	65·59	66·17	66·75	67·32
2	40·71	41·71	59·87	60·51	61·14	61·76	62·37	62·97	63·56	64·15	64·74	65·32	65·90
3	40·71	41·71	42·67	59·55	60·21	60·85	61·48	62·09	62·69	63·29	63·88	64·47	65·05
4	40·70	41·70	42·67	43·61	59·49	60·17	60·82	61·44	62·05	62·66	63·26	63·85	64·44
5	40·70	41·70	42·67	43·61	44·53	59·60	60·28	60·92	61·54	62·15	62·76	63·36	63·95
6	40·70	41·70	42·67	43·61	44·53	45·43	59·51	60·49	61·13	61·75	62·36	62·96	63·56
7	40·69	41·69	42·66	43·60	44·52	45·42	59·34	60·06	60·72	61·36	61·98	62·59	63·20
8	40·69	41·69	42·66	43·60	44·52	45·42	46·34	59·67	60·36	61·02	61·66	62·28	63·89
9	40·69	41·69	42·66	43·60	44·51	45·41	46·33	59·30	60·03	60·71	61·36	61·99	62·61
10	40·69	41·69	42·66	43·60	44·51	45·41	46·33	47·26	59·74	60·45	61·11	61·74	62·30
15	40·68	41·68	42·65	43·58	44·49	45·38	46·29	47·22	48·17	59·01	59·90	60·64	61·33
20	40·66	41·66	42·63	43·56	44·46	45·35	46·26	47·18	48·12	49·08	50·07	59·61	60·41
25	40·65	41·65	42·62	43·54	44·44	45·32	46·22	47·13	48·06	49·01	49·99	51·05	59·46
30	40·63	41·63	42·60	43·52	44·41	45·29	46·18	47·09	48·01	48·95	49·92	50·96	52·13
35	40·61	41·61	42·58	43·50	44·38	45·25	46·14	47·05	47·97	48·90	49·86	50·88	52·02
40	40·60	41·60	42·56	43·47	44·35	45·22	46·11	47·01	47·92	48·85	49·81	50·82	51·92
50	40·57	41·56	42·51	43·42	44·30	45·17	46·05	46·94	47·84	48·76	49·71	50·70	51·74
60	40·54	41·53	42·47	43·38	44·26	45·12	45·99	46·87	47·76	48·67	49·60	50·56	51·57
70						45·08	45·94	46·82	47·71	48·61	49·53	50·47	51·45
80						45·03	45·89	46·76	47·64	48·54	49·45	50·38	51·34
90						44·98	45·84	46·70	47·57	48·46	49·37	50·29	51·27
100						44·93	45·79	46·65	47·52	48·40	49·29	50·19	51·10
150						44·69	45·55	46·41	47·27	48·13	48·99	49·84	50·70
200						44·52	45·37	46·22	47·07	47·91	48·75	49·59	50·42
250									46·92	47·75	48·57	49·39	50·28
300									46·78	47·60	48·41	49·21	50·01
350									46·65	47·46	48·26	49·05	49·85
400									46·52	47·31	48·10	48·88	49·63
500									46·27	47·05	47·83	48·59	49·35
600									46·03	46·80	47·57	48·33	49·00

ENTROPY, CALORIES/MOLE, °K—cont.

Temperature °K													Pressure atm
380	390	400	420	440	460	480	500	520	540	560	580	600	
73·63	74·20	74·76	75·88	76·99	78·10	79·20	80·29	81·37	82·44	83·50	84·55	85·60	0·1
70·42	70·99	71·55	72·67	73·78	74·89	75·99	77·08	78·16	79·23	80·29	81·35	82·40	0·5
69·03	69·60	70·16	61·28	72·39	73·50	74·60	75·69	76·77	77·84	78·90	79·96	81·01	1
67·62	68·19	68·76	69·88	71·00	72·11	73·21	74·30	75·38	76·45	77·52	78·58	79·63	2
66·78	67·35	67·92	69·05	70·17	71·28	72·38	73·47	74·55	75·62	76·69	77·75	78·80	3
66·18	66·75	67·32	68·45	69·57	70·68	71·78	72·87	73·95	75·03	76·10	77·16	78·21	4
65·70	66·28	66·85	67·99	69·11	70·22	71·32	72·41	73·50	74·68	75·65	76·71	77·76	5
65·32	65·90	66·47	67·61	68·74	69·85	70·95	72·04	73·13	74·21	75·28	76·34	77·39	6
64·98	65·56	66·14	67·28	68·41	69·53	70·63	71·72	72·81	73·89	74·96	76·02	77·08	7
64·68	65·27	65·85	66·99	68·12	69·24	70·35	71·44	72·53	73·61	74·68	75·74	76·80	8
64·42	65·01	65·59	66·74	67·87	68·99	70·10	71·20	72·29	73·37	74·44	75·50	76·56	9
64·17	64·76	65·34	66·49	67·63	68·75	69·86	70·96	72·05	73·13	74·20	75·27	76·33	10
63·19	63·79	64·38	65·56	66·72	67·86	68·98	70·09	71·19	72·28	73·36	74·43	75·49	15
62·41	63·03	63·64	64·84	66·02	67·18	68·32	69·44	70·55	71·64	72·72	73·79	74·85	20
61·72	62·38	63·02	64·26	65·46	66·63	67·78	68·91	70·03	71·13	72·21	73·28	74·34	25
61·07	61·77	62·44	63·72	64·95	66·15	67·32	68·47	69·60	70·71	71·80	72·87	73·93	30
60·43	61·20	61·90	63·24	64·50	65·72	66·91	68·07	69·21	70·33	71·42	72·49	73·55	35
59·67	60·59	61·37	62·77	64·08	65·33	66·54	67·72	68·87	69·99	71·09	72·17	73·23	40
56·98	58·92	60·18	61·87	63·28	64·59	65·85	67·07	68·25	69·39	70·50	71·59	72·66	50
55·34	57·14	58·76	61·00	62·60	63·99	65·29	66·53	67·73	68·89	70·02	71·12	72·20	60
54·77	56·07	57·54	60·07	61·88	63·35	64·72	66·02	67·26	68·45	69·60	70·72	71·81	70
54·38	55·47	56·61	59·06	61·14	62·71	64·16	65·52	66·80	68·02	69·19	70·33	71·43	80
54·15	55·16	56·19	58·29	60·36	62·16	63·71	65·09	66·39	67·63	68·82	69·97	71·09	90
53·93	54·91	55·90	57·89	59·80	61·56	63·17	64·65	66·02	67·30	68·51	69·67	70·79	100
53·25	54·10	54·95	56·64	58·32	59·96	61·55	63·07	64·50	65·85	67·14	68·37	69·55	150
52·86	53·67	54·47	56·05	57·62	59·16	60·66	62·12	63·53	64·88	66·18	67·43	68·63	200
52·59	53·37	54·14	55·66	57·16	58·63	60·07	61·48	62·86	64·19	65·47	66·70	67·87	250
52·35	53·11	53·86	55·34	56·80	58·23	59·64	61·02						300
52·12	52·87	53·61	55·07	56·50	57·91	59·30	60·67						350
51·91	52·65	53·38	54·82	56·24	57·63	59·00	60·35						400
51·57	52·30	53·02	54·44	55·83	57·20	58·55	59·88						500
51·27	51·99	52·70	54·11	55·49	56·85	58·19	59·51						600

PROPANE

ENTHALPY, CALORIES/MOLE

Pressure atm	Temperature °K									
	230	240	250	260	270	280	290	300	310	320
0·1	8,965	9,106	9,252	9,403	9,558	9,721	9,889	10,060	10,237	10,418
0·5	8,940	9,084	9,233	9,387	9,544	9,708	9,876	10,048	10,226	10,408
1	4,412	9,057	9,209	9,366	9,526	9,692	9,861	10,034	10,213	10,396
2	4,413	4,648	9,160	9,322	9,487	9,657	9,829	10,005	10,186	10,371
3	4,414	4,649	4,888	9,274	9,444	9,619	9,795	9,974	10,158	10,345
4	4,415	4,650	4,889	5,130	9,393	9,576	9,758	9,941	10,129	10,319
5	4,416	4,651	4,890	5,131	5,376	9,526	9,718	9,906	10,099	10,292
6	4,417	4,652	4,891	5,132	5,377	5,626	9,673	9,868	10,067	10,264
7	4,418	4,653	4,892	5,133	5,378	5,627	9,616	9,826	10,031	10,233
8	4,419	4,654	4,893	5,134	5,379	5,627	5,886	9,778	9,991	10,200
9	4,420	4,655	4,894	5,135	5,380	5,628	5,887	9,722	9,947	10,164
10	4,421	4,656	4,895	5,136	5,380	5,629	5,887	6,156	9,898	10,126
15	4,426	4,661	4,899	5,140	5,384	5,632	5,888	6,155	6,437	9,875
20	4,431	4,666	4,904	5,144	5,388	5,635	5,889	6,154	6,435	6,734
25	4,436	4,671	4,908	5,149	5,392	5,638	5,890	6,154	6,433	6,730
30	4,441	4,676	4,913	5,153	5,396	5,641	5,892	6,154	6,432	6,727
35	4,446	4,681	4,918	5,157	5,399	5,644	5,894	6,155	6,431	6,724
40	4,452	4,686	4,923	5,162	5,403	5,647	5,896	6,156	6,430	6,721
50	4,463	4,697	4,933	5,171	5,411	5,652	5,900	6,158	6,429	6,716
60	4,474	4,708	4,943	5,180	5,418	5,657	5,904	6,161	6,430	6,713
70						5,662	5,908	6,164	6,431	6,711
80						5,667	5,912	6,167	6,432	6,710
90						5,672	5,916	6,169	6,433	6,710
100						5,677	5,920	6,172	6,435	6,711
150						5,702	5,944	6,196	6,458	6,729
200						5,756	5,997	6,246	6,504	6,770
250									6,553	6,817
300									6,615	6,873
350									6,671	6,925
400									6,730	6,982
500									6,849	7,096
600									6,970	7,213

ENTHALPY, CALORIES/MOLE—*cont.*

Temperature °K									Pressure atm
330	340	350	360	370	380	390	400	420	
10,604	10,796	10,993	11,196	11,403	11,615	11,832	12,054	12,513	0·1
10,595	10,788	10,985	11,188	11,395	11,607	11,825	12,047	12,507	0·5
10,584	10,778	10,975	11,178	11,386	11,599	11,817	12,039	12,500	1
10,560	10,756	10,955	11,159	11,368	11,582	11,800	12,023	12,486	2
10,537	10,734	10,934	11,140	11,350	11,565	11,783	12,007	12,471	3
10,513	10,712	10,914	11,120	11,331	11,547	11,766	11,990	12,456	4
10,490	10,690	10,893	11,100	11,312	11,529	11,749	11,974	12,441	5
10,465	10,667	10,872	11,081	11,293	11,511	11,732	11,958	12,426	6
10,438	10,643	10,851	11,061	11,274	11,493	11,715	11,942	12,411	7
10,410	10,619	10,829	11,041	11,255	11,475	11,698	11,926	12,396	8
10,380	10,594	10,808	11,021	11,236	11,457	11,681	11,910	12,381	9
10,349	10,569	10,786	11,000	11,217	11,439	11,664	11,893	12,366	10
10,168	10,425	10,659	10,887	11,113	11,342	11,575	11,808	12,289	15
7,059	10,240	10,515	10,764	11,001	11,239	11,478	11,718	12,208	20
7,051	7,410	10,280	10,595	10,870	11,122	11,370	11,618	12,121	25
7,044	7,396	7,802	10,360	10,707	10,982	11,246	11,505	12,027	30
7,038	7,384	7,776	9,925	10,480	10,809	11,098	11,378	11,925	35
7,032	7,374	7,753	8,192	10,062	10,590	10,910	11,236	11,814	40
7,021	7,354	7,714	8,118	8,660	9,600	10,365	10,860	11,568	50
7,013	7,335	7,684	8,067	8,512	9,030	9,726	10,370	11,292	60
7,007	7,322	7,660	8,026	8,431	8,881	9,382	9,945	10,980	70
7,004	7,315	7,644	7,992	8,362	8,755	9,175	9,626	10,628	80
7,001	7,307	7,629	7,967	8,322	8,696	9,090	9,504	10,375	90
7,000	7,302	7,618	7,948	8,293	8,652	9,027	9,417	10,234	100
7,009	7,297	7,593	7,896	8,207	8,525	8,851	9,186	9,881	150
7,043	7,322	7,608	7,900	8,198	8,502	8,812	9,128	9,777	200
7,086	7,360	7,640	7,925	8,215	8,510	8,810	9,115	9,738	250
7,136	7,405	7,679	7,957	8,240	8,528	8,821	9,119	9,728	300
7,185	7,450	7,720	7,994	8,273	8,556	8,844	9,136	9,735	350
7,239	7,500	7,766	8,036	8,311	8,590	8,874	9,162	9,752	400
7,347	7,603	7,864	8,130	8,400	8,675	8,954	9,238	9,820	500
7,461	7,714	7,972	8,234	8,501	8,772	9,048	9,329	9,906	600

PROPANE

ENTHALPY, CALORIES/MOLE—*cont.*

Pressure atm	Temperature °K								
	440	460	480	500	520	540	560	580	600
0·1	12,992	13,490	14,008	14,545	15,099	15,667	16,250	16,847	17,455
0·5	12,987	13,486	14,003	14,540	15,095	15,664	16,247	16,844	17,452
1	12,980	13,480	13,997	14,534	15,089	15,659	16,242	16,839	17,448
2	12,967	13,468	13,986	14,524	15,079	15,650	16,234	16,831	17,440
3	12,954	13,456	13,974	14,513	15,069	15,641	16,226	16,823	17,433
4	12,940	13,443	13,963	14,503	15,059	15,632	16,217	16,815	17,425
5	12,926	13,430	13,951	14,492	15·049	15,622	16,208	16,807	17,417
6	12,912	13,418	13,939	14,481	15,039	15,613	16,199	16,798	17,409
7	12,898	13,405	13,928	14,470	15,029	15,603	16,190	16,790	17,401
8	12,884	13,392	13,916	14,459	15,019	15,594	16,181	16,782	17,393
9	12,870	13,379	13,904	14,448	15,009	15,584	16,173	16,773	17,385
10	12,856	13,366	13,892	14,437	14,998	15,575	16,164	16,765	17,378
15	12,786	13,300	13,831	14,380	14,946	15,526	16,118	16,723	17,338
20	12,713	13,233	13,769	14,322	14,893	15,476	16,072	16,680	17,298
25	12,637	13,165	13,706	14,264	14,840	15,427	16,026	16,636	17,258
30	12,556	13,094	13,642	14,206	14,786	15,377	15,979	16,593	17,217
35	12,470	13,019	13,576	14,147	14,732	15,327	15,932	16,549	17,176
40	12,379	12,941	13,508	14,087	14,677	15,277	15,885	16,505	17,135
50	12,184	12,777	13,366	13,962	14,565	15,174	15,791	16,417	17,053
60	11,978	12,607	13,219	13,833	14,450	15,072	15,698	16,331	16,974
70	11,758	12,427	13,067	13,704	14,338	14,974	15,611	16,252	16,899
80	11,518	12,233	12,911	13,576	14,231	14,880	15,527	16,176	16,827
90	11,235	12,027	12,755	13,452	14,127	14,790	15,445	16,101	16,757
100	11,056	11,847	12,606	13,332	14,027	14,702	15,365	16,027	16,690
150	10,602	11,340	12,087	12,831	13,563	14,280	14,987	15,686	16,382
200	10,448	11,139	11,845	12,561	13,281	14,004	14,720	15,430	16,137
250	10,382	11,043	11,721	12,413	13,115	13,821	14,526	15,225	15,918
300	10,355	10,999	11,660	12,336					
350	10,352	10,986	11,636	12,302					
400	10,362	10,989	11,633	12,294					
500	10,420	11,038	11,674	12,327					
600	10,500	11,113	11,743	12,391					

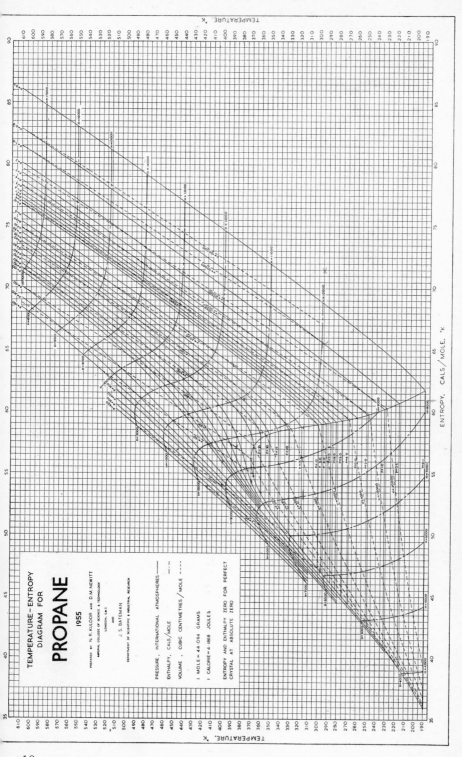

TEMPERATURE - ENTROPY
DIAGRAM FOR

PROPANE

1955

PREPARED BY N. R. KULOOR AND D. M. NEWITT

IMPERIAL COLLEGE OF SCIENCE & TECHNOLOGY
LONDON, S.W.7.

AND

J. S. BATEMAN

DEPARTMENT OF SCIENTIFIC & INDUSTRIAL RESEARCH

PRESSURE , INTERNATIONAL ATMOSPHERES ————
ENTHALPY, CALS / MOLE   — · —
VOLUME , CUBIC CENTIMETRES / MOLE - - - -

1 MOLE = 44·094 GRAMS
1 CALORIE = 4·1868 JOULES

ENTROPY AND ENTHALPY ZERO FOR PERFECT
CRYSTAL AT ABSOLUTE ZERO

TEMPERATURE, °K.

ENTROPY, CALS / MOLE, °K.

ARGON

F. DIN

The British Oxygen Company Limited,
Research and Development Centre, London

SINCE its discovery by RAMSAY at the end of the nineteenth century the physical properties of argon have been extensively studied. Being, in Europe at least, the most readily available of the monatomic inert gases, it has been one of the more convenient materials available for studies in the realm of molecular and atomic physics. At the present time, therefore, there is available a remarkable amount of excellent data for this gas but until comparatively recently these data were mainly of academic interest. In these circumstances it is not surprising that, as far as the present author is aware, there has been no previous correlation of thermodynamic properties in the form of a diagram or tables. In recent years there has been a marked increase in the industrial use of argon and it is certain that this increase will continue. Since this work began MICHELS and his co-workers[1] have published a computation with a skeleton diagram of the thermodynamic functions of argon based on their own *P-V-T* measurements, but these will hardly suffice for the air separation industry where argon separation is becoming an increasingly pressing problem.

SURVEY OF EXISTING DATA

1. The Density of the Gas at N.T.P.

The Landolt–Bornstein tables give the values in Table 1 for the density of argon at N.T.P.

The first five have been adjusted by Landolt–Bornstein to be on a strictly comparable basis. The more recent value of BAXTER and STARKWEATHER[2] is the basis for the internationally accepted atomic weight of argon, 39·944. It agrees to 1 part in 10,000 with the earlier value of SCHULTZE[6], the only one previously given to six significant figures, and in these circumstances it has been used for the present work. It should be noted that the standard atmosphere pressure used by Baxter and Starkweather was not the international atmosphere, $g = 980·665$, but the latitude 45° atmosphere, $g = 980·616$.

F. DIN

TABLE 1

DENSITY OF GASEOUS ARGON AT N.T.P.

Density g/litre	Observer
1·7809	Watson[7] (1910)
1·78375	Schultze[6] (1915)
1·7816	Fischer and Froboese[3] (1911)
1·7823	Leduc[5] (1918)
1·7834	Holst and Hamburger[4] (1915)
1·78394	Baxter and Starkweather[2] (1928–9)

2. The Compressibility Data

The compressibility of argon has been measured by ONNES and CROMMELIN[15] at Leiden, by HOLBORN and his co-workers[9, 10] at the Reichsanstalt, by MASSON and his co-workers[12, 13], by MICHELS and his co-workers[14] at the Van der Waals Laboratory and finally by BRIDGMAN[8]. Landolt–Bornstein also presents two otherwise unpublished isotherms at 0° C and 100° C by OTTO, presumably carried out at the Reichsanstalt, which are of interest in that the pressure range is increased beyond the usual 100 atm for Reichsanstalt data up to 200 atm. The work at Leiden was carried out at room temperature and downwards to − 150° C. The maximum pressure attained was about 60 atm and at the low temperatures very much less, being only 13 atm at − 150° C. The only other comparable data below 0° C are two isotherms from the Reichsanstalt at − 50° C and − 100° C, again at pressures only up to 80 atm and 60 atm respectively. Discrepancies between the Leiden and Reichsanstalt data have been recognized for some time and are attributed by Masson to a fault in the Leiden technique. The Reichsanstalt data cover a wide temperature range. The two isotherms at low temperature have been mentioned and at the other end of the range there are isotherms at 300° C and 400° C. The more recent Amsterdam results cover the usual extensive range, *i.e.* isotherms from 0° C to 150° C in 25° intervals and pressures up to nearly 3000 atm at 25° C and just over 2000 atm at 150° C.

The methods adopted by most of the above investigators call for no special comment; they are well known and have been frequently referred to. The results of Masson and his co-workers were obtained by the use of a refined form of Andrews' apparatus and are presented in terms of the three virial coefficients in the equation:

$$PV = A + BP + CP^2$$

The coefficients for temperatures from 25° C to 174° C are valid for pressures up to 125 atm.

147

The work of Bridgman comes into a special category, being concerned mainly with extremely high pressures, in some cases as high as 15,000 atm.   In Bridgman's method the gas was confined in a variable volume piezometer, the change in volume being indicated by the motion of a leak-proof piston, whilst the absolute values of volume were obtained in a specially calibrated fixed volume piezometer.   The pressures were measured with a manganin wire gauge.   At temperatures from − 90° C to − 150° C the emphasis is on the determination of the freezing curve, but at these temperatures a few values are reported, and at 0° C, 25° C and 55° C several values, for the volume of one gramme of argon.   At these extreme pressures Bridgman, quite rightly, does not distinguish between gaseous and liquid argon but speaks of amorphous argon as distinct from the crystalline solid frozen under pressure.   It should be noted that Bridgman does not claim better than 5 per cent accuracy and reproducibility, although when his results are compared, as far as possible, with those of Michels this would appear to be an underestimate of his own experimental skill.

Before leaving the compressibility data reference should be made to the work of van Itterbeek and van Paemel[11] who calculated the second virial coefficient from velocity of sound measurements at 1 atm using an acoustical interferometer and an ultrasonic quartz crystal. The Leiden and Reichsanstalt data at low temperatures were used in the calculations and van Itterbeek and van Paemel again noted the discrepancy already referred to.

3. The Specific Heats of Gaseous Argon

The specific heats of argon and the ratio γ can be very briefly described.   Being a monatomic gas, the specific heat at constant pressure at zero pressure is $\frac{5}{2}R$, R being the gas constant, and at constant volume $\frac{3}{2}R$, both values being independent of temperature.   The measurements of Heuse[18], Pier[21], Niemayer[20], Strieder[22], Eucken and von Lude[17], Leduc[19] and van Itterbeek and van Paemel[11] all confirm the above values at 1 atm pressure; such discrepancies as exist can be attributed to experimental error or gas imperfection, e.g. Heuse reports an increase in the values of C_p and γ at − 180° C over the values at 15° C.

At pressures above 1 atm there are some interesting results by Clark and Katz[16] who measured γ at 24·2° C and pressures up to 20 atm by a vibrating piston resonance method.   They report an increase in γ with pressure according to the formula:

$$\gamma = 1\cdot6667 + 0\cdot00353P$$

in which P is the pressure in atmospheres.

4. The Joule–Thomson Expansion

The Joule–Thomson expansion of argon has been determined by ROEBUCK and OSTERBERG[23] using the same apparatus as for the original work on air. The integral Joule–Thomson effect was measured, the highest initial pressure being 200 atm with initial temperatures ranging from 300° C to −150° C. Roebuck's results are very convenient to use for the construction of an enthalpy–temperature diagram, but all of the reported pressures have to be corrected[24] by multiplying by 0·9677. Similarly, the calculation of the volume from Roebuck's table of values for the Joule–Thomson coefficient involves applying the correction twice, both to the pressure and to the value of the coefficient.

5. The Vapour Pressure

The first measurement of the vapour pressure of argon which can be regarded as of other than historic interest is that of CROMMELIN[29]. Some of Crommelin's results were incidental to the measurement of the densities of the saturated liquid and vapour phases in equilibrium, but his final presentation covers the range from 67° K, where argon is solid, to the critical point at 150° K. A direct observation of the triple point is also included.

Holst and Hamburger[4] published a few values for the vapour pressure around 1 atm, including the triple point, as part of their work on the argon-nitrogen system. Next follows the work of BORN[25], which again is confined to pressures around 1 atm. Born criticized the purity of Crommelin's argon and went to extreme pains to purify his own; a point considered worthy of special comment by Landolt–Bornstein. All subsequent investigators, however, have failed to reproduce Born's results whilst obtaining substantial agreement amongst themselves and with the earlier work of Crommelin. BURBO and ISCHKIN[26], investigating the argon–oxygen system, report values for the vapour pressure slightly above 1 atm and, whilst claiming no great accuracy for their own work, they note the difference of their results from those of Born. More recently CLUSIUS and FRANK[28] have made meticulous observations of the triple point and normal boiling point of argon. They conclude, as a result of experiments carried out to test the point, that Born over-elaborated the purification of his argon and that in fact it was contaminated with no less than 3 per cent of oxygen at the finish.

Quite recently the vapour pressure of argon from the solid region to the critical point has been firmly established by the jointly published work of MICHELS, WASSENAAR and ZWIETERING and CLARK, DIN and ROBB[27]. These investigators show that the remaining discrepancies between their results are slight, and those of the last-mentioned three authors, which are given in Table 2, include triple point and normal

149

boiling point values in excellent agreement with those of Clusius and Frank, Table 2A.

TABLE 2

VAPOUR PRESSURE OF ARGON

(Clark, Din and Robb[27])

Temperature °K	Pressure mm Hg 0 °C	Temperature °K	Pressure atm
70	57·7	92	1·600
72	83·5	95	2·105
74	118·5	100	3·198
76	165·1	105	4·665
78	226·1	110	6·571
80	304·8	115	8·985
82	405·0	120	11·97
83·78 (T.P.)	515·7	125	15·61
86	661·4	130	19·98
87·29 (B.P.)	760·0	135	25·16
88	818·3	140	31·22
90	1002·5	145	38·26
		150·72 (C.P.)	48·00

TABLE 2A

TRIPLE POINT AND NORMAL BOILING POINT OF ARGON

Triple point		Boiling point	Observer
Temperature °K	Pressure mm Hg, 0° C	Temperature °K	
83·86	516·0	87·32	Crommelin [29]
83·90	521·4		Holst and Hamburger [4]
83·96	512·2	87·50	Born [25]
		87·22	Burbo and Ischkin [26]
83·78	516·8	87·29	Clusius and Frank [28]
83·78	515·7	87·29	Clark, Din and Robb [27]
		87·25	Michels, Wassenaar and Zwietering [27]

All values are adjusted to an ice-point of 273·16° K. The critical point value in Table 2 is that of Crommelin[29].

150

It should be mentioned, however, that there has been no direct observation of the critical point since that of Crommelin, *i.e.* 47·996 atm at −122·44° C.

6. The Density of the Saturated Liquid and Vapour

BALY and DONNAN[30] measured the density of saturated liquid argon in equilibrium with the vapour for the temperature range −189° C to −183° C. They obtained their argon from RAMSAY and TRAVERS and a gaseous density determination confirmed that it was quite pure. Their results are in slight disagreement with the later work of MATHIAS, CROMMELIN and ONNES[31], *Figure 1* and Table 3, carried out by means of the standard Leiden dilatometer.

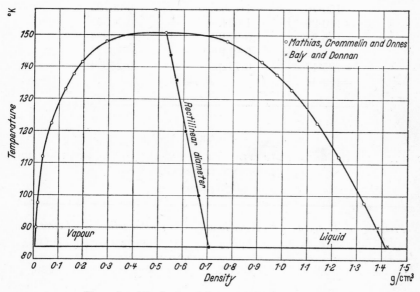

Figure 1.   The density of the saturated liquid and vapour

7. The Freezing and Melting Curves and the Density of the Solid

Considering the rather difficult experimental technique involved in the determination of the course of the freezing and melting curves, it is surprising that no less than three independent investigations on this subject have been undertaken. The work of BRIDGMAN[8], whose results are given in Table 4, has already been mentioned. His values for the melting point under pressure are about 1° higher than the earlier values of SIMON, RUHEMANN and EDWARDS[34] and he attributes the discrepancy to the influence of shear force on the melting point in the blocked tube method used by them. After Bridgman, CLUSIUS and WEIGAND[32] determined the freezing curve by a very elegant method, cooling the liquid under constant pressure in a copper bomb and noting the constancy of the temperature when freezing set in.

TABLE 3

DENSITY OF THE SATURATED LIQUID AND VAPOUR IN EQUILIBRIUM
(Mathias, Crommelin and Onnes[31])

$t\,°C$	Density of liquid g/cm^3	Density of vapour g/cm^3
$-183\cdot15$	$1\cdot37396$	$0\cdot00801$
$-175\cdot39$	$1\cdot32482$	$0\cdot01457$
$-161\cdot23$	$1\cdot22414$	$0\cdot03723$
$-150\cdot76$	$1\cdot13851$	$0\cdot06785$
$-140\cdot20$	$1\cdot03456$	$0\cdot12552$
$-135\cdot51$	$0\cdot97385$	$0\cdot15994$
$-131\cdot54$	$0\cdot91499$	$0\cdot19432$
$-125\cdot17$	$0\cdot77289$	$0\cdot29534$
$-122\cdot44$	$0\cdot53078$ (C.P.)	

TABLE 4

MELTING POINTS, LATENT HEATS OF FUSION, VOLUMES OF THE FREEZING LIQUID
AND MELTING SOLID
(Bridgman[8])

Pressure kg/cm^2	Tempera- ture °K	Volume liquid cm^3/g	Volume solid cm^3/g	Latent heat kg–cm/g
1	$83\cdot9$	$0\cdot702$	$0\cdot622$	280
1000	$106\cdot4$			280
2000	$126\cdot3$	$0\cdot656$	$0\cdot613$	279
3000	$144\cdot9$			277
4000	$161\cdot9$	$0\cdot638$	$0\cdot610$	275
5000	$177\cdot8$			276
6000	$192\cdot9$	$0\cdot628$	$0\cdot607$	277

Clusius and Weigand report melting points for 50 atm increments of pressure up to 200 atm, Table 5, whilst Bridgman's results are reported for 1000 kg/cm^2 increments up to 6000 kg/cm^2. Because of the smaller intervals Clusius and Weigand claim greater accuracy for the derivative $\frac{dP}{dT}$ at the triple point. This derivative has been used by Bridgman to

152

calculate the latent heat from the volume change using the Clausius–Clapeyron equation and by Clusius to calculate the change in volume from his own measurements of the latent heat.

TABLE 5

MELTING POINTS

(Clusius and Weigand[32])

Tempera-ture °K	Pressure atm	Tempera-ture °K	Pressure atm
83·760	0	85·276	100
83·786	1	87·508	150
85·027	50	88·721	250

$$T = 83{\cdot}760 + 2{\cdot}552 \times 10^{-2}\,P - 3{\cdot}57 \times 10^{-6}\,P^2$$

The density of the solid has thus not been determined directly other than by Bridgman. In Table 6 the first three values have been calculated from X-ray crystallographic data, whilst those of Simon, Ruhemann and Edwards and of Clusius and Weigand have been computed with the aid of the Clausius–Clapeyron equation.

TABLE 6

DENSITY OF SOLID ARGON

Tempera-ture °K	Density g/cm³	Observer
0	1·809	Herz[33]
20	1·68	de Smedt and Keesom[36]
40	1·65	Simon and von Simson[35]
83·8 (T.P.)	1·59	Simon, Ruhemann and Edwards[34]
83·8	1·621	Clusius and Weigand[32]
83·8	1·608	Bridgman[8]

8. The Latent Heats

The experimental determinations of the latent heats of fusion and vaporization have been carried out at the triple point and normal boiling point by the schools of EUCKEN[39, 40] and of CLUSIUS[37, 38]. Their results are given in Table 7.

TABLE 7

LATENT HEATS

(f = fusion, v = vaporization)

Tempera- ture °K	Latent heat cal/mole		Observer
(T.P.)	268	f	Eucken[39]
(B.P.)	1501	v	Eucken and Hauck[40]
83·85*	280·8	f	Clusius[37]
(T.P.)			
87·29	1557·5 ± 1·5	v	Clusius and Frank[38]
(B.P.)			

*Clusius later revised this temperature to 83·78° K. See Table 2a.

At higher pressures Bridgman[8] has calculated the latent heat of fusion from the Clausius–Clapeyron equation as already mentioned, shown with the results in Table 4, whilst MATHIAS, CROMMELIN and ONNES[41] have similarly calculated the latent heat of vaporization from the densities of the liquid and vapour phases in equilibrium, Table 8.

TABLE 8

LATENT HEATS OF VAPORIZATION CALCULATED FROM THE CLAUSIUS–
CLAPEYRON EQUATION

(Mathias, Crommelin and Onnes[41])

t °C	Latent heat cal/g	t °C	Latent heat cal/g
− 125·17	10·50	− 150·76	29·62
− 131·54	18·53	− 161·23	33·02
− 135·51	21·74	− 175·39	36·50
− 140·20	24·73	− 183·15	38·15

Compare temperatures with those of Table 3.

These authors point out that the density of the vapour and the pressure are difficult to measure accurately at low temperatures so that the latent heats calculated in this region are consequently least accurate.

9. The Specific Heats of the Saturated Solid and Liquid

The specific heats for the solid and liquid in equilibrium with the saturated vapour arise also from the low temperature calorimetric measurements of Eucken[39, 40] and of Clusius[37, 38]. Where the work

TABLE 9

SPECIFIC HEATS OF THE SATURATED SOLID AND LIQUID

Temperature °K	C_p cal/mole, °K	C_v cal/mole, °K	C_σ cal/mole, °K	Observer
17·8	2·44	2·39		
24·9	3·73	3·56		
30·9	4·54	4·26		
41·25	5·58	4·97		
68·9	6·90	5·43		
78·3	7·80	5·66		Eucken [39]
		Solid		
84·9	10·50			
87·9		5·60		
89·3	10·52			
92·6		5·40		
93·9	10·62			
		Liquid		
90		5·50	10·55	
110		5·50	11·50	
130		4·90	12·80	
150		4·35		Eucken and
		Liquid		Hauck [40]
160		4·00		
170		3·75		
		Gas		
10·51	0·95	0·95		
17·57	2·37	2·34		
24·4	3·61			
32·4	4·64			
43·35	5·53			
70·9	7·04			
80·3	7·77			Clusius [37]
		Solid		
86·6			10·02	
86·9			10·06	
88·9			10·06	
		Liquid		

of these two schools covers the same temperature range appreciable discrepancies appear; Clusius remarks that the 1 per cent to 6 per cent difference in the results is difficult to account for. It is possible, however, that in the case of the earlier work of Eucken the appropriate corrections were not applied to the experimental data when calculating the final values of the specific heat at constant pressure C_p. At low temperatures C_p is virtually the same as C_σ, the specific heat under saturation conditions. In Table 9 typical values reported by these two schools are given.

10. The Velocity of Sound in Argon

The velocity of sound in gaseous argon has been determined by HEUSE[18], STRIEDER[46] and DIXON, CAMPBELL and PARKER[42], the latter at temperatures up to 1000° C, as a means of calculating γ, whilst van Itterbeek and van Paemel[11], as already mentioned, have measured the velocity at low temperatures as a means of calculating the second virial coefficient. LIEPMANN[45] has measured the velocity of sound in liquid argon and used the results with the specific heat data to calculate the compressibility. He notes that there is a 20 per cent discrepancy between the calculated and experimental values. More recently the velocity of sound in liquid argon has been measured by GALT[43] and by VAN ITTERBEEK and VERHAEGEN[44].

CALCULATION OF THE THERMODYNAMIC FUNCTIONS AND CONSTRUCTION OF THE THERMODYNAMIC DIAGRAM

11. Units, Constants and Conversion Factors

For the present work the chosen unit of pressure is the international atmosphere, $g = 980 \cdot 665$, and the unit of volume the cubic centimetre as distinct from the millilitre. An ice point on the Kelvin scale of $273 \cdot 15°$ has been taken, with one exception about to be mentioned, and for the unit of energy the absolute joule has been adopted. The vapour pressure data have been used exactly as reported by Clark, Din and Robb and in this case the ice point is $273 \cdot 16°$ K. It may be mentioned that as far as calculations involving both the saturated vapour and the superheated P-V-T data are concerned this 1 in 30,000 inconsistency has a quite negligible effect.

Baxter and Starkweather's value for the density of argon at 0° C and 1 atm, latitude 45° ($g = 980 \cdot 616$), namely $1 \cdot 78394$ g/litre, is the basis of the internationally accepted atomic weight of argon, $39 \cdot 944$. Converting to the present system this represents a molecular volume at N.T.P. of $22,390 \cdot 4$ cm^3/mole, the Amagat unit, or $560 \cdot 54$ cm^3/g. For an ideal gas the molecular volume per mole has been taken as $22,414 \cdot 6$ cm^3 (0° C, 1 int. atm, chemical scale $0 = 16$). The equation of state at 0° C and 1 atm was assumed to be of the form:

$$PV = RT(1 + BP)$$

and using the data for the true normal volume of argon and the ideal gas volume the value of R in Amagat unit–atm/degree was calculated to be 0·0036649. To convert from Amagat–atm to joules a multiplying factor of 2268·7 was used, based on 1 cm³-atm being equivalent to 0·101325 J.

12. Calculation of the Specific Heat at Constant Pressure, the Entropy and Enthalpy from the P-V-T data

To evaluate the thermodynamic functions in the homogeneous region the specific heat at constant pressure was first established from the P-V-T data.

The thermodynamic equation for calculating C_p from the P-V-T data is:

$$\Delta C_p \Bigg]_{P_1}^{P_2}\Bigg]_T = -T\int_{P_1}^{P_2}\frac{\partial^2 V}{\partial T^2}\Bigg)_P \mathrm{d}P\Bigg]_T = T\int_{P_1}^{P_2}\frac{\partial^2 r}{\partial T^2}\Bigg)_P \mathrm{d}P\Bigg]_T$$

where $r = \dfrac{RT}{P} - V$.

The graphical residual term, r, was worked out for every recorded observation of all the investigators mentioned in section 2. For this purpose the Reichsanstalt and the Bridgman data had to be converted to the Amagat system with pressure in atmospheres. In the case of Masson's data, values were worked out from the series equations. The values of r at points on the freezing line from Bridgman's data were included and also at points on the saturated vapour boundary from the data of Mathias, Crommelin and Onnes. The pressure in the later case was obtained from the vapour pressure data of Clark, Din and Robb, the two sets of data being correlated by constructing a smooth PV versus P curve for the saturated vapour.

The values of r were first plotted against the pressure as isotherms. The anomalous nature of the Leiden data in relation to the Reichsanstalt and other data was apparent. The agreement between the data of Michels, the Reichsanstalt and Masson is excellent apart from slight discrepancies in the Masson data at 150° C and 174° C and also in the Reichsanstalt data at 50° C, probably due to temperature errors. The high pressure data of Bridgman continue the trend of the Michels data but show an initial discrepancy. The Bridgman data can be made to follow on from those of Michels if it is assumed that there is a constant positive error in volume of 0·022 cm³/g in all of Bridgman's values. It may be noted that Bridgman took a value of 580·3 cm³ for the volume of 1 g of argon at 0° C and 1 kg/cm². This is slightly greater than the corresponding value of Baxter and Starkweather but not great enough to explain the above discrepancy. However, Bridgman himself certainly does not claim the extreme precision for his measurements that Michels is able to achieve and therefore it has been considered justified

157

to adjust all of Bridgman's results to make them follow on smoothly from those of Michels.

The curves were re-plotted as isobars, *i.e.* r versus temperature at constant pressures, the Bridgman data being adjusted as described above. The Leiden data were ignored except at the lowest temperatures where they are all that are available. The slopes of the isobars $\dfrac{\partial r}{\partial T}\bigg)_P$ were determined from these curves and without further smoothing the derivatives were plotted against temperature as isobars. The slopes of these latter curves then gave the second differential coefficients $\dfrac{\partial^2 r}{\partial T^2}\bigg)_P$ which were smoothed by plotting both as isotherms and isobars.

From the smooth curves values of $\dfrac{\partial^2 r}{\partial T^2}\bigg)_P$ were read, multiplied by the temperature and tabulated. By plotting these values of $T\dfrac{\partial^2 r}{\partial T^2}\bigg)_P$ as isotherms and integrating graphically the change in specific heat ΔC_p with pressure at the constant temperatures of the isotherms was determined. The integration was carried out from zero pressure, and for the specific heat at zero pressure the constant value independent of temperature $\tfrac{5}{2}R = 20\cdot79$ J/mole, degree was taken. The values of C_p thus calculated were plotted both as isotherms and isobars. In the region covered by the Leiden data the values showed a decrease in C_p with temperature at constant pressure instead of an increase, confirming the uncertain character of these data. These values were therefore ignored, the C_p versus temperature isobars in this region being extrapolated to give an increasing value of C_p along the isobar with temperature decrease. The C_p values were cross plotted as isobars and isotherms until smooth and were then tabulated at regular intervals and smoothed finally by taking differences.

From these smoothed C_p values the changes in entropy and enthalpy along isobars between temperature limits were readily and accurately calculated by graphical integration.

$$\Delta S\bigg]_{T_1}^{T_2}\bigg]_P = \int_{T_1}^{T_2} \frac{C_p}{T}\,\mathrm{d}T\bigg]_P$$

$$\Delta H\bigg]_{T_1}^{T_2}\bigg]_P = \int_{T_1}^{T_2} C_p\,\mathrm{d}T\bigg]_P$$

It was also necessary to know the entropy and enthalpy change with pressure at one isotherm and for this the 300° K isotherm was chosen, since at this temperature P-V-T data up to 5000 atm were available.

The isothermal entropy change with pressure is expressed by the equation:

$$\Delta S\Big]_{P_1}^{P_2}{}_{T} = -\int_{P_1}^{P_2}\frac{\partial V}{\partial T}\Big)_P \, dP\Big]_T = \int_{P_1}^{P_2}\frac{\partial r}{\partial T}\Big)_P \, dP\Big]_T - R\,\log_e\frac{P_2}{P_1}$$

The second term represents the ideal entropy change; the first the change in entropy due to departure from ideal behaviour, which can be evaluated from zero pressure if necessary. In the case of the entropy, however, the values were evaluated from 1 atm pressure.

The isothermal enthalpy change at constant pressure is given by:

$$\frac{\partial H}{\partial P}\Big)_T = V - T\frac{\partial V}{\partial T}\Big)_P = T\frac{\partial r}{\partial T}\Big)_P - r$$

$$\Delta H\Big]_{P_1}^{P_2}{}_{T} = T\int_{P_1}^{P_2}\frac{\partial r}{\partial T}\Big)_P \, dP\Big]_T - \int_{P_1}^{P_2} r\,dP\Big]_T = T\Delta S' - \int_{P_1}^{P_2} r\,dP\Big]_T$$

where $\Delta S'$ is that part of the corresponding entropy change due to departure from ideal behaviour. The isothermal entropy and enthalpy changes at 300° K were calculated by graphically integrating the established values of $\frac{\partial r}{\partial T}\Big)_P$ and r in the above manner. The conversion of the relative values of entropy and enthalpy into absolute values is described later.

13. *Thermodynamic Functions Calculated from the Joule–Thomson Expansion*

The methods described in the previous section enabled thermodynamic functions to be calculated over the large pressure range above 273° K covered by the excellent data of Michels. Below 273° K the pressure range was much reduced and below 200° K the values were established for no higher pressures than 30 atm. As the saturated vapour boundary was approached the values depended on extrapolation of the C_p values since the Leiden data were considered unreliable. In the region immediately above the critical point, however, the Joule–Thomson expansion data of Roebuck and Osterberg are available, and in the absence of other data it was decided to use these to calculate the thermodynamic functions.

Reference was made to the original paper of Roebuck and Osterberg and their recorded experimental results were plotted as isenthalps on a pressure–temperature plane in the same manner as adopted by those authors. The appropriate correction, *i.e.* a multiplying factor of 0·9677, was applied to all the pressures. An enthalpy–temperature diagram was next constructed from the already established data, the isobars on this diagram being extended to lower temperatures by incorporating the data for the integral Joule–Thomson effect. The

159

additional values of enthalpy thus established were tabulated and smoothed by taking differences. The final smoothing by plotting small enthalpy–temperature and enthalpy–pressure diagrams in the critical and compressed liquid regions was carried out when data for the saturation boundary had been calculated. In this manner the limit of the derived thermodynamic functions was extended to 200 atm at 120° K. The C_p values in this region were calculated from the relationship:

$$C_p = \frac{\Delta H}{\Delta T}\bigg)_P$$

and the entropy from the C_p values by integration in the same manner as described in the previous section. The entropy values were also checked for consistency using the relationship:

$$T\Delta S)_P = \Delta H)_P$$

All values were smoothed and reconciled by taking differences and cross-plotting.

The Joule–Thomson coefficients reported by Roebuck and Osterberg were also used to calculate the volume in the manner described in the following section.

14. Calculation of the Volume

The final smoothed values of the volume have been determined throughout by establishing values of the product PV and smoothing them in accordance with the well-known characteristics of the isotherms on the PV versus P diagram. The volume was then simply calculated by dividing by the pressure and converting from Amagat units to cubic centimetres. In the case of the P-V-T data the values of PV were readily computed by returning to the smoothed graphs of the graphical residual r versus pressure and temperature and applying the relationship:

$$PV = RT - rP$$

at regular intervals of pressure and temperature.

In the low temperature region approaching the saturated vapour boundary only the Leiden data were available, but these are known to be unreliable and have been ignored. The volume data in this region were computed from the isotherms on the PV versus P diagram judiciously extrapolated to the saturated vapour boundary. Further details of this process and the method of deriving good values for the saturated vapour volume will be given later.

The calculation of the volume from the Joule–Thomson data in the region where these have been used to establish the thermodynamic functions was a more involved process. Roebuck and Osterberg's table of μ values was first corrected, the pressures being multiplied by

0·9677 and the values of μ divided by this figure. After replotting the values a correct table was drawn up at close intervals of temperature and pressure which was then converted into a table of $\dfrac{\mu}{T^2}$ values.

The thermodynamic equations for the calculation of the volume from μ are:

$$-\frac{\mu}{T^2}=\frac{1}{T^2}\frac{\partial T}{\partial P}\bigg)_H=\frac{1}{T}\frac{\partial V}{\partial H}\bigg)_P-\frac{V}{T^2}\frac{\partial T}{\partial H}\bigg)_P=\frac{\partial\left(\dfrac{V}{T}\right)}{\partial H}\bigg]_P$$

$$\Delta\left(\frac{V}{T}\right)^{H_2}_{H_1}\bigg]_P=-\int_{H_1}^{H_2}\frac{\mu}{T^2}\,dH\bigg]_P$$

The changes in the quotient $\dfrac{V}{T}$ and hence of the volume itself were thus found by plotting the values of $\dfrac{\mu}{T^2}$ against the already established enthalpies as isobars and integrating between appropriate enthalpy limits, care being taken over the units. In this manner values of volume and of the product PV were computed for all pressures and temperatures below 280° K. It was found that these values were in excellent agreement where they overlapped with the Reichsanstalt data and the extrapolated values at the low temperatures and pressures. Where the Joule–Thomson data stand alone they thus provide a valuable contribution to the thermodynamic data. As already indicated, the final values of the volume were calculated by dividing the smoothed products PV by P. In the critical region where the values change their magnitude very rapidly they were ultimately smoothed by plotting volume against entropy along isobars and isotherms. These curves have no sigmoid inflexions in the critical region and are therefore more easily smoothed.

The method of establishing the functions in the homogeneous region at high pressures and low temperatures, i.e. as the freezing and melting lines are approached will be described in a later section after the liquid–vapour boundary has been considered.

15. The Calorimetric Data and the Absolute Values of the Functions

Since calorimetric data for solid argon are available at temperatures down to 10° K it has been possible in the present work to take the entropy and enthalpy as zero for the perfect crystal at the absolute zero of temperature as required by the Third Law of Thermodynamics. Below 10° K the functions were calculated very simply from the Debye relationship:

$$C_p=kT^3$$

where k is a constant readily evaluated from the experimental results at the lowest temperatures. At these very low temperatures C_p, C_v and C_σ, the specific heat at constant saturation are virtually identical. Therefore:

$$S = \int_0^T \frac{C_p}{T} \, dT = \int_0^T k T^2 \, dT = \tfrac{1}{3} k T^3 = \tfrac{1}{3} C_p$$

and

$$H = \int_0^T C_p \, dT = \int_0^T k T^3 \, dT = \tfrac{1}{4} k T^4 = \tfrac{1}{4} C_p T = \tfrac{3}{4} TS$$

Above 10° K the calorimetric data of Clusius have been used to evaluate the thermodynamic functions. The data of Clusius have been chosen because of the meticulous care and fine attention to detail which characterize the experimental work of this school and also because their work shows a keen appreciation of the thermodynamics of the saturated state and the corrections to be applied to experimental results before derived quantities can be accurately evaluated. The C_p values for solid argon up to the triple point were integrated graphically in the usual manner to evaluate both the entropy and enthalpy. The specific heat at constant saturation, C_σ, for the liquid and the latent heats of vaporization and fusion determined by Clusius were also used. Only the enthalpy change of the saturated liquid calls for comment. The equation for this change is:

$$\Delta H \bigg]_{T_1 \sigma}^{T_2} = \int_{T_1}^{T_2} C_\sigma \, dT \bigg]_\sigma + \int_{P_1}^{P_2} V \, dP \bigg]_\sigma$$

V being the volume of the saturated liquid and P_1, P_2 the vapour pressures corresponding with the temperatures T_1, T_2. The $\int V dP$ term amounts to considerably less than 1 per cent of the $\int C_\sigma dT$ term up to the normal boiling point. To convert calories to Joules the multiplying factor 4·1842 as used by Clusius was naturally adopted. The following absolute values of entropy and enthalpy were thus computed.

	Entropy J/mole, °K	Enthalpy J/mole
Perfect crystal at absolute zero	0	0
Melting solid	38·1766	1650·67
Freezing liquid	52·2020	2825·59
Boiling liquid at 1 atm	53·9092	2972·46
Saturated vapour at 1 atm	128·5681	9489·35

Using these values the already computed data for the entropy and enthalpy changes were readily converted to absolute values. It is of interest to compare the entropy of the saturated vapour as calculated above with the value calculated by statistics. First, the value of the entropy for the saturated vapour must be increased to allow for the departure from ideal behaviour. This increase at the normal boiling point was calculated from the existing data for the 1 atm isobar and the 300° K isotherm as follows:

$$\Delta S\Big]_{\substack{P=1 \\ P=0}}^{}{}_{T=87\cdot29} = \Delta S\Big]_{\substack{T=300 \\ T=87\cdot29}}^{}{}_{P=1} - \Delta S\Big]_{\substack{T=300 \\ T=87\cdot29}}^{}{}_{P=0} + \Delta S\Big]_{\substack{P=1 \\ P=0}}^{}{}_{T=300}$$

$$= 25\cdot99 - 25\cdot67 + 0\cdot02$$

$$= 0\cdot34 \text{ J/mole, °K}$$

Making the correction, the value of entropy for the saturated vapour in the ideal gaseous state is 128·91 J/mole, °K. From statistical data Clusius and Frank[28] have calculated the value 129·16 J/mole, °K in excellent agreement with the experimental figure.

16. The Liquid–Vapour Boundary and the Latent Heats of Vaporization

In order to determine the liquid–vapour boundary the following data have been utilized: the densities of the saturated liquid and vapour phases in equilibrium according to Mathias, Crommelin and Onnes, the vapour pressure data of Clark, Din and Robb and the experimental value for the latent heat of vaporization at the normal boiling point of Clusius and Frank, 1557·5 ± 1·5 cal/mole. The data of Mathias, Crommelin and Onnes are a relationship between volume and temperature; the vapour pressure data a relationship between pressure and temperature. The two sets of data taken together are thus equivalent to P-V-T data for the saturation boundary. A PV versus P curve for the saturation boundary was first constructed. Although both sets of original data are quite smooth this method of plotting showed a lack of internal consistency, particularly along the saturated vapour boundary. The measurement of the saturated vapour density, especially at low densities, is the least certain feature of the Leiden experiments. A smooth PV versus P curve was drawn and from this curve new values for the specific volumes of the saturated liquid and vapour were calculated. Using these values the latent heat was then calculated by means of the Clausius–Clapeyron equation after differentiating the vapour pressure equation of Clark, Din and Robb, including the graphical residual term, to obtain the derivative $\dfrac{dP}{dT}$. These latent heat values were plotted and smoothed and it was observed that at 1 atm the calculated value, 5908 J/mole, differed considerably from the experimental value of Clusius and Frank, 6517 J/mole. It was considered that the discrepancy was still due to the inaccurate values for the densities of the saturated vapour at low pressures and accordingly the curve of latent heat values below 7 atm was extrapolated to pass through the experimental value of Clusius and Frank at 1 atm. The new latent heats were then used to re-calculate the specific volume of the saturated vapour at low pressures from the Clausius–Clapeyron equation, assuming that the Leiden liquid densities were accurate. The *PV* versus *P* diagram on the basis of the finally calculated data is shown in *Figure 2*, on which the Leiden compressibility data in the superheated region and the experimental saturated vapour density data correlated with the vapour pressure equation are also shown. The discrepancies in the latter at low pressures are clearly indicated.

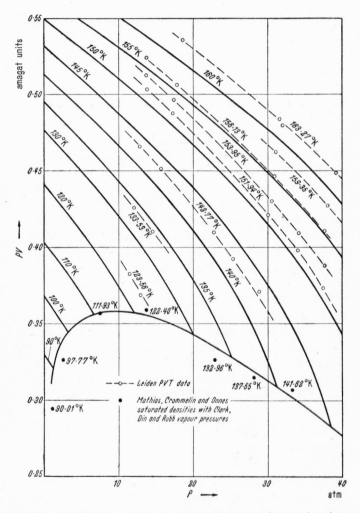

Figure 2.   PV versus P diagram showing the saturated vapour boundary

As mentioned in section 14, the volume data in the low pressure superheated region were calculated by extrapolating the isotherms on the *PV* versus *P* diagram to the saturated vapour boundary. In *Figure 2* these isotherms were constructed by joining the points on the *PV* axis, where the gas can be considered ideal, to those at the same temperature on the saturation line. It will be observed that these isotherms form a consistent family amongst themselves and with the saturated vapour boundary. This would not have been the case had the latent heat value of Clusius and Frank been ignored and the Leiden saturated vapour density data been taken as correct at the low pressures. In this case the 90° K and 100° K isotherms in particular would have been very much steeper on the *PV* versus *P* diagram, indicating a very rapidly increasing value of the second virial coefficient. In *Figure 2* the slope of the 100° K isotherm is $-0 \cdot 0068$ Amagat units, in excellent agreement with the value of the second virial coefficient at this temperature calculated by van Itterbeek and van Paemel from their velocity of sound measurements, namely $-0 \cdot 00673$.

On the temperature–entropy diagram the entropy and enthalpy values for the saturated vapour were determined by extrapolating the tabulated values along the isobars to the appropriate saturation temperatures. The latent heats then enabled the entropy and enthalpy of the saturated liquid to be determined. The smoothness of these saturation values was tested by drawing small diagrams of the saturation boundary with interchanged parameters, *e.g.* enthalpy–temperature, enthalpy–pressure, volume–entropy. The 50 per cent quality line on these diagrams also provided a valuable criterion of smoothness and consistency, particularly in the critical region.

The entropy of the saturated liquid was also calculated by graphical integration of the specific heat data of Eucken and Hauck for the saturated liquid. There are no values for this property by Clusius above 89° K. It was found that the values thus calculated differed considerably from those already established; for example, from the triple point to 130° K the values of Eucken and Hauck lead to an entropy increase of 20·25 J/mole, °K, whereas the previously established values give 22·20 J/mole, °K, a 10 per cent discrepancy. In view of the uncertain nature of Eucken and Hauck's calorimetric data, especially at pressures and temperatures approaching the critical point, it was decided not to consider them further.

17. Extrapolation to the Freezing and Melting Lines

Having derived the additional *P-V-T* values for argon from the Joule–Thomson expansion as described in Section 14, an attempt was made to extrapolate the data to the freezing curve using Bridgman's data for the latter. This was done by plotting the values of the volume residual, *r*, against temperature in the form of isobars. Only five isobars were plotted, namely those for 200, 500, 1000, 2000 and 5000 atm, which were then extrapolated to the appropriate points on the

Bridgman freezing curve. For the 200 atm isobar the extrapolation was over a small temperature interval but for the higher pressures the isobars were extrapolated over an interval of as much as 100°. In spite of the rather large temperature interval it is believed that the extrapolated curves were not seriously out of position. The difficulty arose from the fact that these curves are rather flat and have very little curvature, and consequently an accurate assessment of their slopes is impossible. The first differential coefficient was difficult enough to derive with even nominal accuracy whilst values derived graphically for the second differential coefficient were uncertain in the extreme. It was decided to persevere and values of $\frac{\partial r}{\partial T}\Big)_P$, $\frac{\partial^2 r}{\partial T^2}\Big)_P$ and $T\frac{\partial^2 r}{\partial T^2}\Big)_P$ were derived, tabulated and smoothed. Values of C_p, entropy and enthalpy were then calculated by integration and it was immediately apparent that they were untenable. They showed considerable irregularities when plotted and were in no sense systematic.

It was accordingly decided to try the method of extrapolation and cross-plotting. The volumes at pressures over 1000 atm above 250° K are of similar magnitude to the volumes of the saturated liquid. The small volume isochores on the temperature–entropy diagram were therefore extrapolated over the considerable temperature interval to the appropriate points on the saturated liquid boundary. By drawing isotherms on a volume–entropy diagram for this extrapolated region and extrapolating to even smaller volumes additional small volume isochores could be inserted on the temperature–entropy diagram. Next, isobars on a volume–temperature diagram were drawn using all the experimental data for the freezing liquid and the extrapolated data. Summarizing; at this stage there were isochores on a temperature–entropy plane, isotherms on a volume–entropy plane and isobars on a volume–temperature plane, and therefore it was possible to insert isobars on the temperature–entropy and volume–entropy planes and isentropes on the volume–temperature plane. This process was carried out with numerous adjustments until all three diagrams had been reconciled for smoothness and internal consistency. The isochores and isobars on the temperature–entropy diagram were finally considered sufficiently established. It was then gratifying to observe that the isenthalps on the temperature–entropy diagram calculated from the relationship:

$$\Delta H)_P = T\Delta S)_P$$

and also the specific heats at constant pressure from the relationship:

$$C_p = \frac{\Delta H}{\Delta T}\Big)_P$$

were smooth and systematic.

The solid–liquid boundary was next determined in a precisely similar manner to the liquid-vapour boundary. The freezing points suitably interpolated from the results of Clusius and Weigand and of Bridgman which fall on a single smooth curve, were marked off at the appropriate temperatures on the high pressure isobars on the temperature–entropy diagram to give the entropy and enthalpy values at the freezing liquid boundary. A single smooth curve was drawn for the latent heats of fusion using the Clusius value at the triple point and the calculated Bridgman values at pressures above 1000 atm. Using the latent heats taken from this curve the entropy and enthalpy of the melting solid were readily calculated, all values being finally smoothed graphically and checked for internal consistency. The volumes of the melting solid and freezing liquid were given by the experimental results of Bridgman and of Clusius and Weigand, *Figure 3*.

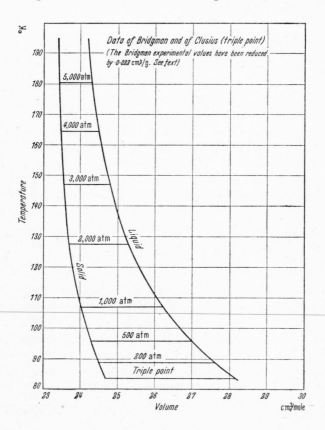

Figure 3. The volume of the freezing liquid and melting solid

18. Interpolation from the Tabulated Data

The tabulated values of entropy both in the superheated region and for saturation conditions enabled isobars and the two-phase boundaries to be drawn on the temperature–entropy plane. Rounded off integral values of enthalpy and volume were then interpolated from the tables along isobars and isotherms as necessary to give the isenthalps and iso-chores. Within the two-phase regions entropy, enthalpy and volume all increase linearly along isobars, and since the saturation values at both ends of the isobars were known, intermediate integral values were readily determined by interpolation.

As already mentioned the various thermodynamic functions were established in the critical region by the method of cross-plotting with interchanged parameters until all were smooth and internally consistent. The method was similar to that which has just been described for the extrapolation to the solid–liquid boundary.

19. The Specific Heat at Constant Volume

Since pressure and temperature have been chosen as independent variables for the present work the specific heat at constant volume could not conveniently be computed until after the final preparation of the diagram. The average slopes of the isochores, $\dfrac{\Delta S}{\Delta T}\bigg)_v$, on the tempera-ture–entropy diagram were measured over 50° intervals and the values multiplied by the average temperature to give values of C_v as a function of temperature and volume. Isochores on a C_v versus temperature diagram were drawn and the points of intersection of isochores and isobars on the temperature–entropy diagram were marked off at the appropriate temperatures on the isochores. These points were joined appropriately to give the isobars on the C_v versus temperature diagram. It was found, with agreeable surprise, that these isobars formed a smooth systematic family and after a further transposition into iso-therms on a C_v versus pressure diagram the final tabulated values as functions of pressure and temperature were quite easily drawn up and checked for smoothness. *Figure 4* shows the final values in the form of isotherms on a C_v versus pressure plane. From *Figure 4* it will be observed that C_v increases regularly on isothermal compression over the whole of the pressure and temperature range. This is different from the apparent behaviour of polyatomic gases, in particular nitrogen and carbon dioxide, for which MICHELS and his co-workers[47, 48] have calculated C_v values which pass through a maximum at the critical density and then show another rise at the highest pressures and den-sities. The intersection of the isotherms on the C_v versus pressure or density diagram is observed with nitrogen but not with carbon dioxide.

168

DISCUSSION

To test the diagram for internal consistency the equation:

$$dH = TdS + VdP$$

has been used in its isothermal integrated form, *i.e.*:

$$\Delta H)_T = T\Delta S)_T + \int VdP)_T$$

In the low pressure region $T\Delta S)_T$ and $\int VdP)_T$ are approximately equal terms of opposite sign and consequently the equation was used to calculate ΔS which could then be compared with the established value. Taking the values from the tables, volume was plotted against pressure along isotherms and graphically integrated to give $\int VdP)_T$. After con-

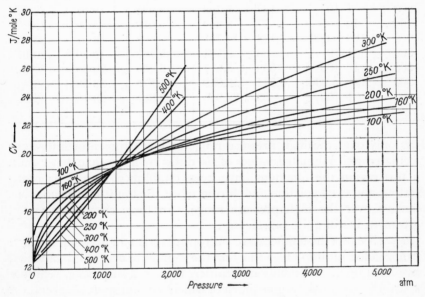

Figure 4. The specific heat at constant volume

verting to Joules/mole this integral was then used with the corresponding tabulated enthalpy change to calculate ΔS which was compared with the tabulated value as shown in Table 11. The agreement between the calculated and tabulated values of ΔS is satisfactory confirmation of the internal consistency of the diagram. Above 300° K over all pressure ranges the agreement is well within 1 per cent. Below 300° K and over pressure ranges from 1 atm to 200 atm the agreement is likewise within 1 per cent. This confirms that the establishment of the functions from the Joule–Thomson expansion and their adjustment at the saturated vapour boundary as described have been carried out without impairing the internal consistency.

169

TABLE 11

TESTING THE DIAGRAM.   CALCULATION OF THE ISOTHERMAL ENTROPY
CHANGE

1	2	3	4	5	6	7
Tempera-ture °K	ΔP atm	ΔH tables J/mole	$\int V dP$ J/mole	$\Delta H - \int V dP$ (3) − (4)	ΔS calc. (5) ÷ (1)	ΔS tables J/mole°K
110	1–5	− 163	1,403	1,566	− 14·24	− 14·32
140	1–10	− 288	2,617	2,905	− 20·75	− 20·49
140	10–30	− 945	1,036	− 1,981	− 14·15	− 14·26
150	50–200	− 784	627	− 1,411	− 9·41	− 9·51
150	200–2,000	4,915	7,894	− 2,979	− 19·86	− 19·27
200	1–10	− 137	3,798	− 3,935	− 19·67	− 19·61
200	10–100	− 1,657	3,359	− 5,016	− 25·08	− 25·32
200	100–5,000	7,183	14,785	− 7,602	− 38·01	− 38·75
300	1–10	− 66	5,721	− 5,787	− 19·29	− 20·87
300	10–100	− 639	5,617	− 6,256	− 20·85	− 20·87
300	100 − 5,000	7,344	18,919	− 11,575	− 38·58	− 38·42
600	1–100	− 53	22,940	− 22,887	− 38·15	− 38·35

It is only over the high pressure range at low temperatures that the calculated and tabulated values of ΔS differ by more than 1 per cent. In this region the functions have been established mainly by cross-plotting and extrapolation and, furthermore, the test itself becomes less sensitive over the high pressure range.   In these circumstances the agreement is still quite satisfactory.

Figure 5 shows the temperature–entropy diagram for argon in skeleton form divided up into areas showing the sources of original data which have been used.   As mentioned earlier, there is a surprising wealth of experimental data for argon, much of which is of indisputable accuracy. Above 0° C the comprehensive P-V-T data of Michels leave nothing to be desired.   Below 0° C the position is not so satisfactory apart from the two isotherms from the Reichsanstalt.   The Leiden data are known to be inaccurate and cover a restricted range only.   It is desirable also that the Joule–Thomson data of Roebuck and Osterberg should be confirmed, and it is hoped, therefore, that the P-V-T data below 0° C will at some future date be measured by Michels and his co-workers with their latest constant volume piezometer and diaphragm manometer. Although the P-V-T data of Bridgman are incomplete in the extreme high pressure homogeneous region, or, as he prefers to call it, the region of amorphous argon, there is little need to make good the deficiency since, as has been shown, the thermodynamic functions cannot be accurately calculated from these data unless the experimental results reach an unattainable standard of accuracy. The phase data of argon have been extensively studied. It is doubtful whether the solid–liquid equilibrium data of Bridgman and of Clusius and Weigand can be improved upon, whilst, returning to more normal pressures, the vapour pressures of liquid and solid argon are now well established. It has

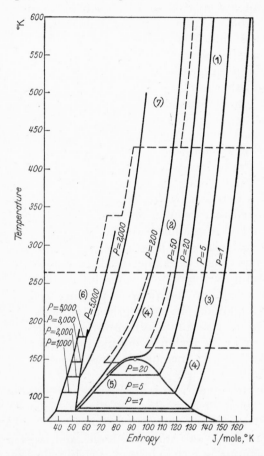

Figure 5. The skeleton temperature–entropy diagram

(1) *P-V-T* data, Holborn and Otto.
(2) *P-V-T* data, Holborn and Shultze; Otto; Tanner and Masson; Michels, Wijker and Wijker.
(3) *P-V-T* data, Holborn and Otto.
(4) Joule–Thomson expansion; Roebuck and Osterberg. Extrapolation to saturated vapour boundary.
(5) Vapour pressure, Clark, Din and Robb. Latent heats of fusion and vaporization at 1 atm, Clusius. Density of saturated liquid and vapour, critical constants, Mathias, Crommelin and Onnes. Latent heats, Clausius–Clapeyron equation. Specific heats saturated solid and liquid, Clusius.
(6) Freezing liquid and melting solid, Clusius (triple point), Bridgman (high pressure). Extrapolation and cross plotting.
(7) Extrapolated.

C_p at zero pressure $= \dfrac{5R}{2}$.

been suggested that the pioneer Leiden data on the density of the saturated vapour are in error, and this may be the case for quite a number of other gases. It appears that since the work at Leiden at the beginning of the century the accurate measurement of densities of saturated vapours has received little attention. Measurements of the specific heats of argon at pressures other than atmospheric would represent a valuable addition to the thermodynamic data. The specific heats are the most difficult functions to derive with accuracy from the P-V-T data and experimental values would confirm whether the derived functions had been satisfactorily evaluated.

There is little other work on the thermodynamic properties of argon with which the present compilation can be compared. A direct comparison is possible only with the evaluation of the thermodynamic properties by the Van der Waals Laboratory from their own measurements of the P-V-T data. Since these data have been the principal source used for the present work above 0° C, these two determinations should agree. Such discrepancies as exist must be attributed to the inevitable errors that arise in the evaluation of the derived data. It may be mentioned that the Van der Waals school do not derive their data by the method of graphical residuals that has been used in this work. In the first place the properties are evaluated as functions of density and temperature by taking the differences in the products PV over 25° temperature intervals at constant density. The properties are then transposed into functions of pressure and temperature by numerical interpolation. It is the present author's opinion that this method is not quite as accurate as measuring the slopes of the residual curves, especially in the region of normal pressures above 0° C where these curves have easily measurable slopes and form a thoroughly systematic family.

The most severe comparison is afforded by the specific heats at constant pressure which are derived in effect by taking a second derivative of the P-V-T data. The values are compared in Table 12 after converting the Van der Waals values to Joules and adjusting to integral values of temperature in Kelvin instead of Celsius degrees. The agreement between the values, considering the difficulty of establishing C_p accurately from the P-V-T data, is considered to be excellent, especially at the higher temperatures. The agreement is not quite so good at 270° K where the values derived in this work rise to a higher peak around 1000 atm before falling again. This region represents the lower limit of temperature and the upper limit of pressure of the Van der Waals data where the derivatives are most difficult to measure and it is not surprising, therefore, that the discrepancy should be largest in this region. The specific heats at constant volume likewise show similar discrepancies.

In view of the good agreement between C_p values the entropy and

172

TABLE 12

COMPARISON OF THE SPECIFIC HEATS AT CONSTANT PRESSURE
J/mole, °K

D = this work.   M = Michels, Lunbeck and Wolkers[1]

Pressure atm	Author	Temperature °K		
		270° K	340° K	400° K
1	M	20·8	20·8	20·8
	D	20·8	20·8	20·8
50	M	24·0	22·6	21·9
	D	23·6	22·5	22·1
200	M	33·9	27·4	24·8
	D	33·3	27·8	25·7
400	M	35·3	30·2	27·0
	D	37·2	30·8	27·7
1000	M	31·6	29·7	27·7
	D	39·0	32·7	27·9
2000	M	30·4	29·0	27·1
	D	37·3	31·0	26·0

enthalpy changes along isobars will also be in excellent agreement.   It is necessary to compare the values of these two functions along one isotherm only and in Table 13 this comparison is made at 273·15° K. In this case the values given for the present work have been inter-polated from the tables and adjusted to entropy and enthalpy zero at 273·15° K and 1 atm to conform with the Van der Waals values.   In the case of the entropy it must be remembered that the correct basis for comparison is between the changes resulting from the departure from ideal behaviour.   Accordingly the ideal value of the entropy is given in Table 13 and also the change resulting from non-ideal behaviour, $\Delta S'$.   Once again it is seen that the agreement is very good except at the high pressures and even in this region the discrepancies of 0·5 J/mole, degree for the entropy and 100 J/mole for the enthalpy represent a displacement of only 2 mm or 3 mm in the lines on a diagram measuring 100 cm by 70 cm.

The only other basis for comparison with the present diagram is the Joule–Thomson data of Roebuck and Osterberg.   In *Figure 6* three pairs of isenthalps at comparable enthalpies have been drawn on a

173

TABLE 13

COMPARISON OF THE ENTROPY AND ENTHALPY AT 273·15° K

D=this work.   M=Michels, Lunbeck and Wolkers[1]. S in J/mole, °K. H in J/mole.

Function	Author	1 atm	50 atm	200 atm	400 atm	1000 atm	2000 atm
S	M	0	− 33·78	− 48·77	− 56·71	− 65·83	− 71·40
	D	0	− 33·69	− 48·66	− 56·55	− 65·79	− 71·93
	Ideal	0	− 32·53	− 44·05	− 49·82	− 57·43	− 63·20
$\Delta S'$	M	0	− 1·25	− 4·72	− 6·89	− 7·95	− 8·20
	D	0	− 1·16	− 4·61	− 6·73	− 8·36	− 8·73
H	M	0	− 444	− 1618	− 2273	− 1865	− 30
	D	0	− 417	− 1583	− 2228	− 1981	− 148

$\Delta S'$ = Entropy change due to departure from ideal behaviour.

pressure–temperature plane.   At low temperatures the data of Roebuck and Osterberg were used to compute the thermodynamic functions and therefore the pair of isenthalps lying between 100° K and 200° K are naturally closely parallel.   At 300° K also the agreement is likewise practically perfect whilst at 450° K there is but a very slight systematic discrepancy between the two isenthalps, the work of Roebuck and Osterberg showing a slightly greater Joule–Thomson effect than the present diagram.   The agreement at the two higher temperatures is particularly pleasing, since when two independent investigations agree with each other the value of both is considerably enhanced.   Confidence in the results of Roebuck and Osterberg at the lower temperatures where they have been used for the present work is therefore justified.

The above comparisons with the work of other authors afford the best means of assessing the accuracy of the present diagram in different regions.   Errors in a thermodynamic diagram arise from two causes; imperfections in the original data and as an inevitable consequence of the differentiation, transposition and smoothing of the data.   In the present case the errors arise almost exclusively from the second cause and an idea of their magnitude can be gained from the comparison with the derived data of Michels as just described.   The Joule–Thomson expansion leads to a very accurate evaluation of thermodynamic functions provided the original experimental data are sound. In the case of argon it has just been shown that the Joule–Thomson data are in substantial agreement with the other experimental data where they overlap, and consequently, where the diagram rests on the Joule–Thomson data alone, it is considered that the errors in the

evaluation of the functions are also small. The low temperature
calorimetry of the Clusius school likewise commends itself for meticulous care and precision and Clusius himself has shown how the
entropy of the saturated vapour at the normal boiling point calculated

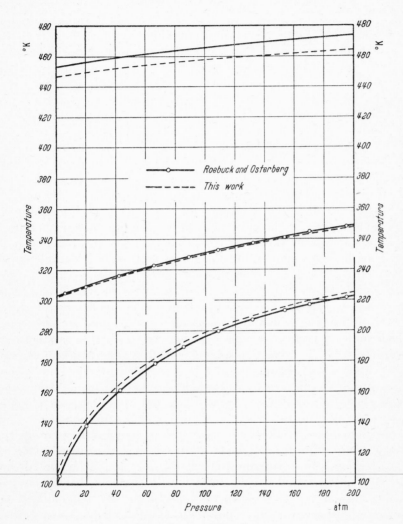

Figure 6. Isenthalps of argon

from his results is in excellent agreement with the theoretical statistical
value. The vapour pressure of argon is also now well established and
unlikely to be proved seriously in error in the future. Unfortunately there
is some doubt about the pioneer Leiden data for the densities of the
saturated liquid and vapour phases in equilibrium which in turn throws
doubt on the latent heats calculated from the Clausius–Clapeyron

equation. Even in this case, however, an attempt has been made to adjust the values to conform with the rest of the data into a thoroughly consistent system. Considerations such as these have led to the drawing up of Table 14 which gives in skeleton form entropy, enthalpy and volume values with their estimated absolute errors over the superheated range. The suggested errors in the volume arise after consideration of the original P-V-T data, the accuracy of evaluating the volume from the Joule–Thomson expansion and the possible errors in the Leiden values for the density of the saturated vapour.

No estimate of errors can be given for the region of extrapolation to the solid–liquid boundary. In this region the data of Bridgman are necessarily of a different order of accuracy from those of the Van der Waals and Reichsanstalt workers. Even if this were not so it is doubtful whether the thermodynamic functions could be established with any greater accuracy than they have been. The methods of extrapolation and cross-plotting in this region which have been described are, it must be admitted, little more than inspired guesswork and it is for this reason that the diagram and functions have been given in skeleton form only. The most that can be said is that the temperature, pressure and volume values are consistent with the experimental data so far as these are known, but there may well be considerable errors in the entropy and, as a consequence, in the enthalpy values. The author would prefer this region to be regarded merely as a pioneer attempt to include the solid–liquid boundary on an authentic diagram.

Both the melting solid and the freezing liquid boundaries have slopes which imply a positive specific heat for both. Solid is produced by compressing the freezing liquid isentropically. The majority of saturated vapours have negative specific heats, i.e. they become superheated on isentropic compression. Nevertheless, some vapours are known for which the reverse is true, and so it seems that from first principles it is quite impossible to say which way any of the saturation boundaries should slope. It is difficult to imagine a liquid with a negative specific heat in equilibrium with its vapour, but not so in the case of a melting solid in equilibrium with the freezing liquid. It may be noted that within the solid–liquid two-phase region the isochores have a positive slope—a necessary condition since C_v must be positive under all circumstances. This would not be possible if the solid–liquid phase boundaries had a very marked negative slope. In the case of a substance like water the solid–liquid boundaries extend downwards in temperature from the triple point since, unlike most substances, the freezing temperature is depressed by application of pressure. It is of interest to speculate on the disposition of the solid–liquid boundaries for a substance whose melting point is completely unaffected by pressure.

The thermodynamic diagram and functions given here are believed to be the first that have appeared for argon. Furthermore, the author

TABLE 14

VALUES OF ENTROPY, ENTHALPY AND VOLUME AND THEIR ESTIMATED MAXIMUM ABSOLUTE ERRORS

S in J/mole, °K. H in J/mole. V in cm³/mole.

Pressure atm		Temperature °K				
		120	160	270	400	600
1	S	135·34 (±0·10)	141·41 (±0·10)	152·36 (±0·10)	160·55 (±0·10)	168·99 (±0·10)
	H	10,183 (±6)	11,026 (±6)	13,327 (±6)	16,034 (±6)	20,197 (±6)
	V	9,722 (±1)	13,053 (±0)	22,131 (±0)	32,819 (±0)	49,240 (±1)
10	S	114·21 (±0·22)	121·33 (±0·16)	133·01 (±0·12)	141·31 (±0·12)	149·83 (±0·12)
	H	9,810 (±20)	10,804 (±15)	13,249 (±11)	15,996 (±13)	20,198 (±16)
	V	837 (±1)	1,235 (±1)	2,194 (±0)	3,281 (±0)	4,935 (±0)
100	S	67·62 (±0·55)	84·20 (±0·40)	111·62 (±0·15)	121·34 (±0·15)	130·64 (±0·15)
	H	4,723 (±60)	7,051 (±50)	12,465 (±20)	15,666 (±25)	20,250 (±30)
	V	32·8 (±0·5)	48·6 (±1·0)	204·3 (±0)	329·8 (±0)	505·3 (±0·1)
500	S			93·20 (±0·20)	106·04 (±0·25)	
	H			10,972 (±35)	15,173 (±65)	
	V			51·2 (±0)	77·2 (±0)	
1000	S			86·37 (±0·30)	99·64 (±0·40)	
	H			11,290 (±60)	15,629 (±120)	
	V			38·0 (±0)	50·3 (±0)	
2000	S			80·24 (±0·40)	92·82 (±0·50)	
	H			13,128 (±90)	17,235 (±160)	
	V			31·5 (±0·1)	35·8 (±0·1)	
5000	S			72·44 (±0·50)		
	H			19,592 (±110)		
	V			26·0 (±0·3)		

knows of no other diagram for any substance that covers such a wide range of pressure and temperature. Wherever possible the best modern original data have been used as a basis, and much time and trouble have been spent in smoothing out the functions and reconciling them with each other.   It is the author's hope that this work will stand the test of closest scrutiny.

REFERENCES

1 MICHELS, LUNBECK and WOLKERS, *Appl. Sci. Res. Hague*, A2 (1950) 345.
2 BAXTER and STARKWEATHER, *Proc. nat. Acad. Sci. Wash.*, 14 (1928) 57; *Proc. nat. Acad. Sci. Wash.*, 15 (1929) 441.
3 FISCHER and FROBOESE, *Ber. dtsch. chem. Ges.*, 44 (1911) 92.
4 HOLST and HAMBURGER, *Proc. Acad. Sci. Amst.*, 18 (1915) 872.
5 LEDUC, *Ann. Phys. Paris*, 9 (1918) 5.
6 SCHULTZE, *Ann. Phys. Lpz.*, 48 (1915) 269.
7 WATSON, *J. chem. Soc.*, 97 (1910) 833.
8 BRIDGMAN, *Phys. Rev.*, 45 (1934) 930; *Proc. Amer. Acad. Arts. Sci.*, 70 (1935) 1.
9 HOLBORN and OTTO, *Z. Phys.*, 23 (1924) 77; 30 (1924) 320.
10 HOLBORN and SCHULTZE, *Ann. Phys. Lpz.*, 47 (1915) 1089.
11 VAN ITTERBEEK and VAN PAEMEL, *Physica, 'sGrav.*, 5 (1938) 845.
12 MASSON and DOLLEY, *Proc. roy. Soc.* A, 103 (1923) 524.
13 MASSON and TURNER, *Proc. roy. Soc.* A, 126 (1930) 268.
14 MICHELS, WIJKER and WIJKER, *Physica, 'sGrav.*, 15 (1949) 627.
15 ONNES and CROMMELIN, *Commun. phys. Lab. Univ. Leiden*, 118b (1910.
16 CLARK and KATZ, *Canad. J. Res.*, 21A (1943) 1.
17 EUCKEN and VON LUDE, *Z. phys. Chem.*, B5 (1929) 413.
18 HEUSE, *Ann. Phys. Lpz.* (4), 59 (1919) 86.
19 LEDUC, *Chem. Rev.*, 6 (1929) 13.
20 NIEMAYER, *Diss. Halle* (1902).
21 PIER, *Z. Electrochem.*, 15 (1909) 536; 16 (1910) 897.
22 STRIEDER, *Diss. Marburg* (1915).
23 ROEBUCK and OSTERBERG, *Phys. Rev.* (2), 46 (1934) 785.
24 ROEBUCK and MURRELL, *Temperature—Its Measurement and Control in Science and Industry*, Reinhold, New York, 1941, pp. 60–73.
25 BORN, *Ann. Phys. Lpz.* (4), 69 (1922) 473.
26 BURBO and ISCHKIN, *Phys. Z. Sowjet.*, 10 (1936) 271.
27 CLARK, DIN and ROBB; MICHELS, WASSENAAR and ZWIETERING, *Physica, 's Grav.*, 17 (1951) 876.
28 CLUSIUS and FRANK, *Z. Electrochem.*, 49 (1943) 308.
29 CROMMELIN, *Commun. phys. Lab. Univ. Leiden*, 138c (1913); 140a (1914).
30 BALY and DONNAN, *J. chem. Soc.*, 81, (1902) 911.
31 MATHIAS, CROMMELIN and ONNES, *Commun. phys. Lab. Univ. Leiden*, 131a (1912).
32 CLUSIUS and WEIGAND, *Z. phys. Chem.*, B46 (1940) 1.
33 HERZ, *Z. anorg. Chem.*, 105 (1919) 171.
34 SIMON, RUHEMANN and EDWARDS, *Z. phys. Chem.*, B6 (1929) 331; B7 (1930) 80.
35 SIMON and VON SIMSON, *Z. Phys.*, 25 (1924) 160.
36 DE SMEDT and KEESOM, *Commun. phys. Lab. Univ. Leiden*, 178b (1925).
37 CLUSIUS, *Z. phys. Chem.*, B31 (1936) 459.
38 CLUSIUS and FRANK, *Z. phys. Chem.*, B42 (1939) 395.
39 EUCKEN, *Verh. dtsch. phys. Ges.*, 18 (1916) 4.

[40] EUCKEN and HAUCK, *Z. phys. Chem.*, 134 (1928) 161.
[41] MATHIAS, CROMMELIN and ONNES, *Commun. phys. Lab. Univ. Leiden,* 162a (1923).
[42] DIXON, CAMPBELL and PARKER, *Proc. roy. Soc.*, A 100 (1921) 1.
[43] GALT, *J. chem. Phys.*, 10 (1948) 505.
[44] VAN ITTERBEEK and VERHAEGEN, *Proc. phys. Soc. Lond.*, 62 (1949) 800.
[45] LIEPMANN, *Helv. phys. Acta.*, 12 (1939) 421.
[46] STRIEDER, *Verh. dtsch. phys. Ges.*, 16 (1914) 615.
[47] MICHELS and DE GROOT (CO_2), *Appl. Sci. Res. Hague*, A1 (1948) 94.
[48] MICHELS, LUNBECK and WOLKERS (N_2), *Physica, 's Grav.* 17 (1951) 801.

TABLES OF THERMODYNAMIC FUNCTIONS OF ARGON

The properties are given for 1 gramme mole of argon (39·944 g) as functions of the pressure in international atmospheres ($g=980·665$) and temperature in degrees Kelvin (0° C$=273·15$° K). Entropy and enthalpy are zero for the perfect crystal at the absolute zero of temperature.

Molecular weight	$=39·944$
Density of the gas at N.T.P.	
(latitude 45°, $g=980·616$)	$=1·78394$ g/litre
(international atm, $g=980·665$)	$=0·00178398$ g/cm^3
Molecular volume at N.T.P.	
(International atm, $g=980·665$)	$=22,390·4$ cm^3
Normal boiling point	$=87·29$° K
Triple point: temperature	$=83·78$° K
pressure	$=515·7$ mm
Critical constants: temperature	$=150·72$° K
pressure	$=48·00$ atm
volume	$=75·2$ cm^3/mole

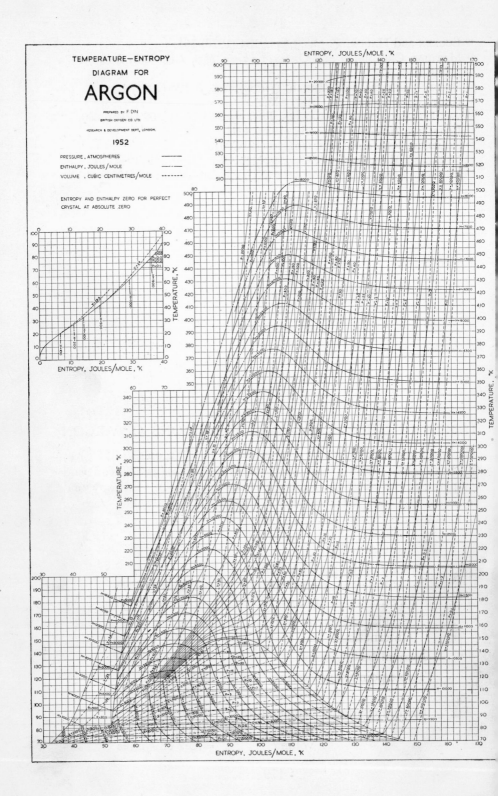

TEMPERATURE—ENTROPY

DIAGRAM FOR

ARGON

PREPARED BY F. DIN

BRITISH OXYGEN CO. LTD.

RESEARCH & DEVELOPMENT DEPT., LONDON.

1952

PRESSURE , ATMOSPHERES

ENTHALPY , JOULES / MOLE

VOLUME , CUBIC CENTIMETRES / MOLE

ENTROPY AND ENTHALPY ZERO FOR PERFECT
CRYSTAL AT ABSOLUTE ZERO

PROPERTIES OF THE SATURATED SOLID AND VAPOUR

Temperature °K	Pressure mm	J/mole, °K		J/mole		cm³/mole	
		S sol.	S vap.	H sol.	H vap.	V sol.	V vap.
0		0		0		23·1	
10		1·27		9·51		23·5	
20		6·36		88·29		23·8	
30		12·51		241·01		24·0	
40		18·35		445·2		24·2	
50		23·55		682·4		24·4	
60		28·22		940·2		24·5	
70	57·7	32·53	146·50	1,219	9,197	24·5	87,110
75	140·2	34·60	139·60	1,369	9,244	24·6	31,670
80	304·8	36·65	134·44	1,526	9,349	24·6	15,650
83·78 (T.P.)	515·7	38·18	131·10	1,651	9,436	24·6	9,961

PROPERTIES OF THE SATURATED LIQUID AND VAPOUR

Pressure atm	Temperature °K	J/mole, °K		J/mole		cm³/mole	
		S liq.	S vap.	H liq.	H vap.	V liq.	V vap.
0·6785 (T.P.)	83·78	52·20	131·10	2,826	9,436	28·2	9,961
1	87·29	53·91	128·57	2,972	9,489	28·7	6,999
2	94·43	57·42	124·21	3,293	9,600	29·6	3,714
3	99·20	59·73	121·61	3,514	9,652	30·2	2,553
5	105·97	63·02	118·32	3,855	9,715	31·3	1,578
7	110·98	65·45	116·01	4,128	9,739	32·3	1,144
10	116·81	68·26	113·51	4,441	9,727	33·4	802·5
15	124·22	71·63	110·40	4,865	9,681	35·3	529·3
20	130·03	74·40	107·85	5,241	9,590	37·2	383·6
25	134·86	76·79	104·59	5,582	9,466	39·6	294·7
30	139·06	78·95	103·55	5,905	9,326	42·3	233·8
40	146·12	82·77	99·93	6,499	9,006	48·7	155·6
48·00 (C.P.)	150·72	91·41		7,829		75·2	

PROPERTIES OF THE FREEZING LIQUID AND MELTING SOLID

Pressure atm	Temperature °K	J/mole, °K		J/mole		cm³/mole	
		S sol.	S liq.	H sol.	H liq.	V sol.	V liq.
0·6785 (T.P.)	83·78	38·18	52·20	1,651	2,826	24·6	28·2
200	88·7	39·39	52·37	2,270	3,422	24·5	27·6
500	95·8	40·87	52·73	3,002	4,138	24·3	27·0
1,000	107·0	42·80	53·19	4,231	5,343	24·0	26·2
2,000	127·5	45·93	54·47	7,080	8,169	23·7	25·3
3,000	147·0	48·81	56·15	9,928	11,007	23·5	24·8
4,000	164·3	51·06	57·62	12,748	13,826	23·5	24·5
5,000	180·3	53·13	59·13	15,549	16,630	23·4	24·3

ARGON

ENTROPY, JOULES/MOLE, °K

Pressure atm	Temperature, °K								
	90	100	110	120	130	135	140	145	150
1	129·24	131·48	133·50	135·34	137·03	137·83	138·59	139·33	140·05
2		125·45	127·51	129·39	131·11	131·92	132·70	133·45	134·18
3		121·79	123·89	125·80	127·55	128·37	129·16	129·92	130·66
5			119·18	121·17	122·99	123·84	124·66	125·45	126·20
7				117·92	119·81	120·69	121·54	122·35	123·13
10				114·21	116·26	117·20	118·10	118·96	119·79
15				69·71	111·72	112·78	113·79	114·75	115·66
20				69·58	74·41	109·09	110·27	111·37	112·40
25				69·45	74·21	105·60	107·09	108·40	109·58
30				69·32	74·02	76·60	103·84	105·54	106·98
40				69·06	73·63	76·04	78·58	81·76	102·12
50				68·81	73·27	75·57	77·97	80·69	85·57
60				68·56	72·94	75·17	77·44	79·87	82·69
70				68·32	72·63	74·79	76·96	79·21	81·59
80				68·08	72·32	74·43	76·52	78·66	80·91
100			63·26	67·62	71·72	73·74	75·73	77·73	79·79
120				67·19	71·18	73·11	75·02	76·91	78·81
140				66·79	70·67	72·54	74·37	76·17	77·96
160				66·41	70·19	72·01	73·78	75·51	77·23
180				66·06	69·75	71·52	73·25	74·93	76·60
200	53·02	57·66	61·87	65·73	69·33	71·07	72·76	74·42	76·06
250									
300		56·59	60·50	64·09	67·41		70·52		73·46
350									
400									
500		54·44	58·08	61·38	64·41		67·21		69·84
600									
800									
1000			54·12	56·95	59·60		62·09		64·45
1500									
2000					55·10		57·45		59·65
2500									
3000									56·79
4000									
5000									

ENTROPY, JOULES/MOLE, °K—*cont.*

Temperature, °K								Pressure atm
155	160	170	180	190	200	210	220	
140·05	141·41	142·68	143·88	145·02	146·10	147·12	148·09	1
134·88	135·56	136·85	138·06	139·21	140·30	141·33	142·31	2
131·37	132·06	133·37	134·60	135·76	136·86	137·90	138·88	3
126·93	127·63	128·97	130·22	131·40	132·51	133·56	134·55	5
123·88	124·60	125·98	127·26	128·46	129·59	130·66	131·67	7
120·58	121·33	122·76	124·09	125·33	126·49	127·58	128·60	10
116·53	117·36	118·91	120·33	121·64	122·86	123·99	125·04	15
113·37	114·29	115·98	117·51	118·90	120·17	121·34	122·43	20
110·68	111.71	113·54	115·17	116·65	117·99	119·21	120·33	25
108·24	109·39	111·43	113·21	114·78	116·19	117·46	118·62	30
103·90	105·39	107·80	109·85	111·62	113·18	114·57	115·82	40
98·67	101·43	104·50	106·91	108·91	110·63	112·13	113·47	50
87·20	95·90	101·39	104·28	106·57	108·47	110·10	111·53	60
84·87	89·85	97·95	101·68	104·32	106·43	108·21	109·74	70
83·50	86·94	94·18	99·21	102·26	104·59	106·52	108·16	80
81·93	84·20	89·60	94·52	98·32	101·17	103·44	105·33	100
80·73	82·68	87·04	91·28	95·00	98·15	100·74	102·86	120
79·76	81·58	85·36	89·09	92·57	95·67	98·36	100·64	140
78·95	80·70	84·18	87·57	90·78	93·72	96·38	98·72	160
78·26	79·94	83·23	86·39	89·38	92·15	98·70	97·01	180
77·67	79·26	82·39	85·39	88·21	90·85	93·29	95·52	200
								250
	76·26	78·96	81·55	84·02	86·36	88·56	90·62	300
								350
								400
	72·32	74·67	76·92	79·08	81·15	83·13	85·03	500
								600
								800
	66·69	68·83	70·88	72·85	74·75	76·59	78·37	1000
								1500
	61·73	63·71	65·62	67·46	69·24	70·96	72·63	2000
								2500
	58·83	60·76	62·60	64·37	66·08	67·74	69·35	3000
		58·68	60·47	62·20	63·87	65·49	67·06	4000
				60·78	62·42	64·01	65·55	5000

ARGON

Pressure atm	Temperature, °K								
	230	240	250	260	270	280	290	300	320
1	149·02	149·91	150·76	151·57	152·36	153·12	153·85	154·56	155·90
2	143·24	144·13	144·98	145·79	146·58	147·34	148·07	148·78	150·12
3	139·82	140·72	141·58	142·40	143·19	143·95	144·68	145·39	146·74
5	135·50	136·40	137·26	138·09	138·89	139·65	140·39	141·10	142·45
7	132·63	133·54	134·41	135·24	136·04	136·80	137·54	138·26	139·62
10	129·57	130·49	131·37	132·21	133·01	133·78	134·52	135·24	136·61
15	126·03	126·97	127·86	128·71	129·52	130·30	131·05	131·77	133·15
20	123·45	124·41	125·32	127·18	127·01	127·80	128·56	129·29	130·68
25	121·38	122·36	123·29	124·17	125·01	125·82	126·59	127·33	128·73
30	119·69	120·69	121·63	122·52	123·37	124·19	124·97	125·72	127·13
40	116·95	117·99	118·96	119·88	120·75	121·58	122·38	123·14	124·58
50	114·68	115·78	116·80	117·75	118·64	119·49	120·31	121·09	122·56
60	112·79	113·93	114·98	115·96	116·88	117·75	118·59	119·38	120·88
70	111·09	112·29	113·39	114·40	115·35	116·24	117·10	117·91	119·44
80	109·58	110·83	111·96	113·00	113·97	114·89	115·77	116·60	118·16
100	106·92	108·29	109·50	110·60	111·62	112·58	113·50	114·37	115·99
120	104·62	106·10	107·38	108·54	109·62	110·63	111·58	112·48	114·16
140	102·55	104·14	105·50	106·73	107·85	108·90	109·89	110·83	112·57
160	100·71	102·39	103·83	105·10	106·27	107·36	108·39	109·37	111·17
180	99·04	100·79	102·29	103·63	104·85	106·00	107·07	108·08	109·93
200	97·55	99·34	100·89	102·29	103·57	104·76	105·87	106·91	108·81
250			98·14	99·61	100·97	102·23	103·40	104·49	106·47
300	92·54	94·32	95·96	97·46	98·85	100·14	101·34	102·46	104·50
350			94·17	95·69	97·11	98·43	99·66	100·81	102·90
400			92·67	94·20	95·63	96·97	98·22	99·39	101·53
500	86·85	88·58	90·21	91·75	93·20	94·56	95·84	97·05	99·26
600			88·41	89·95	91·41	92·79	94·09	95·32	97·57
800			85·43	86·98	88·46	89·87	91·20	92·46	94·78
1000	80·09	81·75	83·35	84·89	86·37	87·78	89·12	90·39	92·72
1500			79·88	81·38	82·82	84·20	85·52	86·77	89·04
2000	74·25	75·83	77·36	78·83	80·24	81·59	82·87	84·08	86·29
2500			75·44	76·87	78·24	79·55	80·80	81·98	84·11
3000	70·91	72·42	73·88	75·28	76·62	77·90	79·11	80·26	82·33
4000	68·58	70·04	71·45	72·80	74·10	75·35	76·54	77·66	79·69
5000	67·03	68·45	69·83	71·16	72·44	73·67	74·84	75·95	77·94

ENTROPY, JOULES/MOLE, °K—*cont.*

Temperature, °K								Pressure atm
340	360	380	400	450	500	550	600	
157·16	158·35	159·48	160·55	163·00	165·19	167·18	168·99	1
151·38	152·57	153·70	154·77	157·22	159·41	161·40	163·21	2
148·00	149·19	150·32	151·39	153·85	156·04	158·03	159·84	3
143·72	144·92	146·05	147·12	149·59	151·79	153·79	155·60	5
140·90	142·11	143·24	144·31	146·79	148·99	150·99	152·80	7
137·89	139·10	140·24	141·31	143·80	146·01	148·02	149·83	10
134·44	135·65	136·79	137·86	140·36	142·58	144·59	146·41	15
131·98	133·20	134·35	135·43	137·94	140·17	142·19	144·02	20
130·04	131·27	132·43	133·52	136·04	138·28	140·31	142·15	25
128·45	129·69	130·86	131·96	134·50	136·76	138·80	140·66	30
125·92	127·18	128·37	129·48	132·04	134·32	136·38	138·26	40
123·93	125·22	126·43	127·56	130·15	132·46	134·54	136·44	50
122·27	123·57	124·79	125·93	128·55	130·88	132·97	134·88	60
120·86	122·18	123·42	124·58	127·23	129·58	131·69	133·62	70
119·60	120·94	122·20	123·38	126·06	128·43	130·56	132·51	80
117·48	118·86	120·14	121·34	124·07	126·49	128·66	130·64	100
115·69	117·10	118·41	119·64	122·43	124·89	127·09	129·10	120
114·15	115·60	116·95	118·21	121·06	123·55	125·78	127·82	140
112·80	114·29	115·67	116·96	119·86	122·39	124·65	126·71	160
111·60	113·13	114·54	115·86	118·80	121·37	123·66	125·74	180
110·52	112·08	113·51	114·85	117·83	120·43	122·74	124·84	200
108·25	109·87	111·35	112·72	115·76	118·40			250
106·33	107·99	109·51	110·91	114·02	116·70			300
104·78	106·48	108·03	109·45	112·58	115·27			350
103·44	105·16	106·73	108·17	111·33	114·03			400
101·22	102·98	104·58	106·04	109·22	111·93			500
99·56	101·34	102·95	104·41	107·58	110·29			600
96·81	98·61	100·22	101·68	104·85	107·56			800
94·77	96·57	98·18	99·64	102·81	105·51			1000
91·03	92·79	94·36	95·78	98·85	101·45			1500
88·23	89·94	91·46	92·82	95·74	98·18			2000
								2500
								3000
								4000
								5000

ARGON

ENTHALPY, JOULES/MOLE

Pressure atm	Temperature, °K								
	90	100	110	120	130	135	140	145	150
1	9,547	9,759	9,971	10,183	10,394	10,499	10,605	10,710	10,816
2		9,721	9,937	10,153	10,368	10,475	10,582	10,688	10,795
3		9,670	9,891	10,111	10,330	10,439	10,548	10,656	10,765
5			9,808	10,037	10,264	10,377	10,490	10,602	10,714
7				9,955	10,191	10,308	10,424	10,540	10,655
10				9,810	10,066	10,192	10,317	10,441	10,563
15				4,621	9,849	9,991	10,131	10,268	10,403
20				4,630	5,234	9,756	9,918	10,075	10,227
25				4,639	5,234	9,471	9,675	9,862	10,037
30				4,647	5,234	5,575	9,372	9,614	9,827
40				4,664	5,235	5,553	5,903	6,353	9,335 ⊙
50				4,677	5,235	5,541	5,870	6,258	6,978
60				4,688	5,235	5,531	5,842	6,187	6,604
70				4,697	5,236	5,522	5,820	6,141	6,492
80				4,706	5,236	5,515	5,803	6,108	6,440
100			4,224	4,723	5,237	5,504	5,779	6,064	6,367
120				4,740	5,238	5,493	5,756	6,026	6,037
140				4,757	5,242	5,490	5,742	6,000	6,264
160				4,774	5,246	5,487	5,731	5,978	6,231
180				4,790	5,251	5,486	5,723	5,978	6,209
200	3,479	3,920	4,362	4,806	5,257	5,486	5,718	5,963	6,194
250									
300		4,056	4,466	4,878	5,293		5,713		6,139
350									
400									
500		4,395	4,675	5,055	5,435		5,816		6,197
600									
800									
1,000			5,441	5,769	6,101		6,439		6,781
1,500									
2,000					8,248		8,565		8,884
2,500									
3,000									11,109
4,000									
5,000									

ENTHALPY, JOULES/MOLE—*cont.*

Temperature, °K								Pressure atm
155	160	170	180	190	200	210	220	
10,921	11,026	11,237	11,447	11,656	11,866	12,075	12,284	1
10,901	11,007	11,220	11,432	11,643	11,854	12,064	12,274	2
10,873	10,981	11,195	11,409	11,623	11,836	12,048	12,259	3
10,825	10,936	11,156	11,375	11,592	11,808	12,023	12,235	5
10,769	10,883	11,109	11,333	11,555	11,775	11,993	12,209	7
10,684	10,804	11,041	11,274	11,503	11,729	11,952	12,173	10
10,536	10,666	10,922	11,171	11,413	11,650	11,882	12,110	15
10,375	10,519	10,798	11,065	11,322	11,570	11,811	12,046	20
10,204	10,366	10,668	10,954	11,227	11,488	11,739	11,981	25
10,021	10,203	10,532	10,839	11,129	11,404	11,665	11,915	30
9,607	9,841	10,239	10,597	10.926	11,230	11,514	11,782	40
8,982	9,418	9,924	10,345	10,715	11,050	11,359	11,647	50
7,292	8,660	9,566	10,072	10,495	10,865	11,201	11,509	60
6,992	7,780	9,122	9,776	10,265	10,676	11,040	11,369	70
6,835	7,375	8,575	9,457	10,023	10,480	10,876	11,228	80
6,692	7,051	7,947	8,812	9,518	10,072	10,537	10,942	100
6,600	6,905	7,627	8,371	9,061	9,675	10,205	10,660	120
6,537	6,824	7,448	8,101	8,744	9,349	9,901	10,390	140
6,494	6,769	7,342	7,933	8,526	9,100	9,646	10,148	160
6,463	6,727	7,270	7,820	8,375	8,915	9,438	9,934	180
6,441	6,693	7,209	7,733	8,255	8,770	9,271	9,751	200
								250
	6,573	7,018	7,472	7,929	8,385	8,837	9,280	300
								350
								400
	6,581	6,969	7,362	7,761	8,165	8,572	8,981	500
								600
								800
	7,128	7,481	7,840	8,205	8,576	8,953	9,335	1,000
								1,500
	9,206	9,533	9,867	10,207	10,554	10,907	11,266	2,000
								2,500
	11,423	11,739	12,060	12,388	12,722	13,062	13,407	3,000
		14,001	14,315	14,635	14,961	15,293	15,630	4,000
				16,935	17,255	17,580	17,910	5,000

ENTHALPY, JOULES/MOLE—*cont.*

Pressure atm	Temperature, °K								
	230	240	250	260	270	280	290	300	320
1	12,493	12,702	12,910	13,119	13,327	13,536	13,744	13,952	14,369
2	12,484	12,694	12,903	13,112	13,320	13,529	13,737	13,945	14,363
3	12,470	12,681	12,891	13,101	13,310	13,519	13,728	13,937	14,356
5	12,448	12,660	12,871	13,082	13,293	13,503	13,713	13,923	14,343
7	12,424	12,638	12,851	13,063	13,275	13,486	13,697	13,908	14,329
10	12,391	12,607	12,822	13,036	13,249	13,462	13,674	13,886	14,309
15	12,334	12,555	12,774	12,991	13,207	13,422	13,636	13,850	14,277
20	12,276	12,502	12,725	12,945	13,164	13,381	13,597	13,813	14,244
25	12,217	12,448	12,675	12,898	13,120	13,340	13,559	13,777	14,212
30	12,157	12,393	12,624	12,851	13,076	13,299	13,520	13,741	14,180
40	12,038	12,284	12,523	12,758	12,989	13,217	13,444	13,669	14,117
50	11,917	12,174	12,422	12,664	12,902	13,136	13,368	13,598	14,055
60	11,794	12,063	12,321	12,571	12,815	13,054	13,292	13,527	13,993
70	11,671	11,951	12,218	12,476	12,727	12,973	13,216	13,457	13,932
80	11,547	11,840	12,115	12,380	12,638	12,891	13,140	13,386	13,870
100	11,299	11,620	11,915	12,194	12,465	12,731	12,991	13,247	13,750
120	11,055	11,404	11,719	12,014	12,298	12,576	12,848	13,115	13,636
140	10,819	11,195	11,527	11,840	12,137	12,427	12,710	12,989	13,527
160	10,598	10,994	11,346	11,672	11,983	12,285	12,579	12,867	13,424
180	10,392	10,804	11,172	11,513	11,839	12,153	12,458	12,756	13,330
200	10,207	10,628	11,009	11,367	11,707	12,033	12,349	12,656	13,244
250			10,725	11,101	11,461	11,806	12,138	12,459	13,073
300	9,711	10,128	10,529	10,913	11,282	11,637	11,979	12,310	12,942
350			10,385	10,772	11,147	11,510	11,861	12,200	12,849
400			10,280	10,670	11,049	11,417	11,774	12,120	12,784
500	9,390	9,796	10,196	10,588	10,972	11,347	11,712	12,068	12,751
600			10,169	10,563	10,950	11,330	11,702	12,065	12,761
800			10,253	10,648	11,040	11,427	11,807	12,180	12,898
1,000	9,722	10,113	10,506	10,899	11,290	11,678	12,061	12,437	13,159
1,500			11,404	11,788	12,172	12,552	12,927	13,295	13,999
2,000	11,631	12,002	12,377	12,753	13,128	13,499	13,863	14,219	14,902
2,500			13,406	13,770	14,133	14,493	14,848	15,195	15,856
3,000	13,757	14,112	14,469	14,826	15,181	15,533	15,879	16,217	16,858
4,000	15,971	16,313	16,657	17,002	17,346	17,689	18,028	18,359	18,987
5,000	18,243	18,577	18,914	19,253	19,592	19,930	20,264	20,591	21,208

ENTHALPY, JOULES/MOLE—*cont.*

Temperature, °K								Pressure atm
340	360	380	400	450	500	550	600	
14,785	15,202	15,618	16,034	17,075	18,116	19,157	20,197	1
14,780	15,197	15,614	16,030	17,072	18,114	19,156	20,197	2
14,774	15,192	15,609	16,026	17,069	18,112	19,155	20,197	3
14,762	15,181	15,599	16,017	17,063	18,108	19,153	30,197	5
14,750	15,170	15,589	16,008	17,057	18,104	19,151	20,197	7
14,732	15,154	15,575	15,996	17,048	18,099	19,149	20,198	10
14,703	15,128	15,552	15,975	17,033	18,090	19,145	20,199	15
14,674	15,102	15,529	15,955	17,019	18,081	19,141	20,200	20
14,645	15,076	15,506	15,935	17,005	18,073	19,138	20,202	25
14,617	15,051	15,484	15,916	16,992	18,066	19,136	20,205	30
14,562	15,003	15,442	15,879	16,967	18,051	19,132	20,210	40
14,508	14,956	15,401	15,843	16,942	18,037	19,128	20,216	50
14,454	14,909	15,360	15,808	16,919	18,024	19,125	20,222	60
14,400	14,862	15,319	15,772	16,895	18,011	19,122	20,229	70
14,346	14,815	15,278	15,737	16,872	17,998	19,119	20,235	80
14,241	14,722	15,196	15,666	16,826	17,975	19,116	20,250	100
14,142	14,636	15,122	15,602	16,784	17,954	19,113	20,265	120
14,049	14,556	15,054	15,544	16,748	17,936	19,112	20,280	140
13,962	14,483	14,992	15,492	16,717	17,920	19,111	20,295	160
13,882	14,416	14,936	15,446	16,690	17,905	19,111	20,311	180
13,808	14,354	14,885	15,404	16,665	17,890	19,112	20,326	200
13,659	14,225	14,774	15,308	16,601	17,854			250
13,546	14,127	14,689	15,236	16,554	17,823			300
13,467	14,059	14,631	15,186	16,518	17,795			350
13,414	14,016	14,595	15,157	16,500	17,781			400
13,399	14,015	14,605	15,173	16,522	17,808			500
13,419	14,043	14,639	15,210	16,560	17,848			600
13,570	14,198	14,794	15,364	16,713	18,001			800
13,835	14,465	15,060	15,629	16,976	18,258			1,000
14,656	15,272	15,853	16,407	17,711	18,946			1,500
15,542	16,141	16,703	17,235	18,476	19,635			2,000
								2,500
								3,000
								4,000
								5,000

ARGON

VOLUME, CUBIC CENTIMETRES/MOLE

Pressure atm	Temperature, °K									
	90	100	110	120	130	135	140	145	150	155
1	7,223	8,056	8,889	9,722	10,555	10,973	11,390	11,806	12,222	12,638
2		3,949	4,373	4,796	5,220	5,433	5,645	5,856	6,067	6,277
3		2,579	2,867	3,154	3,441	3,585	3,729	3,872	4,015	4,157
5			1,654	1,836	2,017	2,107	2,196	2,285	2,373	2,461
7				1,267	1,404	1,471	1,537	1,603	1,669	1,734
10				837	942	993	1,043	1,092	1,140	1,188
15				34·2	577	618	647	694	729	763
20				34·1	37·3	424	459	490	520	549
25				34·0	37·1	296	334	364	392	418
30				33·9	36·9	39·1	240	273	302	328
40				33·7	36·6	38·6	41·5	46·8	182	209
50				33·5	36·4	38·2	40·5	44·0	54·9	127
60				33·4	36·2	37·8	39·9	42·8	48·3	60
70				33·2	35·8	37·3	39·2	41·7	45·4	51
80				33·1	35·4	36·9	38·6	40·8	43·8	48
100			31·1	32·8	34·9	36·2	37·7	39·5	41·8	44
120				32·6	34·5	35·7	37·0	38·5	40·4	42
140				32·3	34·2	35·2	36·4	37·8	39·4	41
160				32·0	33·8	34·8	35·9	37·2	38·6	40
180				31·8	33·5	34·4	35·5	36·6	37·9	39
200	28·0	29·1	30·3	31·7	33·2	34·1	35·1	36·2	37·4	38
250										
300		28·8	29·8	30·9	32·0		33·2		34·7	
350										
400										
500		27·9	28·7	29·5	30·3		31·1		31·9	
600										
800										
1,000			26·9	27·5	28·1		28·6		29·2	
1,500										
2,000					25·4		52·9		26·3	
2,500										
3,000									24·9	
4,000										
5,000										

VOLUME, CUBIC CENTIMETRES/MOLE—*cont.*

Temperature, °K									Pressure atm
160	170	180	190	200	210	220	230	240	
13,053	13,883	14,711	15,538	16,364	17,189	18,014	18,838	19,662	1
6,488	6,908	7,326	7,743	8,158	8,573	8,987	9,401	9,815	2
4,299	4,583	4,864	5,144	5,423	5,701	5,978	6,256	6,533	3
2,548	2,722	2,894	3,065	3,235	3,404	3,572	3,740	3,907	5
1,798	1,925	2,050	2,174	2,297	2,419	2,540	2,661	2,782	7
1,235	1,327	1,417	1,505	1,593	1,680	1,767	1,853	1,938	10
796	861	924	985	1,046	1,106	1,165	1,224	1,282	15
576	628	678	725	772	819	864	909	954	20
442	488	529	569	608	646	684	721	758	25
351	393	430	465	499	532	564	596	627	30
233	273	306	335	362	388	414	439	463	40
157	197	229	256	280	302	324	345	364·9	50
97·0	144	176	202	225	245	264	282	299·7	60
66·0	105	138	164	186	204	221	237	253·2	70
56·0	82·5	110	135	156	174	189	204	218·6	80
48·6	61·6	78·8	97·3	115	132	146	158	170·4	100
45·4	53·1	64·3	77·5	91·1	105	117	128	138·9	120
43·4	49·2	57·0	66·5	77·0	87·5	97·7	108	117·0	140
42·0	46·6	52·5	59·7	68·1	76·6	85·0	93·4	101·5	160
40·9	44·7	49·6	55·4	62·0	68·9	76·0	83·1	90·3	180
40·0	43·3	47·4	52·1	57·5	63·4	69·4	75·6	81·8	200
									250
36·4	38·5	40·8	43·4	46·2	49·3	52·5	55·9	59·4	300
									350
									400
32·8	33·8	35·0	36·4	38·0	39·7	41·5	43·3	45·2	500
									600
									800
29·7	30·3	30·8	31·4	32·0	32·7	33·4	34·2	35·0	1,000
									1,500
26·8	27·2	27·7	28·1	28·5	29·0	29·4	29·8	30·2	2,000
									2,500
25·2	25·5	25·9	26·2	26·5	26·9	27·2	27·5	27·9	3,000
	24·6	24·8	25·0	25·3	25·5	25·7	26·0	26·3	4,000
			24·3	24·5	24·7	24·9	25·1	25·3	5,000

VOLUME, CUBIC CENTIMETRES/MOLE—*cont.*

Pressure atm	Temperature, °K							
	250	260	270	280	290	300	320	340
1	20,485	21,308	22,131	22,954	23,777	24,599	26,244	27,889
2	10,228	16,641	11,054	11,467	11,879	12,292	13,116	13,939
3	6,809	7,086	7,362	7,638	7,914	8,189	8,740	9,290
5	4,074	4,242	4,409	4,575	4,742	4,908	5,240	5,571
7	2,902	3,023	3,143	3,263	3,382	3,502	3,740	3,977
10	2,024	2,109	2,194	2,279	2,363	2,447	2,614	2,781
15	1,340	1,398	1,456	1,513	1,570	1,627	1,739	1,852
20	999	1,043	1,087	1,130	1,174	1,217	1,302	1,387
25	794	830	865	901	936	971	1,040	1,109
30	657	688	718	748	777	807	865	923
40	487	511	534	557	580	602	647	691
50	384·7	404·3	423·5	442·4	461·1	479·6	516·1	551·8
60	316·8	333·6	350·1	366·3	382·2	398·0	428·9	459·2
70	268·4	283·3	297·8	312·0	326·0	339·8	366·7	393·1
80	232·3	245·7	258·7	271·4	283·9	296·2	320·2	343·6
100	182·1	193·4	204·3	214·9	225·3	235·4	255·2	274·5
120	149·2	159·1	168·5	177·7	186·6	195·3	212·2	228·7
140	126·2	135·0	143·4	151·5	159·4	167·0	181·8	196·2
160	109·5	117·4	125·0	132·3	139·3	146·0	159·2	172·1
180	97·3	104·2	111·0	117·6	123·9	130·0	141·9	153·5
200	88·0	94·1	100·2	106·2	111·9	117·4	128·3	138·8
250	72·3	77·0	81·8	86·5	91·1	95·6	104·4	113·0
300	63·0	66·8	70·6	74·5	78·3	82·1	89·3	96·4
350	56·8	60·0	63·2	66·5	69·7	72·9	79·0	85·0
400	52·7	55·3	58·1	60·8	63·6	66·3	71·6	76·7
500	47·1	49·1	51·2	53·4	55·6	57·7	61·8	65·7
600	43·4	45·2	47·0	48·7	50·5	52·2	55·5	58·7
800	38·6	40·1	41·5	42·9	44·2	45·4	47·8	50·1
1,000	35·9	36·9	38·0	39·2	40·3	41·3	43·2	45·0
1,500	32·7	33·2	33·7	34·3	34·9	35·5	36·8	38·0
2,000	30·7	31·1	31·5	31·9	32·3	32·7	33·5	34·1
2,500	29·2	29·6	29·9	30·3	30·6	30·9	31·6	
3,000	28·2	28·5	28·9	29·2	29·5	29·8	30·5	
4,000	26·5	26·8	27·1	27·4	27·7	28·0	28·6	
5,000	25·6	25·8	26·0	26·3	26·5	26·8	27·3	

VOLUME, CUBIC CENTIMETRES/MOLE—*cont.*

Temperature, °K							Pressure atm
360	380	400	450	500	550	600	
29,533	31,176	32,819	36,925	41,031	45,136	49,240	1
14,762	15,585	16,408	18,463	20,518	22,572	24,625	2
9,840	10,389	10,938	12,310	13,681	15,051	16,421	3
5,902	6,232	6,562	7,387	8,211	9,035	9,857	5
4,214	4,451	4,687	5,278	5,868	6,457	7,045	7
2,948	3,115	3,281	3,696	4,110	4,523	4,935	10
1,964	2,076	2,187	2,465	2,742	3,018	3,294	15
1,472	1,556	1,641	1,850	2,058	2,266	2,473	20
1,177	1,245	1,313	1,481	1,648	1,815	1,981	25
980	1,037	1,094	1,235	1,375	1,514	1,653	30
735	778	821	927	1,033	1,138	1,243	40
587·2	622·2	656·9	743·0	828·4	913·1	997·1	50
489·0	518·5	547·8	620·2	691·8	762·8	833·1	60
419·0	444·6	469·9	532·5	594·3	655·5	716·0	70
366·6	389·3	411·6	466·8	521·3	575·1	628·2	80
293·4	311·9	329·8	375·0	419·1	462·5	505·3	100
244·8	260·6	276·0	313·8	351·0	387·3	423·2	120
210·3	224·0	237·4	270·3	302·3	333·7	364·6	140
184·6	196·8	208·7	237·8	265·9	293·4	320·6	160
164·7	175·7	186·5	212·5	237·6	262·2	286·4	180
149·0	159·0	168·8	192·3	214·9	237·1	259·0	200
121·3	129·5	137·5	156·3	174·3			250
103·3	110·1	116·8	132·4	147·3			300
90·9	96·6	102·3	115·5	128·1			350
81·8	86·7	91·6	103·0	113·9			400
69·6	73·4	77·2	86·1	94·8			500
61·8	64·9	68·0	75·3	82·5			600
52·4	54·6	56·8	62·3	67·7			800
46·8	48·5	50·3	54·7	58·9			1,000
39·3	40·4	41·6	44·5	47·3			1,500
34·7	35·3	35·8	37·2	38·4			2,000
							2,500
							3,000
							4,000
							5,000

ARGON

SPECIFIC HEAT AT CONSTANT PRESSURE, JOULES/MOLE, °K

Pressure atm	Temperature, °K								
	90	100	110	120	130	135	140	145	150
1	21·24	21·21	21·18	21·15	21·13	21·11	21·10	21·08	21·07
2		21·64	21·58	21·52	21·47	21·44	21·41	21·38	21·36
3		22·10	22·00	21·91	21·82	21·77	21·73	21·69	21·65
5			22·96	22·78	22·61	22·53	22·45	22·37	22·29
7				23·81	23·52	23·38	23·25	23·12	22·99
10				25·74	25·18	24·92	24·68	24·45	26·23
15				57·3	28·75	28·18	27·66	27·17	27·73
20				56·6	71·0	33·00	31·81	30·81	29·95
25				56·0	66·7	43·50	38·82	36·13	34·19
30				55·5	63·6	—	53·5	45·1	40·45
40				54·5	61·1	68·3	—	—	60·0
50				53·7	59·0	64·4	—	—	—
60				53·0	57·3	61·3	67·2	—	—
70				52·3	55·9	58·9	62·9	70·0	—
80				51·7	54·7	57·0	60·0	65·2	74·0
100			49·7	50·5	52·6	54·2	56·2	59·6	63·6
120				49·2	50·8	51·9	53·3	55·5	58·0
140				48·0	49·2	50·0	51·1	52·6	54·6
160				46·8	47·8	48·5	49·4	50·6	52·2
180				45·7	46·6	47·3	48·1	49·1	50·4
200	44·1	44·2	44·3	44·6	45·6	46·2	47·0	48·0	49·0
250									
300		41·0	41·1	41·3	41·7		42·3		43·2
350									
400									
500		38·0	38·0	38·0	38·1		38·1		38·2
600									
800									
1000			32·8	32·9	33·6		34·0		34·4
1500									
2000					31·8		31·9		32·1
2500									
3000									31·3
4000									
5000									

SPECIFIC HEAT AT CONSTANT PRESSURE, JOULES/MOLE, °K—*cont.*

Temperature, °K										Pressure atm
155	160	170	180	190	200	210	220	230	240	
21·06	21·04	21·01	20·99	20·96	20·94	20·91	20·89	20·87	20·86	1
21·33	21·30	21·24	21·19	21·14	21·09	21·04	20·99	20·95	20·93	2
21·61	21·57	21·48	21·40	21·32	21·24	21·17	21·10	21·04	21·00	3
22·21	22·13	21·98	21·83	21·69	21·56	21·44	21·33	21·23	21·15	5
22·86	22·74	22·50	22·28	22·07	21·89	21·72	21·57	21·43	21·31	7
24·01	23·81	23·43	23·08	22·76	22·46	22·19	21·95	21·74	21·56	10
26·31	25·92	25·19	24·53	23·95	23·43	22·98	22·59	22·26	21·99	15
29·19	28·50	27·26	26·20	25·29	24·49	23·81	23·25	22·79	22·42	20
32·68	31·46	29·53	27·97	26·69	25·59	24·67	23·93	23·33	22·86	25
37·24	34·96	32·03	29·88	28·18	26·76	25·58	24·63	23·88	23·31	30
50·1	44·0	37·77	34·18	31·48	29·28	27·52	26·12	25·04	24·23	40
—	62·0	45·66	39·34	35·20	32·08	29·65	27·73	26·27	25·19	50
—	—	59·0	45·8	39·35	35·19	31·97	29·47	27·58	26·20	60
—	—	—	55·2	44·4	38·63	34·51	31·35	28·99	27·27	70
—	—	—	66·0	50·4	42·4	37·27	33·37	30·47	28·40	80
69·3	86·0	89·0	81·0	61·2	50·4	43·2	37·74	33·64	30·73	100
61·1	65·0	74·0	72·5	65·2	57·1	49·0	42·1	36·92	33·01	120
56·8	59·5	64·6	65·3	62·5	57·8	52·1	45·9	40·1	35·17	140
54·0	55·8	58·4	59·4	58·5	56·2	52·6	47·6	42·2	37·25	160
51·8	53·1	54·7	55·4	54·6	53·3	51·1	47·7	43·6	38·85	180
50·0	50·9	52·1	52·3	51·9	50·8	49·2	46·9	43·9	39·80	200
										250
	44·1	45·0	45·6	45·7	45·4	44·8	43·8	42·4	40·8	300
										350
										400
	38·60	39·09	39·59	40·1	40·6	40·8	41·0	40·8	40·4	500
										600
										800
	35·02	35·60	36·19	36·80	37·40	37·96	38·49	38·94	39·27	1000
										1500
	32·53	33·12	33·73	34·35	34·98	35·60	36·20	36·78	37·28	2000
										2500
	31·5	31·85	32·46	33·08	33·67	34·23	34·76	35·23	35·60	3000
		31·12	31·70	32·30	32·88	33·42	33·88	34·22	34·37	4000
			31·73	32·29	32·77	33·15	33·42	33·62		5000

ARGON

SPECIFIC HEAT AT CONSTANT PRESSURE, JOULES/MOLE, °K—*cont.*

Pressure atm	Temperature, °K						
	250	260	270	280	290	300	320
1	20·85	20·84	20·83	20·83	20·83	20·83	20·82
2	20·91	20·89	20·88	20·87	20·87	20·87	20·86
3	20·97	20·95	20·93	20·92	20·91	20·91	20·90
5	21·09	21·05	21·02	21·01	21·00	20·99	20·97
7	21·22	21·16	21·12	21·10	21·08	21·07	21·04
10	21·42	21·33	21·27	21·24	21·21	21·19	21·14
15	21·78	21·63	21·54	21·48	21·44	21·40	21·33
20	22·14	21·94	21·81	21·73	21·67	21·62	21·52
25	22·51	22·26	22·09	21·98	21·90	21·84	21·71
30	22·89	22·58	22·37	22·24	22·14	22·07	21·91
40	23·64	23·24	22·97	22·78	22·64	22·53	22·31
50	24·43	23·93	23·59	23·34	23·15	23·00	22·72
60	25·25	24·64	24·22	23·91	23·67	23·49	23·14
70	26·10	25·36	24·86	24·49	24·21	23·98	23·56
80	26·97	26·08	25·52	25·09	24·76	24·48	23·99
100	28·71	27·54	26·84	26·29	25·86	25·49	24·84
120	30·40	29·00	28·16	27·49	26·96	26·49	25·69
140	32·05	30·45	29·47	28·68	28·04	27·48	26·52
160	33·65	31·89	30·76	29·85	29·09	28·44	27·33
180	35·22	33·32	32·03	30·98	30·10	29·35	28·11
200	36·76	34·72	33·26	32·05	31·05	30·20	28·82
250	38·52	36·81	35·24	33·84	32·64	31·56	29·92
300	39·24	37·68	36·18	34·83	33·61	32·56	30·87
350	39·40	38·10	36·84	35·63	34·48	33·39	31·66
400	39·52	38·38	37·23	36·14	35·10	34·11	32·32
500	39·64	38·82	37·94	37·01	36·06	35·10	33·25
600	39·72	39·07	38·36	37·58	36·73	35·82	33·95
800	39·63	39·36	38·93	38·35	37·65	36·84	34·75
1000	39·36	39·24	38·98	38·56	37·96	37·14	34·96
1500	38·44	38·42	38·21	37·87	37·26	36·28	34·04
2000	37·56	37·57	37·31	36·81	36·02	35·13	33·10
2500	36·40	36·37	36·18	35·76	35·12	34·20	31·70
3000	35·71	35·64	35·40	34·93	34·23	33·30	30·30
4000	34·45	34·49	34·39	34·11	33·57	32·70	29·65
5000	33·80	33·94	33·89	33·62	33·09	32·22	29·18

SPECIFIC HEAT AT CONSTANT PRESSURE, JOULES/MOLE, °K—*cont.*

Temperature, °K								Pressure atm
340	360	380	400	450	500	550	600	
20·82	20·82	20·82	20·82	20·81	20·81	20·81	20·81	1
20·85	20·85	20·84	20·84	20·83	20·83	20·83	20·82	2
20·89	20·88	20·87	20·87	20·86	20·85	20·85	20·84	3
20·95	20·94	20·93	20·92	20·91	20·90	20·89	20·88	5
21·01	20·99	20·98	20·97	20·95	20·94	20·93	20·91	7
21·11	21·08	21·06	21·05	21·02	21·00	20·99	20·97	10
21·28	21·24	21·21	21·18	21·14	21·11	21·09	21·07	15
21·45	21·39	21·35	21·31	21·26	21·22	21·19	21·17	20
21·62	21·55	21·49	21·44	21·38	21·33	21·30	21·28	25
21·80	21·71	21·63	21·57	21·49	21·44	21·40	21·38	30
22·15	22·02	21·91	21·83	21·72	21·65	21·61	21·58	40
22·51	22·34	22·19	22·09	21·94	21·86	21·82	21·78	50
22·87	22·65	22·47	22·34	22·17	22·07	22·02	21·98	60
23·23	22·96	22·75	22·60	22·39	22·28	22·22	22·17	70
23·59	23·27	23·03	22·85	22·61	22·48	22·41	22·35	80
24·31	23·89	23·58	23·36	23·04	22·87	22·77	22·70	100
25·04	24·53	24·14	23·86	23·47	23·25	23·12	23·03	120
25·75	25·15	24·69	24·36	23·87	23·59	23·44	23·34	140
26·45	25·76	25·23	24·84	24·24	23·91	23·73	23·61	160
27·12	26·34	25·74	25·29	24·57	24·20	23·99	23·85	180
27·77	26·87	26·20	25·68	24·85	24·44	24·19	24·03	200
28·78	27·84	27·07	26·44	25·42	24·82			250
29·58	28·55	27·71	27·00	25·80	25·05			300
30·24	29·09	28·17	27·40	26·03	25·19			350
30·79	29·51	28·49	27·70	26·16	25·30			400
31·56	30·12	28·94	28·00	26·32	25·45			500
32·02	30·45	29·14	28·11	26·38	25·52			600
32·54	30·67	29·24	28·11	26·35	25·49			800
32·66	30·58	29·08	27·93	26·17	25·31			1000
31·80	29·86	28·33	27·16	25·26	24·27			1500
30·96	28·97	27·29	25·99	23·90	22·51			2000
								2500
								3000
								4000
								5000

ARGON

SPECIFIC HEAT AT CONSTANT VOLUME, JOULES/MOLE, °K

Pressure atm	Temperature, °K									
	90	100	110	120	130	135	140	145	150	155
1	12·94	12·84	12·76	12·70	12·65	12·63	12·61	12·60	12·58	12·57
2		13·05	12·93	12·84	12·76	12·73	12·70	12·68	12·65	12·63
3		13·23	13·08	12·96	12·86	12·82	12·78	12·75	12·72	12·69
5			13·33	13·17	13·03	12·97	12·91	12·87	12·83	12·79
7				13·34	13·18	13·10	13·03	12·98	12·93	12·88
10				13·59	13·37	13·27	13·19	13·12	13·06	13·01
15				16·60	13·65	13·53	13·43	13·35	13·28	13·21
20				16·62	16·37	13·76	13·65	13·56	13·48	13·40
25				16·65	16·40	13·97	13·86	13·76	13·66	13·57
30				16·67	16·43	16·28	14·06	13·95	13·84	13·74
40				16·72	16·48	16·33	16·17	15·97	14·21	14·08
50				16·76	16·53	16·38	16·22	16·03	15·79	14·55
60				16·80	16·57	16·43	16·28	16·10	15·86	15·05
70				16·84	16·62	16·47	16·32	16·14	15·92	15·38
80				16·88	16·66	16·52	16·37	16·19	15·98	15·58
100			17·16	16·96	16·74	16·61	16·46	16·29	16·09	15·79
120				17·03	16·82	16·69	16·54	16·38	16·20	15·96
140				17·11	16·89	16·76	16·62	16·47	16·30	16·11
160				17·18	16·96	16·84	16·71	16·57	16·41	16·24
180				17·25	17·03	16·91	16·88	16·65	16·51	16·36
200	17·89	17·71	17·52	17·32	17·10	16·99	16·87	16·74	16·61	16·47
250										
300		18·00	17·81	17·62	17·42		17·22		17·01	
350										
400										
500		18·44	18·28	18·12	17·96		17·81		17·66	
600										
800										
1000			18·94	18·89	18·85		18·81		18·77	
1500										
2000					20·40		20·39		20·39	
2500										
3000									21·50	
4000										
5000										

SPECIFIC HEAT AT CONSTANT VOLUME, JOULES/MOLE, °K—*cont.*

Temperature, °K										Pressure atm
160	170	180	190	200	210	220	230	240	250	
12·56	12·54	12·52	12·51	12·50	12·50	12·50	12·49	12·49	12·49	1
12·62	12·59	12·56	12·54	12·52	12·52	12·52	12·52	12·51	12·51	2
12·67	12·63	12·60	12·57	12·55	12·54	12·54	12·54	12·53	12·53	3
12·76	12·71	12·67	12·63	12·60	12·58	12·57	12·57	12·56	12·56	5
12·85	12·78	12·73	12·69	12·65	12·63	12·62	12·61	12·60	12·59	7
12·97	12·89	12·82	12·77	12·73	12·70	12·68	12·66	12·65	12·64	10
13·16	13·05	12·97	12·90	12·85	12·82	12·79	12·76	12·74	12·72	15
13·34	13·21	13·11	13·03	12·97	12·93	12·89	12·85	12·83	12·80	20
13·50	13·36	13·24	13·15	13·08	13·03	12·98	12·94	12·91	12·88	25
13·66	13·50	13·37	13·27	13·19	13·13	13·07	13·02	12·98	12·95	30
13·97	13·78	13·62	13·49	13·39	13·31	13·24	13·18	13·13	13·09	40
14·28	14·03	13·84	13·69	13·57	13·48	13·40	13·33	13·27	13·22	50
14·60	14·25	14·03	13·87	13·74	13·64	13·56	13·48	13·41	13·35	60
14·89	14·45	14·20	14·03	13·90	13·79	13·70	13·62	13·55	13·48	70
15·14	14·64	14·36	14·18	14·05	13·94	13·85	13·76	13·68	13·61	80
15·49	14·99	14·66	14·46	14·32	14·21	14·11	14·02	13·94	13·86	100
15·72	15·26	14·93	14·72	14·57	14·46	14·35	14·26	14·17	14·08	120
15·90	15·49	15·18	14·96	14·81	14·69	14·58	14·48	14·38	14·28	140
16·05	15·70	15·41	15·19	15·03	14·90	14·78	14·67	14·56	14·46	160
16·19	15·88	15·61	15·40	15·23	15·09	14·96	14·84	14·73	14·62	180
16·32	16·04	15·79	15·59	15·42	15·27	15·13	15·00	14·88	14·77	200
									15·12	250
16·81	16·61	16·42	16·24	16·07	15·92	15·79	15·67	15·55	15·44	300
									15·73	350
									15·99	400
17·52	17·38	17·25	17·13	17·01	16·90	16·79	16·69	16·59	16·49	500
									16·94	600
									17·71	800
18·73	18·68	18·64	18·60	18·56	18·52	18·48	18·45	18·42	18·39	1000
									19·80	1500
20·41	20·42	20·45	20·50	20·56	20·61	20·67	20·75	20·84	20·94	2000
									21·90	2500
21·56	21·63	21·72	21·83	21·86	22·01	22·17	22·34	22·53	22·74	3000
	22·25	22·42	22·61	22·83	23·07	23·32	23·58	23·86	24·16	4000
		23·42	23·65	23·92	24·23	24·57	24·94	25·33		5000

ARGON

SPECIFIC HEAT AT CONSTANT VOLUME, JOULES/MOLE, °K—*cont.*

Pressure atm	Temperature, °K						
	260	270	280	290	300	320	340
1	12·49	12·49	12·48	12·48	12·48	12·48	12·48
2	12·51	12·50	12·50	12·49	12·49	12·49	12·49
3	12·53	12·52	12·51	12·51	12·51	12·51	12·50
5	12·55	12·54	12·54	12·54	12·53	12·53	12·53
7	12·58	12·57	12·57	12·56	12·56	12·55	12·55
10	12·63	12·62	12·61	12·60	12·59	12·58	12·57
15	12·70	12·69	12·67	12·66	12·65	12·64	12·63
20	12·78	12·76	12·74	12·72	12·71	12·69	12·68
25	12·85	12·83	12·81	12·79	12·77	12·75	12·73
30	12·92	12·89	13·87	13·85	12·83	12·80	12·78
40	13·05	13·02	13·00	12·97	12·95	12·91	12·88
50	13·18	13·15	13·12	13·09	13·07	13·02	12·98
60	13·31	13·27	13·24	13·20	13·18	13·12	13·07
70	13·43	13·39	13·35	13·31	13·28	13·21	13·15
80	13·55	13·50	13·46	13·41	13·37	13·30	13·23
100	13·79	13·73	13·67	13·61	13·56	13·47	13·39
120	14·00	13·93	13·86	13·79	13·73	13·62	13·54
140	14·19	14·11	14·03	13·96	13·89	13·77	13·68
160	14·36	14·27	14·19	14·11	14·04	13·91	13·81
180	14·52	14·43	14·34	14·26	14·19	14·05	13·94
200	14·67	14·58	14·49	14·41	14·33	14·19	14·07
250	15·01	14·91	14·82	14·74	14·66	14·51	14·38
300	15·33	15·22	15·13	15·04	14·96	14·81	14·67
350	15·62	15·52	15·42	15·33	15·25	15·10	14·96
400	15·88	15·78	15·69	15·61	15·53	15·38	15·24
500	16·39	16·30	16·21	16·13	16·05	15·90	15·77
600	16·85	16·77	16·69	16·61	16·54	16·40	16·27
800	17·65	17·60	17·54	17·49	17·44	17·34	17·24
1000	18·36	18·33	18·30	18·28	18·26	18·20	18·16
1500	19·83	19·87	19·90	19·94	19·98	20·07	20·17
2000	21·04	21·15	21·25	21·36	21·47	21·71	21·97
2500	22·07	22·25	22·42	22·59	22·77	23·14	
3000	22·96	23·19	23·43	23·67	23·91	24·40	
4000	24·47	24·80	25·15	25·50	25·86	26·58	
5000	25·74	26·17	26·61	27·07	27·54	28·50	

SPECIFIC HEAT AT CONSTANT VOLUME, JOULES/MOLE, °K—*cont.*

Temperature, °K							Pressure atm
360	380	400	450	500	550	600	
12·48	12·48	12·48	12·48	12·48	12·47	12·47	1
12·49	12·49	12·49	12·49	12·49	12·48	12·48	2
12·50	12·50	12·50	12·50	12·50	12·49	12·49	3
12·52	12·52	12·52	12·51	12·51	12·50	12·50	5
12·54	12·54	12·54	12·53	12·52	12·51	12·51	7
12·57	12·56	12·56	12·55	12·54	12·53	12·52	10
12·62	12·61	12·61	12·59	12·57	12·55	12·54	15
12·67	12·66	12·65	12·62	12·60	12·58	12·57	20
12·72	12·70	12·69	12·66	12·63	12·61	12·59	25
12·76	12·74	12·73	12·69	12·66	12·63	12·61	30
12·85	12·82	12·80	12·76	12·72	12·69	12·66	40
12·94	12·90	12·87	12·82	12·78	12·74	12·71	50
13·02	12·98	12·94	12·88	12·83	12·79	12·76	60
13·10	13·05	13·01	12·94	12·89	12·84	12·80	70
13·18	13·13	13·08	13·00	12·94	12·89	12·85	80
13·33	13·27	13·22	13·12	13·05	12·99	12·94	100
13·47	13·40	13·35	13·23	13·15	13·09	13·03	120
13·60	13·53	13·47	13·34	13·25	13·18	13·12	140
13·72	13·65	13·58	13·45	13·35	13·28	13·22	160
13·84	13·76	13·69	13·55	13·44	13·37	13·31	180
13·96	13·87	13·80	13·65	13·54	13·46	13·40	200
14·26	14·16	14·07	13·91	13·78			250
14·55	14·44	14·34	14·16	14·01			300
14·83	14·71	14·61	14·41	14·24			350
15·10	14·98	14·88	14·67	14·48			400
15·64	15·52	15·41	15·19	14·99			500
16·15	16·04	15·94	14·73	15·54			600
17·15	17·07	17·00	16·83	16·67			800
18·12	18·08	18·04	17·94	17·85			1000
20·27	20·38	20·49	20·80	21·13			1500
22·26	22·57	22·90	23·76	24·70			2000
							2500
							3000
							4000
							5000

8 8276

9 8276